WINGS OF AN ANGEL

Colin Barrett

MINERVA PRESS
LONDON
MIAMI RIO DE JANEIRO DELHI

WINGS OF AN ANGEL
Copyright © Colin Barrett 2001

All Rights Reserved

ISBN 0 75411 442 2

First Published 2001 by
MINERVA PRESS
315–317 Regent Street
London W1R 7YB

Printed in Great Britain for Minerva Press

WINGS OF AN ANGEL

This book is dedicated to those who did not survive, and their memorial is my remembrance and to Spit, my friend.

About the Author

Colin Barrett was born in Maymyo, near Mandalay, Burma, in 1930. Shortly before his second birthday, his father died from tuberculosis. In 1940, his mother married Sergeant Arthur Townend, serving with the King's Own Light Infantry who were garrisoned there. With the war raging in the East in 1942, all families attached to the British Forces were evacuated. His formal schooling was over. The family, which included a younger brother and baby sister, were flown to India by an American bomber group. They eventually arrived in England in January 1944.

Mr Barrett is divorced, and has three children. Now retired, he lives in Selby, North Yorkshire.

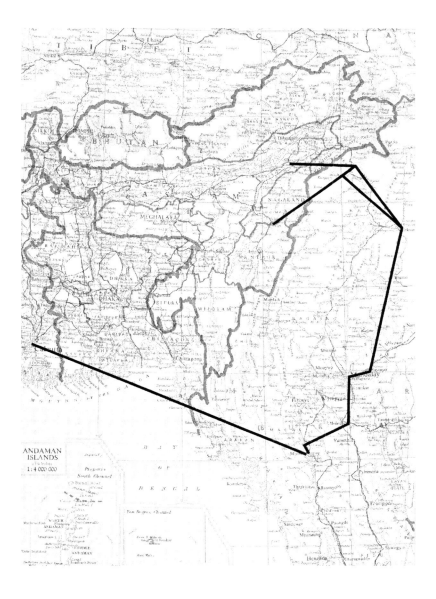

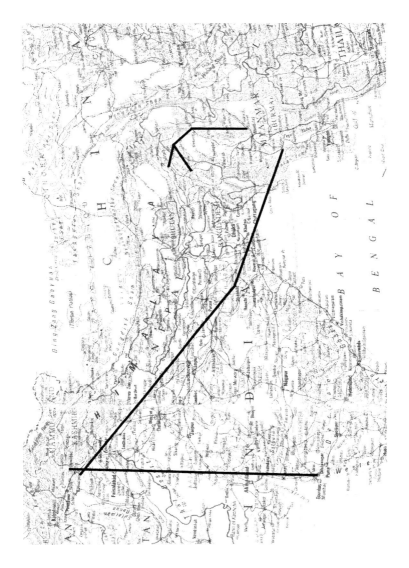

Preface

Numerous military memoirs of the Japanese invasion of Burma exist. It is the personal accounts of the ordinary people, which are rare. Yet, in the swift and relentless advance of the enemy, thousands of civilians suffered and died in sordid captivity. Countless others embarked on a perilous journey, which was later to be known as 'the trek', a horrendous pilgrimage through an unforgiving and duplicitous land. The majority were to succumb, but some lived through that pitiless exodus. Among them were members of my family.

This story begins in the winter of 1951, when an insane decision of mine almost cost me my life, triggering memories from the past, recollections of my early childhood in Maymyo, near Mandalay, Burma. I was born in that country, then under a British Colonial regime.

This is the factual chronicle of various incidents and events endured by some of my relatives on that terrifying and horrific journey, as they struggled through the heart of darkness, in a ferocious jungle, across hundreds of miles of formidable terrain, from Northern Burma to the safety of the Indian border, during the early months of 1942. It is an account of the desperate attempts to avoid capture by the advancing Japanese army, of families with small children, weak with exhaustion, despondent, and forever haunted by fear, with insufficient food and without adequate medical supplies or help, to combat the illnesses they contracted in those extreme conditions. Constantly pursued by a remorseless enemy, they were regularly in prayer for safe guidance, with a glistening passion of intensity, to a friend in whom they had faith. Fear was their inseparable companion throughout their gruelling ordeal. From these elements many came, and in these elements many were to perish.

Finally, those who failed to escape their adversary suffered the atrocities of internment. This imprisonment resulted in malnutrition, deprivation and despair. The proliferation of flies spread numerous diseases and as they were deprived of medication many of the internees died. A few survived this onslaught of evil and the horrors of neglect.

This then is their story, and mine…

Prologue

I was a child, but that is without relevance. These problems arose because there was a war. I soon learnt about fear, adversity, and grief. I travelled with apprehension and confused emotions, and visited many places that didn't exist 'over the rainbow'. I prayed with conviction to that unseen power many times, when everything appeared layered with pain and sorrow. Those of you, who haven't experienced the horrors of war, may commiserate when your eyes focus on my story. I survived, and will endeavour to express the depth of human values and resolution, which I never imagined possible.

Chapter I

4 p.m. Monday, 12 November 1951

The wind had moved round to the north-east, turning colder, and dark grey clouds were shifting what little daylight there was left in the sky. Now summer was just a vague memory, its warmth nothing more than an illusion. A few months ago it had been so hot one could never imagine ever being cold again. I stepped into the kitchen, rubbing my hands furiously trying to remove the chill that gripped my knuckles. I had just spent two hours outside preparing my cycle for the long journey ahead. These were difficult times, and the very thought of owning a motor vehicle was out of the question. Unfortunately the bus service for my intended route was inadequate, almost non-existent. So the laborious journey ahead of me had to be undertaken with a cycle partnered with will power and determination.

I sat alone in the lounge of the house, which belonged to my in-laws, thinking of my dear wife who was in a maternity hospital. She had given birth to our first child, a son, and would be waiting patiently for my regular visit. Although it was inconvenient, we were obliged and grateful to stay with her parents, until the local council could offer us one of the numerous houses that were being built on the new estate. I was employed in a job that I loved, as a locomotive fireman on the London North-Eastern Railway. Having arrived in the quaint little market town of Selby as a small boy, during the Second World War, I was soon accepted by its inhabitants, who were intrigued by the arrival of the young stranger. At present, tiredness was creeping in, as I had just completed my first shift which had begun at 4 a.m., transporting some of the local women employed at the Rowntrees chocolate factory, based in York, a beautiful historical city fourteen miles away.

I had finished the meal prepared for me by my mother-in-law;

it was the usual fry-up of leftovers from Sunday's dinner, affectionately known to everyone as bubble and squeak. I slipped into a thick overcoat, scarf and gloves, much needed protection against the bitter cold. It was time to start my journey to Hazelwood Castle, now modified into a reputable maternity home, on the outskirts of Tadcaster. The return trip was approximately forty-one miles but well worth the effort, and tonight would be no different to any other. The day had been cloudy, grey and overcast, when even the sky seemed to hang close to the ground. I stepped outside the house into the impending darkness, secretly concealing the human passion for anxiety under the mercy of the bleak weather. As I passed the swirling River Ouse, a chilling breeze wrung tears from my eyes. There was a heaviness in the air and I noticed the gathering of storm clouds, which were slowly covering the galaxy of flashing white stars peeping down through the window of heaven. Here, desire and determination were almost inseparable, as I followed the road through a lane of brick houses bordered by plots of well-tended gardens.

It started to rain as I continued down a slight hill, where a swiftly flowing stream crossed the bottom of the road. I could faintly hear the ripple of water passing through the railings, which were waist-high, although they sounded frail by the way they creaked with the flow. I continued without pause or hesitation, perhaps even with a touch of bravado, through this wash with virtually no current at all. I cycled through the dimly lit streets of a small village, which looked like something left over from a bygone age. After passing an ancient-looking public house, where the villagers spent their leisure hours enjoying a quiet drink and pleasant conversation, I came to an abrupt halt. There was a general build-up of traffic, so I waited patiently, a potent virtue absent in my personal attitude. Suddenly, I was approached by a scruffy-looking gent draped in a shabby beige raincoat. On his head was a ragged trilby revealing more curves than a corrugated sheet. The mud and manure that clung to his boots suggested that he was a farm labourer. A brief conversation soon developed, when I had to withstand a ghastly odour of stale beer.

'I'd keep away from this place, mate,' he said with an Irish-

Yorkshire dialect.

'I'm only passing through, pal,' I replied.

'It's a good job because it floods terribly around here in the winter, the river rises quickly and there's no holding the water,' he replied.

I thanked him and followed the traffic, which had started to move through the darkness. I pedalled furiously to make up the lost time, as an icy wind from the north dampened my face, and the darkness hurtled past. Finally, arriving at the intersection near Tadcaster, I headed towards Bramham crossroads and my intended rendezvous. My anxiety was over when I reached the main entrance to the hospital, just off the carriageway.

I didn't know too much about the castle, only that it was built early in the thirteenth century. It was then owned until 1908 by the Vavasour family, who were prominent Catholics throughout the penal times. Now, with constant additions over the years, it had grown into one of the largest maternity hospitals in the north-east, especially during the Second World War, when it covered the district of Leeds. In 1967 it was bought by the Carmelites, who took up residence in 1972 and transformed it into a magnificent guest house known as The Carmelite Friars.

The castle stood well back off the main road, like a community in a state of grace tucked away behind a forest of trees. The long winding path, bathed in total silence, led me to the main entrance. Here autumn leaves of red and yellow carpeted the area, mute testimony that winter would soon be arriving.

After visiting my family, I stepped outside into the darkness, but it was a different night. The clouds had rolled back, and the moon shone down unimpeded, looking cold and bleak. I continued on my journey home, when I reached that small village of Ryther once again. The darkness had plummeted and the narrow streets were deserted, except for the sound of a barking dog which chilled the night air. I reached the area where the stream crossed the road; it was deeper now and appeared to be rising slowing. The sporadic shafts of moonlight brightened the gloomy stretch as I pedalled across. Beneath my feet the viscous element coiled and vibrated, throwing up mantles of cold spray.

Suddenly the storm broke and there was an enormous deluge, the tremendous force impelling me against the wooden railings. I grabbed at the barriers with both hands frantically, as the swirling current rushed past, trapping my legs inside the cycle frame. Now the worst fear was drowning in the freezing cold, as it pierced through my clothing. The water was rising quickly, and my mood grew darker like a peat bog.

I needed help and soon, so I turned in the direction of that public house, now bathed in darkness, then bawled at the top of my voice several times. There was no instant reply but a moment later light appeared in the upstairs window. My heart jerked with excitement when a strange voice shouted, 'Is there someone out there?'

I yelled, raising one arm, 'Please help me, I'm over here trapped near the railings.'

Then the stranger's voice replied, 'Hang on, I'll be with you in a minute.'

High up in the sky the moon appeared to be gibbous, casting a cold bland eye on the trees and the swirling current. Retreating into this new belief of being rescued, I hung on desperately. Suddenly, a tractor lurched forward onto the bumpy surface of the road, headlights blazing on full beam. It turned away, then reversed slowly towards me, cautiously avoiding any contact before coming to a halt.

'Are you all right?' shouted the driver. I nodded with a certain amount of conviction.

He handed me a short length of rope. 'Fasten this to the crossbar and give me your hand quickly, the water is rising too fast,' he shouted.

I did what was asked of me, although floundering in the darkness, then reached out at the outstretched arm in random desperation. Once on the platform, the machine pulled away from the flood hauling the cycle behind it. I climbed off the tractor but my saturated body wobbled with fatigue and my legs were so weak that I fell to the ground. The world grew dark as I lay there, and shadows of doubt passed across my face as my mind went spinning backwards. Within minutes a tall stranger lifted me up, slipped an arm around my waist and half carried me to the front entrance of The Ryther Arms. As we stepped into the cosy lounge, it looked inviting and peaceful, although cigarette smoke lingered inside, reminders of the past evening's pleasure.

'Hello son, you look like a drowned rat,' she said, in soft voice and a pleasant smile that glowed with warmth. 'I'm Nell, the landlady.'

I nodded slowly seeing her compassionate face. She had intelligent, deep brown eyes, with long brown hair that cascaded down and around her shoulders like sheep's wool.

She then handed me a large towel and said, 'I've run a hot bath for you and left some of Jack's clothes for you to change into.' She glanced at her husband, then back to me, smiling. 'They may be a trifle on the large side,' she added, 'but I'm sure they will be more comfortable. It's better than catching a severe cold.'

Taking the towel, I thanked her, feeling my face burn with embarrassment. I also promptly swallowed a tot of rum, which Jack had handed to me. It glowed in my throat and a surge of warmth spiralled through my entire body. After soaking up the warm water and drying myself, I climbed into the garments left for me, a large, thick, white polo-necked jumper, dark-blue corduroy trousers, a pair of enormous, white woollen stockings, and some oversized wellingtons. The reflection in the mirror was of a comic Guy Fawkes, which brought a modest smile to my face and memories of maritime days.

When I arrived back in the lounge, Nell handed me a tray containing a bowl of hot soup, sandwiches, and a warm drink.

'Feeling better, son? I hope you enjoyed the bath,' she said, her voice floating through the air.

'Yes,' I replied and thanked her for everything. As I glanced at both her and Jack, they appeared to be curious and concerned about the young stranger who had caused all the confusion. While eating the meal in front of a blazing log fire, I gave them a detailed account of what had happened, then apologised for all the disturbance, explaining that I had to be getting home for my early shift the next day. Jack decided on an alternative route because of the atrocious conditions, one in the opposite direction through Bishops Wood but with extra mileage on my path. He also couldn't believe my decision to try to cross the stream, and handed me another portion of rum. He then said that I was extremely fortunate to have survived and could easily have drowned in those conditions. Should that have happened, I would never have seen my family again.

I gulped down the remains in the glass, staring anxiously into the roaring fire. The logs appeared to be splintering and crackling, forming prefabricated images in the shimmering flames. I could feel the alcohol flowing through my veins, paralysing my perception and weakening my reactions. But his few sympathetic words triggered a memory from the past, as my mind whirled in a slow-motion dream and not without purpose. The room suddenly grew colder, cutting away from the cosiness within. My innermost feelings were subjugated in a hushed surrender, born not out of dedication but nonchalance, as though I cared little about what happened tonight, or whether there would be a tomorrow. My brain was now spinning on an axis, oblivious to everything. I shouted aloud but there was no sound, only a muffled tone as the words seemed to hang in the air. Then darkness shrouded my own existence as I drifted slowly, effortlessly, disappearing into an echoing abyss which I never thought I would enter, one that encompassed a weary traveller in another time, another place, a whole lifetime ago, in Maymyo[1], Burma, where I was born.

---

[1] Pronounced *Maymuo*.

Chapter II

Walter Emanual Barrett, a Freemason, was a kind, decent and highly respected gentleman, employed on the Burma Railways as a passenger guard. Standing at six feet, with dark-brown hair, brown eyes and of medium build, he was the youngest of three sons, along with two sisters who were his junior. The family had supposedly originated from Ireland. He met and courted Gwendoline May Harding, a sales representative from Whiteway & Laidlaw, a high-class British drapery store, for a number of years. She was the second of eight children, and had grown up fast after the early death of her parents. Her short brown hair and dark-brown eyes framed an intelligent face. She was incredibly dedicated to her work and her five feet three inches design belied her precocious nature. They shared all the important experiences and observed the laws that early twentieth century bureaucracy demanded, without breaking any of the rules. They eventually married on 28 July 1928, the ceremony taking place at the All Saints Memorial Church in Maymyo, upper Burma. He was twenty-eight years old and she was twenty-five.

I was born from this alliance on 30 August 1930, at the Civil Hospital in Maymyo, into a world enchanted by the living. During the early part of 1932, my father became very ill, and the doctors didn't detect the imminence of any real danger until it was too late. He had contracted tuberculosis. Several weeks were spent in hospital as the degeneration progressed and a huge cavity developed in one of his lungs. They watched him struggle in the limited silence and loneliness. When the illness worsened he became very quiet and unresponsive. There was nothing that anyone could do and all the praying soon proved to be a waste of time. With the great loss of weight, his breathing got heavier and his sunken eyes darted around in confusion. My mother and Aunty Iris wept inconsolably on hearing his last few words, 'I've been very fortunate in my life, dears.' Suddenly the beat of a weak human heart stopped, as the mirror of life clouded over, shortly before my second birthday and he entered the last and greatest journey when all is revealed. We then discovered that there could be no brotherhood of man without a father. There was no comfort, no thoughts, just a huge chasm of emptiness and pain.

During the weeks that followed in a veiled slow agonising chain reaction, severe depression and bitterness enveloped my mother. She regressed into self-imposed isolation with an impenetrable sorrow. Through her sense of isolation she became a reserved and lonely woman, imprisoned by her own sacred beliefs, concepts deeply embedded in her thoughts. Ambition overcame maternal instincts and she eventually purchased a new residence not far away. Moving on to redeem her own shattered life, she left me in the capable hands of her youngest sister, Iris. The latter was unmarried and willingly accepted the new responsibility into her humble home, graciously and with no grudges borne. She was determined to prove this a satisfactory arrangement.

Although not living under the same roof as my mother, I always felt a deep reverence for her. She possessed an instinctive authority and just looking at her made it easy to respect her austere image. She abided by the rules that she laid down, and always set the perfect illustration, although controlled by necessity. I was never seriously aware of her deep affection for me or ever being taken into her arms as a small child and embraced with affection. So, by an early age uncertainty and insecurity were already buried in my young life. Under my aunt's gentle reassurance and expert guidance, all this was to change dramatically. She adjusted and rearranged my childhood, by disposing of all the tension within me. Then by showering me with love, affection and kindness, she eliminated my loneliness, my childish anxieties and my sadness. These early days of my youth were wonderful and I grew to savour every single moment of them. It was the beginning of everything that mattered in my life, so I suppose I could say that I had everything that would make me happy.

Iris was also an intelligent, skilful and highly respected school teacher, tutoring mathematics and English to a high degree in the

Anglo-Vernacular school on Lodge Road in Maymyo. She was twenty-two years old, five feet two inches tall, strong and slender, with short black hair and dark-brown eyes, which sparkled with life, a small straight nose and a smiling mouth. She seldom wore make-up, was naturally graceful and certainly didn't concern herself with what was deemed sophisticated. It showed in the way she dressed and the way she carried herself. As far as I was concerned she was the most elegant, the most charismatic and the most immaculate person that ever lived. I loved her.

Our home was sectioned in the railway quarters, an end house. It had been the original residence of my father, and Iris was granted the lease for another three years. It was surrounded by a luxurious spread of lawn banked with a border of breathtaking flowers to the front. The garden to the rear overlooked the main railway line to Mandalay. It was meticulously tended by the gardener, who worked to a method rather than with instinct, with unlimited energy and knowledge. In the centre of the yard grew a huge mulberry tree, around which was a wooden seat often providing the perfect platform for solitude and fantasy. It was also the principle source for relaxation on warm summer evenings. The numerous branches catered cosily for flocks of mating doves, the exquisitely plumaged lorikeets, with their metallic tints of reds and blues, and endless streams of the dreaded caterpillar.

The house was not out of proportion with the other dwellings in the vicinity, having two large rooms on the ground floor, with a separate kitchen to the rear. The three rooms on the first floor above served as bedrooms. There was nothing fashionable about it, such as characterised many of the larger houses, but it was comfortable. The feeling of warmth glowed within, a place of strength. To the side was a huge, lush green meadow, where the older children spent numerous leisure hours performing amazing tricks with their kites of all sizes and spectacular colours. The younger ones would play games, furnished by their own imagination, with a growing mischievousness during the dry season. It was an exciting and challenging lifestyle. The house was situated on Lodge Road, aptly named because the imposing Masonic Lodge was the principal structure. Its huge sturdy gates at the front entrance peppered the avenue adjacent to our home.

The Hardings of Maymyo were very prominent members of the community, and had a large family by social standards, comprising four girls, Myrtle, Gwen, Irene and Iris, who were the eldest, and four boys, Oswald, Stanley, Leo and Ronald, who was the youngest. It was also considered traditional practice that a high standard of education was the essential qualification required to survive and function within the pomp and splendour among the elite under the British Colonial rule. The competition to establish oneself in eminent positions and participate amongst the wealthy and influential was fierce and stringent. Many searched for work either to become adults or for necessity. Throughout the early years, Mr and Mrs Harding constructed and carefully prepared with infallible precision a prodigious calendar for each of their children, revolting against anything that threatened their desires. They had witnessed pain and sympathy over the years, and neither of them was by nature predisposed to not follow the rules. Unfortunately they both passed away before their children reached adolescence and sadly were never to witness or cherish some of their achievements.

The children were immediately relocated into the care of an aunt and through the civil court she was granted sole custody, thus becoming their legal guardian. As she was a spinster, the task ahead was a formidable one. She had an openness and a capacity to love but was herself a casualty of inadequate funds. She promptly enrolled the girls into St Joseph's convent, the boys would continue at St Michael's school. On completion of this early tuition, she had hoped that they would continue and finalise their education at the university in Rangoon, the capital, although this was not the normal pattern, which troubled her. However, her motives were commendable, and it also gave her a certain freedom. She couldn't identify with this inconvenient legacy, but it was something she had to overcome and take some comfort from the fact that this sacrifice would be all worthwhile. There were certain rules governing this relationship, and she would have to abide by these, but with loyalty, conviction and spiritual guidance, she was to accomplish an objective that was unthinkable under the circumstances.

Eventually, the pressure was soon to materialise as the shortage of finance intensified. Myrtle, who was the eldest and Gwen, who was later to become my mother, were conscious of the difficulties ahead and entertained no illusions concerning the circumstances that could develop. To overcome this disadvantage, they forfeited their own personal desires and dismissed the opportunity to further their education. Together, they engaged themselves in permanent employment, to assist in relieving the enormous financial pressures that were forthcoming. They worked to an unregulated scale of hours stretching into uncharted territory, because there was no specific contract. Working with mutual contemplation, they were to make a powerful impression, but the demands of the working day inevitably gave rise to heated exchanges. However, it was an immediate success and between them they established a basic foundation, which the rest of them were to follow throughout their early lives.

When the remainder of the siblings were firmly established in high school and college, Myrtle married Ben Unitt, who was a traffic inspector on the Burma Railways. They purchased a huge residence in the small town of Myingre[1], which incorporated the railway workshops. They had five children, Rex, Deryck, Hazel, Joy and Terence. Gwen also married and resided in railway quarters in Maymyo.

Irene and Iris, who brought me up, completed their education at university and both received their teachers' degree. Irene later married Richard De'Santos, a passenger guard on the railways, settling down in private residence near the locomotive sheds in Maymyo. There were three children, Peter and John who were twins, and Maureen, their daughter. Irene was always fascinated with rural activity and had an abiding love affair with nature. She established a small holding at the rear of her home, where numerous cattle, goats, geese, ducks and chickens often enticed me on countless mischievous romps. The huge spacious compound also billeted the servants who had a permanent dwelling and a steady source of revenue. She also provided many of the citizens in the area with a daily supply of fresh milk, eggs

---

[1] Pronounced *Mingair*.

and the occasional table dressing.

Oswald, the eldest of the boys, achieved his degree in electrical engineering. He was a man of integrity and possessed an excellent intelligence; to most observers he spoke of money and position. After taking up a post on the railways, he moved further south away from the family. With his European background, he was beyond criticism; it was also a source of admiration, which he enjoyed quietly. He was a bachelor and, although he dressed casually, a streak of harshness ran through him as ferocious as the moss that grew in the undergrowth of the jungle. He made decisions quickly and sincerely believed that excuses were a waste of precious time.

Stanley was the enigmatic one, showing absolutely no interest in the academic qualities achieved by the others. He joined the railways at an early age as a locomotive fireman. He soon settled down, marrying Eileen Dunning, whose parents originated from the British Isles. She had a well-deserved reputation for outstanding good looks and sharp stunning features. Her eyes, almost black, sparkled with warmth and long, silky, brown flowing hair touched her waist. She was intelligent, thoughtful and serene and there appeared to be a certain chemistry between them. Although they weren't given to luxury, they enjoyed a charmed and contented marriage, having four children, two girls and two boys, Peggy, Peta, Leon and Richard.

Leo secured his Master's degree at an early age, and taught at the Government English High School in Maymyo. He occasionally acted as vice-head when called upon, and resided at the school quarters during the early years. He frequently enjoyed a move to his sister Iris's residence, when he sought additional comfort and polite conversation in her company. He was also a bachelor, adventurous and powerfully built. He enjoyed the outdoor life, sleeping in the open and staying in the scattered villages. He was a good judge of character and firmly believed that marching in and out of classrooms was a stuffy affair. Shrewd and patient, he despised unwarranted conversations, dismissing them by keeping his distance, with a general air of haste.

Ronald, the youngest, was energetic, studious and a perfectionist by nature. With the lithe build of an athlete, he was an avid sportsman and applied his ability with enthusiasm to almost any venture when called upon. He was a passionate young man, and it showed in his mobility and the way he handled things. His eyes were forever observant, yet concealed the warmth that lay behind them. Although still young, he could endure almost anything beyond question. He studied for a degree in journalism, eventually taking up a teaching post in the Shan states until the outbreak of the war in the Far East in 1941. He then worked secretly behind the enemy lines deep in the jungle for American intelligence.

The town of Maymyo, situated forty miles north-east of the old capital, Mandalay, in central Burma, was rather peaceful, but had its fair share of excitement, such as the impressive Military Tattoo at the end of March, demonstrating British influence in the country. The water festival of Thingyan in mid-April celebrated the Burmese New Year; the old year would be washed away and the new one baptised with the deluge of water bringing peace and prosperity. This was symbolised by the launching of water on everyone who dared to venture into the streets. No one was exempt from this spectacular ceremony. The whole country greeted this visitation with an explosion of celebrations when fêtes, parades and every sort of display was approved of. Water from buckets and bowls was hurled at everybody, squirted from pumps and hydrants, cascaded from balconies and windows. This usually lasted from three to four days. There was also the Indian colour festival, when a similar pattern would continue. This time, coloured powder would be dispatched on everyone in the streets, embellishing them with a flashing assortment of stains and shades. Any deviation from this ceremony would also be resented by the town's inhabitants.

In October, the season of Thadingyat would be celebrated, accepted as the happy festival of light, marking the end of Lent and all its restrictions and solemnity. For almost a week, lights would blaze radiantly throughout the country. Lamps of all types and descriptions drifted down the rivers on floats, and fire balloons of various sizes and shapes burst forth from the sky. The streets were full of carnivals, and huge fireworks displays illuminated the heavens with spectacular colours. The houses and shops were decorated with torches and coloured lanterns in memory of Buddha's return from heaven. It was a rapturous and joyful occasion all over the country, as the people congregated in celebration and time slid into a different schedule.

Over eighty per cent of the Burmese people were Buddhists and nowhere else in the world would you find a country more influenced by religion. It was an integral part of their everyday lives, and the majority of homes had a shrine or a Buddha image high on a wall. Christians, accustomed to the Sunday-best solemnity, had their own churches. Those of the Church of England denomination worshipped in the All Saints Church situated close to the General Civil Hospital in the town centre. The Roman Catholics pursued their divinity at Saint Joseph's, which was attached to the convent near the Alexandra Barracks. Here the British regiment, The King's Own Yorkshire Light Infantry was garrisoned. This military precinct also provided the families with married quarters if they chose to be billeted in the grounds, a school, a hospital and churches for the various faiths. The Baptists, who had the largest unwavering congregation, had their own place of worship plus an accommodating school. The remaining ethnic groups worshipped in their own pyramidal temples close to their habitation, each one maintaining a stronghold of faith in the future.

The town also had an assembly of citizens known to us as *dhobies*, who by arrangement would dispose of all the dirty garments from the house. They would mark and check them before removing them and return them the following week, washed, ironed and in immaculate condition. This was a continuous process. All these people were inhabitants from the hill tribes and, apart from growing vegetables and fruit, which they sold regularly in the market, this was the only employment available to them. They were diligent, trustworthy and very appreciative, receiving a reasonable revenue for their tasks. The dominant citizens of the town were employed in authoritative occupations, thus enjoying a very luxurious lifestyle. This was considered conventional, so it was considered a natural compulsion to engage various servants for any specific tasks on a regular basis. They would contribute their skills to all the daily activities and chores in return for wages; some acquired limited but adequate accommodation from their employers, thus allowing their bosses considerable freedom of movement in keeping with their existence.

In our household we had a female servant, who assisted my aunt with the customary shopping and prepared all the daily meals on a regular basis. In addition, her husband attended to the upkeep of the garden and contributed the remainder of his spare time to the various other jobs that were required. He was known as the *Mali* and would be paid accordingly.

I was fortunate enough to have a personal chaperon during my early years and her name was Tye. She was only in her teens, but a remarkable young woman, possessing all the natural qualities that were needed. Her skin was very fair akin to the inhabitants from the hill states, her features delicate and small, with round cheeks which came down to a rigid chin. She had dark-brown eyes and straight black hair, which spilled over her shoulders, and a wide disarming smile. She attended to all my desires and controlled my erratic nature with compassion and loving tenderness. I depended on her rather heavily during my growing-up years, spending all my leisure hours in her company, and found it impossible to ignore her naturally tender voice. Overcoming the language barrier was never a problem. Her tone was playful, joking, yet within it I could sense an honest note. Every now and then she would nod as if to reassure me that she was paying strict attention to everything I had to say. A good deal of my happiness revolved around her personal support and tolerance. As the years slipped by she became the central figure in my early life, and I grew up never to forget her.

Chapter III

It was the autumn of 1935 and a warm wind from the north had displaced the deplorable monsoon season. I had completed one full year in the kindergarten under the expert guidance of Miss Amy Nicholas, and had arrived home on a Friday evening, having finished my first week of primary education at St Michael's School on Circular Road. My Aunty Iris had also entered the house after finishing her duties as a teacher. A short distance away, opposite her school, stood the impressive Railway Institute. Here, all the official functions, sports galas and parties were held for the children whose parents were employed in that industry. Dances were a special feature every Saturday night throughout most of the year.

In the kitchen, the evening meal was being hastily prepared, and for a few moments silence reigned in the lounge. Throwing a quick glance through the window at the gathering dusk, as the setting sun reflected its early departure, Aunty Iris spoke.

'Please take Colin for a short walk before it gets too dark, then finish for the day,' she requested of Tye with a friendly smile. Her relationship with Tye far exceeded the usual affinity shown between two people of vastly different ages and distant cultures.

'I certainly will, lady,' she replied in perfect English, although brought up in the Shan states herself. Her voice was deep and not at all in keeping with her petite figure. Her smile glowed with an expression as soft as a feather. She was rather pretty and demure, looking charming in her pale-yellow lace blouse buttoned up to the neck. A long silk dark green *loungyi*[1] and open white sandals completed her outfit. The weekends were her own, allowing her many hours of pleasure, when she would spend time with her family. During the weekdays she would remain in the servants' quarters with the others, avoiding the unnecessary long journey

---

[1] Pronounced *loonghi*.

home.

The kerosene lamps were reflecting faint shadows in the room, and the house glowed in the darkness. In the background, the dining table was already set for dinner. A slight breeze blew the dust along Lodge Road as we strolled, but the weather remained warm and heavy with smells of the eucalyptus trees. I held her hand tightly when we passed the Masonic Lodge, sneaking a hurried glance from the corners of my eyes as my heart began to pump. We mingled with the echo of other footsteps, walking briskly down the avenue in the peace and early dusk. The strength of the sun weakened and even the birds were settling down for the night. Some of the houses were lit up and through distant windows people moved about, getting on with their lives, chatting, consuming food, oblivious to our movements. The road to the north was flat and sturdy woods blocked the view. To the east, the large green meadow stretched out beyond the houses, where some of the older children were pulling in their kites for the night. Here the land rose gently to a golden summer dream, and everything was still and silent. Suddenly a cool breeze whispered its approach high into the heavens. Overhead a few scattered clouds hung suspended, moving towards the horizon of an incredible tawny colour.

We had walked for about an hour when it briskly grew colder and Tye decided to return as the light was paling above the distant woods. The horizon was starting to disappear and the remainder of the sunset was strange, as we halted at the front gates of the Masonic Lodge. I held on to its closed barriers and shuddered as I peered through, yet it wasn't with the cold, it was with a feeling of being alone. It was powerful and persuasive. In the splendid twilight, I could see this imposing building as it dominated the road like a fortress, an enormous, faceless, commanding mansion standing in its own perimeter as if protesting against the violation of its privacy. There were extensive gardens, lawns trimmed and shaped with precision. The battalions of flowers of all descriptions sent out an aroma that penetrated the brain with delight. The mansion towered at the end of a long driveway, which led to a colossal teak door and was flanked on each side by huge oak trees. The lodge itself appeared sinister yet spellbinding and its magnetism terrified me. It held a mystery, which drew me to the front entrance, intensified by the faint haunting music that wafted from within. As we left, I turned and glanced at the movements of shadows from behind the heavy, deep-yellow curtained windows which revealed the undeniable presence of some secret, some dark secret. We walked in silence, but there was an impenetrable sorrow there and I felt it. I wondered if someone was trying to call me. There was a constant humming in my head, and my flesh began to creep and my mouth became dry.

I was sitting patiently at the dining table directly opposite my aunt, waiting for the evening meal to be served. We sat in silence until I spoke.

'Aunty, what is that strange building across the road?' I asked very innocently.

There was a tight ironic smile on my mouth, which revealed a sense of hesitation in my speech. She raised her eyes slowly from the table and it was painfully obvious that, despite her friendly smile, she was rather surprised and reluctant to answer my question. Suddenly her expression changed, caught in the plane of light that streamed through the window. There were tears in her eyes when she answered in a voice like a whisper.

'Now, listen very carefully, my son. When you are a little older I will tell you everything that you need to know, but for now just finish your dinner.'

I never mentioned that building again, although my sceptical nature kept me fascinated by its presence and the mystery that lurked within. With the passing of the seasons I soon settled down and was never afraid of its stature during my travels. However, the time did arrive when I wouldn't pass those towering gates again.

The previous year, my mother had moved around and worked for the sheer joy of it. Then she married a Sergeant Breward, who was from the United Kingdom and at that time was attached to the Buffs, a regiment stationed in Rangoon, the capital. I also had a younger brother, Trevor. He was born on 27 July 1935, although we were not to meet for a number of years. However, shortly after his birth, the Army authorities were notified that Sergeant Breward was not officially divorced from his wife in England. That marriage was immediately annulled.

The summer of 1937 had arrived, and we had moved out of railway quarters, the lease having subsided. The new residence was at the opposite end of Lodge Road and quite close to the railway station. All the servants accompanied us, as adequate premises were provided at the rear of the building for their use. The building was fairly large and subdivided to accommodate two families; the ground floor was already inhabited. A heavy, open, wooden staircase led to a small verandah, which surrounded the front of the first floor. This was to be our temporary home until more suitable housing could be established. My aunt wasn't too keen on the steep flight of stairs.

As I entered the long hallway a feeling of constriction made me feel restless. There was an eerie atmosphere about the place that frightened me and, as the weeks drifted into months, the fears were to intensify. I was always conscious of a strange and unidentifiable scent that haunted me. I never settled and sleep became an affliction, not a desire. Finally there were dreams, bad dreams, even nightmares. Maybe I was just fearful and so keyed up that I hallucinated. Yet there may be some truth in the belief that houses absorb the emotions that are spent in them, for I certainly wasn't prone to imagination. So I remained composed and tentative; after all children are condemned to silence and solitude.

However, during the months that followed, I was not my usual mischievous self. Even my school reports began to deteriorate rapidly and time was to prove a revelation.

I had now commenced at the juniors at St Michael's School, which catered for girls and boys up to the second standard. This part occupied a separate area of the huge premises. It was also clearly distinguishable because it was under the comprehensive control of the Church of England sisters. We knew the superior as Sister Harriet. She never indulged in teaching the pupils, but everyone would remember her with respect. She was a tall commanding figure, dressed in a black and white habit. A pinnacle of authority and diplomacy, although she was rarely seen, her very presence could be felt. Her astuteness and impartial opinion was held in the highest esteem, and she was a staunch disciplinarian. Having to confront her for an elucidation was to have a penetrating and everlasting effect. Following a harrowing incident that took place concerning myself, I was to have the displeasure of such a visit. Trivial as it may seem now with the passing of time, this particular episode is still embedded in my memory.

It was late August and the summer holidays weren't too far away, when the lush green days of the tropics disappeared and the days seemed to grow shorter. Classes were over and spirits were high as the children strolled casually to the main entrance. There was a subtle change in the air, but it was still soothing even in shirtsleeves. However, this was strictly against school regulations. Although my aunt worried needlessly about my physique, I was not afraid or fragile in that respect. I was a typical boy in most ways and extremely mischievous; school fights had never scared me. My cousins, Rex and Deryck, were attending the same school, although they were slightly older than I was. They would shortly be leaving to continue their education at the Government English High School as boarders. This institution on Bund Road, catered entirely for boys.

The clumsy blue school buses were making their appointed rounds, picking up the children who were waiting patiently for the homeward-bound journey. The atmosphere outside the school grounds was jovial and full of laughter. Most of the children were giggling, chatting, and busy chasing each other. Some of the boys had their stockings rolled down and their shirt tails hanging out of their trousers, a custom they adhered to when they pursued anyone vigorously, swinging their school bags at whoever came within striking distance. Outside the school, between the perimeter boundary and the main road, ran a dyke. However, due to the recent dry weather, it was void of water. I was perched on top of the bank with my feet dangling in space, when Rex was provoked into a fight with a lad of his own age. I had always admired Rex, occasionally looking on him as an older brother. He was broad and thickset with black hair and a swarthy complexion, more like an American. As far as I was concerned, he was tough, reliable and would never let me down.

I remembered a friendly scrap we had once had, rolling all over the floor at his home. When we eventually stood up and parted with exhaustion and with sweat pouring from our bodies, there was a flow of blood streaming down Rex's left leg. I was terrified and ran to my aunt; he just stood there and laughed. She finally discovered that, tucked away inside his pocket, was a one-sided Ever-ready razor blade. This had carved a deep gash in his thigh, which had to be stitched at the hospital. His humour changed quickly when we arrived at the clinic; he passed out as soon as he saw the needle. Injections seemed to terrify him.

I watched anxiously as Rex and the other boy rolled down to the dry bottom of the dyke. Unfortunately, the lad who was involved in the fight was on the receiving end of some severe punishment. He was screaming as Rex sat on top of him and punched him across his face. It was what I had expected and laughed with enormous delight. Amidst all the cheers and shouts, a mate of the lad decided to assist his pal and save him from a relentless thrashing. I wasn't for one moment going to allow this and decided to engage myself in this unfair scrap. I casually picked up a brick that lay close by and then slid down the embankment and delivered a thundering blow to the unfortunate lad's head. There was a crunching sound like the breaking of bone china. His screams were piercing as he staggered about holding his injured head, his face masked in an endless flow of blood. I gazed at him without blinking, afraid, unable to move a muscle. Now the scene was ugly as the cheers turned to screams of hysteria. Then there was more anguish, as he fell silent to the ground.

I needed to escape from my own company and I stood there feeling alone and petrified, my eyes blinded with tears, the brick, speckled with blood, still clenched in my hand. There was nothing but dark walls, dark shapes standing on the walls, shadows of people rocking backwards and forwards, shadows of classmates, shadows of others, strangers. Then I heard voices of schoolmates, anxious voices of the sisters who had been called to the scene and were staring at me as though outraged. I was trembling. The voices seemed to penetrate then float away into the sunlight, and the relentless faces on the bank filled me with dread. The poor lad was finally rushed away by the sisters. The school bus had arrived and the remainder of the pupils climbed inside heading for home, without me. I was immediately marched off under supervision to the superior's office, silently blaming myself for getting involved in the scuffle. The atmosphere inside the building was sombre; there was an icy stillness and I felt that I was going to be violently sick. I sat trembling outside the main office, and gazed at the ceiling, thinking of home and the rolling meadows with the children playing.

Suddenly the door opened and a sister beckoned me inside, then left. It was a large panelled room, with a huge glass window, which overlooked a great lawn on the south side. The walls were decorated with Oriental sketches, with colourful artistic creatures swimming in decorated seas, grotesque beasts and sea snakes. Everything looked forbidding and frightening to the eyes of a young lad. Several books, stacked tidily, added a little warmth to the atmosphere. In one corner, perched strikingly on a compact table, a pair of candelabra glowed with the light of long-stemmed candles. It was pleasantly cool and the window stood open, as the fading sun danced through the shadows cast by a giant tree that stood outside.

Sister Harriet, still dressed in her habit and exhibiting an air of authority, sat on something that looked like a great carved oak throne. She looked at me with a somewhat bemused expression, then confronted me with a barrage of extremely difficult questions. She demanded explanations for my horrible behaviour, her strict countenance hiding any hint of emotion. My brain was blanketed by my fear didn't fall far away from it, and acted as a brake on any thoughts. I tried desperately to think of what to say or to find some excuse, but the words didn't come out, only settled in my throat like pebbles on a beach. If I could just be alone, away from all the confusion.

'I've sent for your aunt,' she said abruptly, looking visibly distressed, her tone informal. She possessed a wealth of wisdom and knowledge, gained through decades of experience. I felt that my retribution was about to begin, when my impudence was slowly stifled by her huge stature. I lowered my eyes and did not reply as a feeling of shame crept over me. Finally I received a severe reprimand, a verbal caution for violating the high standard held by the school, and ten painful lashes of the cane on my backside. All this was considered a disgrace and I hurt pretty badly.

I sat outside Sister Harriet's office in a lot of discomfort, waiting patiently for my aunt to arrive. Time passed and the silent fear suddenly disappeared, when I saw her walk gracefully through the main doors, with a gentle smile on her face. I felt a surge of excitement flooding through my body, and drew in a breath of instant relief. She was immediately followed by the boy's parents looking extremely disturbed, their faces twisted with sarcasm. However, I was not to be intimidated; the nearness of my aunt's presence just brought a total calm, like reassuring clouds. I felt isolated from society, when she slowly disappeared into the sister's office. I leaned forward with my elbows resting on my knees, face cupped in my hands and my ears strained for any words that might filter through the door. But they spoke quietly and deliberately so, their muted conversation designed not to be heard. The passage of time only increased the tension and confusion, aggravating my emotions. I sat patiently facing the evening twilight, which streamed through the window and formed images on the floor, but all my senses were turned inwards whispering words of assurance.

There was a seemingly long wait. Predictions, evaluations, and opinions of human behaviour filtered in and out of my exhausted brain. I despised the endless delay with thoughts invisible to the outside world. Suddenly I was startled by my aunt's presence, her smile deep with warmth and satisfaction. I jumped to my feet and placed my arms around her waist, overcome with emotion. The lad was all right; he'd had his head shaved and stitched, and, except for a large swelling and a severe headache, he was comfortable at home.

Through all the trauma my aunt had remained perfectly calm and undaunted. There was no anger, there was no nervousness. I felt a little humiliated and guilty for her sake and broke into tears. I didn't get to hear that familiar phrase, 'Boys don't cry', for when I raised my eyes she was standing there motionless, looking at me with eyes as full as mine. We walked slowly down the corridor into the open night where a blast of warm air greeted us. I searched for a few right words to say but couldn't speak, only make a formless sound. A moment later she patted me on the head and slipped an arm around me for support.

'Let's go home, son. Everything will be fine now,' she said in a deep resonant voice.

My serenity spread like bright sunlight on a summer's day. I smiled gratefully at her as she proceeded to take me home; it didn't matter any more, she was there, strong, courageous, and full of compassion. She considered it more important that I should feel secure with her, and I did.

Summers and monsoons came and went, with the celebrations of the New Years soon over. I had finally completed my formal education at St Michael's, which concluded at the second standard. The customary procedure was that the girls would remain behind and continue with their schooling. The boys would leave and further their education at another school. January 1939 signalled my entry into the Government English High School on Bund Road, commencing at the third standard, this being the reception standard. Mrs D Fisher was to initiate my introduction by making her presence felt with a stamp of towering authority.

'I would like to welcome all of you to your new class,' she said in a tone slightly tinged with irony. 'You will be under my supervision for at least another full year,' she added with a friendly smile. The term used to address her was 'Master', a process customary throughout the school. Her husband, Donald, also a member of the teaching set, lectured at the seventh standard. She had a dumpy stature, with a roly-poly figure, short brown hair and brown eyes, and was in her late thirties. I didn't especially like her, the guard dog expression bothered me. However, I respected her position and got on with my education, regardless of her authoritative methods. Their son, Patrick, being a little older than me, was in the next class, but we were to become close friends.

This immense complex was one of the largest schools in Burma, covering several acres of land. Magnificent well-tended lawns with gardens extended across the entire front and gazed over the busy thoroughfare. A huge assortment of breathtaking blossoms, arranged with regimental precision, embellished the whole exterior with authority. Although governed by the relative light they received each day, they brooked no resistance from public admiration and approval. The drive from the main road led directly to the steps of the assembly hall. Extended on either side of this theatre were the classrooms. Entry to them was made via long windowed corridors. Each class accommodated no fewer than sixty boys of all denominations, regardless of colour, race and creed. Numerous highly qualified teachers moved systematically from classroom to classroom, lecturing on issues in which they were qualified. The pupils remained in their own grade during these periods, reducing the confusion of movement and maintaining a steady rhythm. This proved to be a far more beneficial and a generally friendly system.

There were also numerous staff quarters for those billeted in the school. A number of servants were employed to maintain the prestigious high standards required by the school authorities. The cooking, cleaning, laundry, servicing and preservation of the grounds would come under their jurisdiction. Finally, the elegantly constructed and preserved dormitories housed the boarders, who remained at the school during the whole term and only returned home to their families for the annual holidays. To the rear, bound and regulated, were all the facilities for the sporting activities, which were an essential part of the school's heritage. Secured squarely in one corner was the impressive open-air swimming bath. The remainder of the grounds was divided into sections, comprising football and hockey pitches, tennis courts, assorted athletic tracks and a recreation area. The balance of this vast arena was carpeted in plush green velvet grass, tended and trimmed regularly by the gardeners.

The school was divided equally into three houses. During each term they would compete against each other in scholastic issues and sporting events as part of the national curriculum, thus adhering to the great tradition. They were known as the Boarders, the Saint John's and the Adventurers. I belonged to the latter, family convention saw to that. My Uncle Leo, who was a master at the school, and his three brothers were all members of that house during their schooldays.

The school uniform was khaki shirts and shorts, navy blue stockings with light-blue tops, black shoes and a navy blue blazer with light-blue piping, the top pocket bearing the insignia GEHS embroidered in gold. These were the school colours signifying a whole syndrome of perfection and a hallmark of great quality. To a young scholar it was intimidating, yet awe-inspiring.

Each year a fierce tournament took place between this school and the Diocese college from Rangoon. A burning desire to compete in any of the sporting events, which were organised on an age basis, was swift testimony to those who were committed in their search of success. To represent one's school was considered an honour and to prevail was an uplifting experience and the avenue to personal achievement. I desperately wanted to compete and to triumph. All my uncles had accomplished success in their youth. I thought very carefully on how to conduct my search for acceptance. The vision that I had of myself as a boxer was my foremost objective. I had arrived home on the bus after completing my preliminary day, feeling pleasantly at ease and sat down next to my aunt, who was delighted to see me.

'How did you enjoy your first day at school?' she asked with a look of pleasure, her eyes sparkling with life.

'Oh, it wasn't too bad but it's so big!' I replied, feeling a little complacent.

I glanced nervously down at my small hands clasped together under the table, wondering if I'd been too cocky and daring in volunteering for the school's boxing squad. Not having a father figure to depend on, I desperately needed a male reference point in proving something, at least to myself. The news that my Uncle Leo was coming to stay with us shortly was encouraging and lifted my spirits, as he was a keen sportsman himself. Surely his experience and helpful advice would channel some impetus into my enthusiasm; besides, engaging in this kind of activity would require his stamp of approval. At nine years of age, I was the eldest of the new generation of the Harding family residing in the town. My two older cousins, Rex and Deryck, who were boarders at the school, and were themselves involved in the sporting project, lived in Myingre[2] some distance away. I couldn't very well bombard them with a barrage of questions. Besides, they were

---

[2] Pronounced *Mingair.*

usually immersed in their own functional progress. Rex had also found himself a girlfriend, Florence Nortsquires. I often teased him about his new sweetheart. She was really pretty, with long dark hair and dark eyes.

My aunt soon noticed out of the corner of her eye the mischievous glint on my face, and giving me a vacant stare, she asked, 'Have you been doing anything out of the ordinary today, son?'

I didn't answer her question directly, but then replied with fierce determination, 'I've joined the boxing team, Aunty.'

There was a small hiccup and a sustained hush before she answered. 'You've done what?' she asked, looking at me rather annoyed. Stirring emotions crossed her face with changing swiftness. 'What utter nonsense! You are far too young, son,' she added, her voice soft and cultured. She was probably justified in her fear but unable to disguise her displeasure.

'Don't worry, Aunty, I'm going to be trained first,' I spluttered feebly, then ran off to chat with my pals about my exciting new-found adventure, leaving her to continue with her paperwork, and also to avoid being buried under an avalanche of questions. She certainly didn't want me fighting, although she was immensely supportive during my early life. The potential rewards appeared to have blown away; besides, what would my mother have to say?

It wasn't going to be a carefree life for us. There would be immense difficulties, but circumstances could be controlled. Love and affection would release much of the pressure. She wanted goodness, a fine mind and for me to have the right values in life. She accepted my harmless pranks and high spirits without question or embarrassment, but with an unusual sense of humour that delighted in confounding people by her unexpected remarks. I was the apple of her eye, and she was eternally grateful that Tye was still with us, contributing her personal style of excellence, when she wasn't around. I was pugnacious, observant, curious, with a rebellious streak and a trace of mischievous immaturity that touched a nerve. As I grew, I needed the answers to everything. Although I was not clever at to mathematics, science and foreign languages, it was history, English and geography that gave me what I wanted the most, some hint, some picture of the country I'd been born in, and a lot more about the world in general. Sport created enormous excitement, public adulation and a good vehicle in which I enjoyed competing with mercurial enthusiasm, invariably a chosen form of defence against verbal accusation. But I hated any injustice that was inflicted by the very same system responsible for administering it.

We were sitting on the verandah, absorbed in the peaceful atmosphere of an evening sunset when she questioned me once again.

'Why didn't you choose a more delicate sport?' she asked anxiously, trying to sound discreetly irritated. The study of biology always fascinated her; now tiny fragments of a distorted invisible picture were forming in her mind.

I didn't answer her directly but stared sullenly before replying.

'I'm going to run as well, Aunty,' I said, with a cheeky smile and a glint in my eyes.

Somehow there still seemed to be a strain of contradictions hanging in the air. All she could visualise was a bloody nose, lumps and stitches patterned all over my face.

'I'm must have a serious talk with your Uncle Leo when he arrives. I think that you are far too young and too small,' she said, feeling a little apprehensive, then buried herself in some paperwork. I glanced up surprised at the forcefulness of her tone and feeling a little upset.

By the time Uncle Leo came home, it was getting late. Nevertheless, this wasn't going to prevent her from discussing this aggravating situation. I listened as they talked in the soothing atmosphere of the lounge. Everything that could be said was said. Suddenly he just laughed with a full-blooded sound, which drifted off into the air like the smoke from a cigarette. He was genuinely delighted to hear that I had chosen to compete. She seemed more surprised than angry about his advice, although his powerful and candid opinion was always respected. He was a burly tough gentleman, standing well over six feet, with black wavy hair and bespectacled brown eyes. He was built like a truck, with a rugged face like granite, but his personality was as impressive as his stature and his idea of teaching was simple and uncomplicated. He was a man who taught by example.

As soon as the uneasiness drifted away, I felt relaxed and revelled in the secure feeling this had given me. I began thinking ahead about how I might actually enjoy it. With these thoughts in my mind a distinct change came over me, a fierce pull of desire. Suddenly Aunty Iris was pleased, her face covered with a fleeting thought of solace, and she smiled with satisfaction as if her expectation would prove conclusive. At least she would take comfort from my eagerness to participate, and my zest for sport continued.

The monsoon rains came and went now that September had arrived with all its intensity. Being a hill station, the town and the surrounding areas never flooded. The eagerly awaited holidays also drew nearer. The noise of a few streets took on a new hold, initiated by the sporting gala between the schools. The town joined in the hysteria and the atmosphere was electric in the school grounds. The hard surface and grass verges teemed with excited families, shouting for relatives and close friends engaged in activities. There was no single voice, just a cacophony of discordant high-pitched tones. My aunt watched with pride and her eyes danced with delight, as I struggled to succeed in the junior one hundred yard sprint in an atmosphere void of air. My legs ached with a deep agonising pain, but my heart pumped with satisfaction. It was a laborious effort just to run to her.

With the completion of the field events outside, the assembly hall was now transformed into a boxing arena for the more hardy competitors. I waited patiently for my turn to arrive, as the tension in my stomach increased. I waited to step into the ring, but was not so confident and assured for this event. It was unfamiliar and uncharted territory for me. I was praying hard, concentrating, and for a moment my anger surfaced. Time passed and my arms ached. I wanted to kill him, but something happened. I hit out with all my remaining strength; it was the best I could manage but it didn't connect solidly. I know that it hurt him. I could tell as he took a few steps backwards and winced. With an enormous effort, I struggled to my feet for the final round. He was a good boxer, better than I had expected. I didn't see the next punch, but my head was rumbling in my neck.

Exhaustion and unsteadiness were all the same; with my second wind my eyes were seeing two heads. I was badly shaken, bruised and my chest felt tight. My lips were dry and swollen. The infuriating part was that I thought that I had won.

'It's nice to have you back,' my aunt said in a whisper. Tears welled up in her eyes, and coursed down her cheeks at my endeavour.

I tried not to cry. I didn't want her to see any weakness, remembering something important she had once said: 'It's taking part that counts.' I thought that maybe all this was just a dream, unfortunately, no, it wasn't a dream. It was a drug called losing.

Our school finally won the tournament outright for that year, and would be the visiting delegation the following season. I felt extremely proud to have contributed a little towards accomplishing that accolade. The tournament was finally brought to a close before the early hours of the morning with a magnificent dance, which included a buffet displaying a huge concentration of mouth-watering dishes. It was to be a cardinal day in my life, a day that was to signal the end of my childhood. Unknown to me at that time I would never again participate in any of the future tournaments.

It was now October and with the holidays over we had returned to school. Preparations for the final examinations, due at the end of November, were the main topic. Then the entire school would participate for advancement to higher standards. England was savaged by a World War and the whole of Europe trembled in its wake, creating a chilling undercurrent that would eventually destroy countless lives. After two strenuous weeks of self-determination, I had completed my exams successfully and would advance to the fourth standard. The school finally closed for the long Christmas holidays, and suddenly my life was good.

January 1940 had arrived. In company with a couple of pals I walked into my new classroom. My teacher's name was Miss Alice Baker. She was slightly older than my aunt but knew her personally; they had studied together at the teachers' training college in Rangoon. She had a pallid complexion with sharp features, and black hair that was shaped into a huge bun at the back. She certainly wasn't creative with make-up and had a stern upright stature and a 'jumble sale' image. She had the appearance of a governess rather than a teacher. However, I was fortunate enough to become her favourite pupil and had to restrain my overconfidence as I settled down to a slightly tougher routine.

Mid-April fell from the clouds with the advent of the water festival of Thingyan, introducing the celebration of the Burmese New Year when water is launched on everybody who dares to venture into the streets. Because of this democratic ceremony, we had finished dinner early that evening and were looking forward to participating in the festivities, and although the weather was at its hottest period, outside the sunlight had been struck from the sky by a glorious purple twilight.

'Is Uncle Leo coming with us tonight,' I asked my aunt eagerly, putting on my coat hurriedly. I felt protected by his company.

'As soon as he has completed all his paperwork,' she replied, then smiled without opening her lips.

She turned slowly to face him, as if the balance of power was in his hands, then they lapsed into polite chatter. He went into the lounge to pocket his things, then returned, wrapped in his overcoat and looking forward to the evening's pleasures.

'Shall we go and enjoy the festivities?' he remarked, putting an arm around my shoulder but not failing to notice the joy and eagerness stretched across my face.

We left the house more quickly than I expected and his company gave rise to a boisterous gaiety that had been missing. We walked slowly down the avenue. There was an eerie stillness in the night air and the day trembled on the edge of darkness. A slight breeze sighed through the trees making them rustle secretly. There was chaos everywhere, oxen, carts and rickshaws pushed through narrow paths. Street-traders sat behind stalls of various types of fruit; some traders were roasting Indian corn on charcoal fires. Further on towards the town centre the area was being flooded by torrents of water cascading from balconies and fire hydrants. Firework displays and massive fire balloons, spectacularly decorated with oriental insignia and emblems, illuminated the iridescent sky. We blended in with the throng of excited spectators, greeting a few acquaintances. It was virtually impossible to move around in comfort, as numerous processions blocked many of the entrances in this watery wilderness. But there were periods of relative calm as the furry clouds slowly unravelled and gently blew away.

We moved around in company with close friends, and enjoyed the festival for a number of hours. By the end of the evening the majority of the residents were saturated and tired, including myself. Although I said nothing, I began to feel a little unwell and thoroughly exhausted with all the commotion.

'I think it's time for us to leave,' said my aunt anxiously, noticing my strange behaviour.

Her motives were good, and she looked troubled, judging by her immediate reaction. A distinct change had come over me. I felt very cold with a dull incessant pounding in my head. I also found it very difficult to keep from shivering in this cyclone of discomfort.

'We need to be getting home soon,' she urged, with an expression of worry stretching across her face.

We arrived back later than expected and by now I was feeling very weak after a spasm of sickness.

'Now go quickly to your room and remove all those wet clothes,' she said. 'I'll be with you in a minute.'

Everything seemed still and all sound appeared distant, as I stripped off. She rubbed me down thoroughly, after I had stepped out of the hot bath, and stood on rubbery legs. I hurried out of the bathroom with a sense of urgency, changed into my pyjamas and inched my way into the bed. My heart was pounding as, still trembling with the cold, I clutched the hot-water bottle. The room was full of shapes and shadows. I tossed and turned endlessly as my head rolled on the pillow, and sleep was a long time coming.

I awoke the next morning with a weight of fever on my eyelids. My body began to shake and the side effects were affecting my vision. I had never felt as bad as this before, and the heaviness was already surging through my body. My condition was worse, so my aunt immediately sent for the family doctor, fearing a reoccurrence of a previous illness from which I had suffered, malaria. After a close examination, the physician diagnosed an early form of pneumonia but the uncertainty was a source of anxiety to him so he promptly arranged for my removal to the civil hospital. The days passed into weeks and my condition worsened. The sickness seemed to heighten with the weight loss, and through heavy-lidded and swollen eyes I could see faintly the outlines of my aunt and mother. They were sitting beside the bed, their heads buried in their hands and seemed to be ever present, night and day. I felt protected by the constant darkness and the sheltered location. Occasionally even the huge glass windows seem to throb with a misty light, as I lay there motionless. The pounding in my chest frightened me, and there was a silence. I didn't want to die.

If only I could have cried but I couldn't. I just felt sorrow and sadness in a world where things were going wrong without any proper reason. But the fever, the doctors, the nurses and the beds were ever constant and I felt condemned to silence and seclusion, alone and helpless. There was a jumbled disharmony; even the room suddenly appeared to be getting much colder. Now icy shivers ran up and down my spine. I desperately needed to talk with somebody. I needed to talk with God, the unseen guest in every household and the silent listener to every conversation. I turned my head very slowly and saw a faint light in the distance; it revealed a wilderness. Then a warm glow encircled my entire body. The light seemed to grow much larger in a night of stars. Then someone approached me very slowly, shrouded with a radiant light. Almost instantly I felt a deep sensation which frightened me. The power of this fear closed my eyes, but the power of curiosity was the stronger and reopened them again. They persisted in seeing something I really didn't want to look at, as a strange silhouette came towards me, indistinct, then more distinct, as it came much closer, walking effortlessly, gliding along the surface without touching the floor. I reached out to touch the stranger, and caress the halo but couldn't move. It was then that I noticed it was faceless. I watched entranced and fascinated by this vision and without any fear. Then I heard a man's voice distinctly say, 'You must go back this time, son, and be careful of that step.' The voice was soft and it flowed over me like a golden stream of beauty. Then the stranger turned very carefully and moved away from me as the light faded. Sadly he was gone before I could touch or speak to him.

I tried desperately to say something, but only a faint moan escaped from my throat as delicate as a silver strand of a spider's web. I awoke to a deathly silence and a great feeling of exultation. Nothing could ever match this highly emotional feeling, even the air seemed to reverberate with high expectation. I was very happy to see my aunt and mother still sitting beside the bed, with tears streaming down their faces, but they were tears of joy. I was hesitant to mention my strange and touching story to them. The vivid details appeared full of so many contradictions, which only added to the turmoil of my deep emotions. When I finally confessed the events that happened on this particular occasion to my aunt, she accepted my story as unguided childish innocence, caused by the lengthy periods of delirium and endless days and nights in a breathless lull when an angel is supposed to pass.

I gradually recovered from my horrendous ordeal, and my health improved sufficiently for me to return home. Soon I was able to stand on my own two feet and my sole determination was set for another short journey. The stranger's words of warning haunted me a lot more than my aunt, as the curtains of doubt traipsed constantly through my active mind. However, I decided to keep my discomfort to myself.

Finally, one Saturday morning shortly after our breakfast, she noticed the anxiety was still in my eyes. Willingly she agreed to examine the steps from the apex of the wooden verandah, although the full significance of her suggestion was really only to satisfy my infectious enthusiasm. Curiosity accompanied us carefully down the wooden steps. We paused frequently as they creaked with our weight, while searching for any slight damage in the rather ancient open staircase. Our interest was soon replaced by fear and anguish, when my aunt knelt down to secure better vision on the underside. Suddenly she shuddered with a look of trepidation on her face. Tears filled her eyes when she discovered a huge crack under the sixth step. It was eerie and sinister, and the silence was palpable. I felt a jolt of panic, and my whole body convulsed as I stared for a long time at the deep crack, for I needed to believe. Then quite suddenly there was no pain, no sobs, only thoughts. It also explained to me why we met, and why he spoke. I wanted to see him again so badly. The memories are now etched into my brain. They will be there for ever.

Here in the white heat of the tropics sadly our summer holidays whispered their warning, but some things really never do change with the passing of time, like the sun, the wind, and the rain. The highlight of the customary break was the occasional visit to the immensely popular Arnisakan Falls, only a few miles away to the north. Uncle Dick being employed on the railways allowed us the privilege of free travel on the train. I enjoyed tagging along for this lavishly organised picnic with Aunty Irene and her children, Peter and John, the twins, who were five years old, and Maureen, the baby, was barely one. This part of the wooded area was really picturesque, surrounded by big tree jungle and the recurrent villages with huts made of palm thatch, although somewhere in the high jungle even the road might die, as the graceful gum trees rustled in the breeze. Here the miniature falls, cascading into the lake in the morning light, were unforgettably striking. They created an expression of charm and tranquillity by bringing civilisation to a rural corner of the earth and leaving an indelible image in one's mind. The scenic picnic area served as a living playground, under the great dimension of the beckoning sky, while some of the shallow sections of the lake provided a paddling haven for the younger children and illustrated an exotic landscape of a dream.

On the home front, we had also recently coped with the stressful burden of moving once again to a new residence, financially assisted by Uncle Leo. It was a bungalow situated at the extreme end of a small private road, which led directly to a dead end. Open grassy fields spread over the outlying area, and a narrow footpath, which ran down one side of the house, led to the main road, later to bear a famous name, the 'Burma Road'. This continued over a small bridge and directly to the right of it stood one of the centrepieces of the town, the Empire Bioscope. There were two other cinemas, to help quench the people's insatiable thirst for films. The Regal faced the clock tower in the town centre, and the Rialto stood next to Hadji Sulimans, the largest grocery store in the main street.

The front of the bungalow, where most of the brickwork was concealed beneath a dense growth of ivy, faced the rear entrance of the intimidating Masonic Lodge. For me this was still a haunting sight, but it never troubled me. The windows at the front looked upon a small lawn, regularly bathed by the pale rays of a late afternoon sun. Towards the rear, enormous eucalyptus trees coiled lazily towards the sky and seemed to press forward, with a twilight of tangled branches, against the house. The long, thin, leaves rustled softly and the cry of many colourful birds broke the silence. At dusk, the cosy night air was furnished with an alluring sweet fragrance. Extending to the right of the property was a huge triangular-shaped garden, bordered with numerous fruit trees, a plush green lawn, with plots of flower bushes neatly arranged, forming a treasure chest of sparkling colours. In the middle, elegantly perched, was a little wishing well, with sturdy ivy covering the exterior and wooden planking concealing the opening. The winding handle, which was connected to the rope and bucket, was locked for my benefit. Finally, in the far corner, were the servants' quarters, sufficiently large enough for all of them to live in relative comfort, although they were easily accessible for my regular jaunts for a chat, plus the occasional taste of intricate dishes served up by them.

I was now experiencing a new kind of excitement. Suddenly the unhappy memories of bygone days were comfortably locked away in the characterisation of a child's emotional mind. The constant recreation also played a major part in that transition. As usual, the sports gala between the schools had taken place in Rangoon. Unfortunately, still frail and rather weak following my recent illness, I hadn't competed. I tended to disappear out of sight to brood and suffer alone, rather than let anyone know that I was still very deeply hurt. The final examinations approached as November showed its face, but there were some doubts about whether or not I would return to school in time. I had already assumed that I would be returning; for me not to reappear would have been an admission of defeat. My aunt was equally proud to hear that I had the courage to see it through. Contrary to all expectations I failed miserably. I had no conception of knowing that it was going to be so tough and felt thoroughly ashamed of myself, constantly hiding behind a horrible mask of defeat. The thought of remaining behind in the same standard for another complete year was also painful.

The passing of the Christmas festival and the New Year celebrations brought January 1941. Then I began my new term in the same class once again with Miss Baker. There were others who had also failed, and although I had many excuses, it was a blemish on the Harding trait. The shame clung like unrelenting snow. However, my devoted teacher soon decided to remove the paralysis I'd furrowed myself into by setting me a challenge. A very friendly and pleasant agreement was made between us respectfully. Should I finish at the top of the class during each of the monthly examinations, and complete my term in prime position in the finals, she would present me with a precious gift. I was a good listener and even with her influence, integrity, and belief in my capabilities, the challenge was a difficult one. Then, with extreme reluctance and after a long hesitation, I accepted. Gradually the days passed into weeks, and the months progressed steadily towards the summer holidays and the examinations.

Here I must digress.

During the late thirties, among the late traders of numerous strikes, a young man named Aung Sang came to the forefront. He was an ardent Burmese nationalist, and his sole ambition was for an independent Burma. With many comrades, he threatened to overhaul the present British government. He was soon considered a menace to the stability of the country. Immediate plans were to have him arrested and interrogated for political reasons. However, disguised as a Chinaman, he secretly booked a passage on a Norwegian freighter and escaped to Japan. Ignoring Japanese fascism, he was obsessed by the belief that they would agree to his passionate philosophy for his beloved country. So he decided to collaborate with them, and was eventually trained in jungle warfare on Hainan Island.

Following the Japanese attack on the American fleet at Pearl Harbour on 7 December 1941, a huge force of Japanese aircraft relentlessly bombed the city of Rangoon and its docks on

23 December 1941. This assault created widespread havoc, and decimated countless lives. Not satisfied with this initial attack, they arrived again on Christmas morning, strafing the streets as children ran out waving their flags jubilantly. It was a violation of maniacal brutality and ruthlessness. The human carnage left the city looking like a principle ghost town, like a vanquished civilisation. In March 1942, Aung Sang was smuggled back into the capital Rangoon with a band of associates. They were all expertly trained in guerrilla tactics, and were known as 'The Thirty Comrades'. Then he and his so-called liberation army helped Japan to invade the lower regions of Burma on 16 January 1942.

The governor, Sir Reginald Dorman-Smith, requested that there should be no immediate panic. He also confirmed that the Allies were capable of repelling any onslaught from the enemy. Many civilians lived religiously with this belief; they danced, they drank and enjoyed themselves, not contemplating any serious attack. They stubbornly refused even to consider it, even after the invasion of Malaya and Thailand. Finally, as panic and fear intervened, nothing could prevent the mass exodus that had already begun heading north from the southern regions. With the Allied forces heavily engaged all over Europe, those serving in the Far East weren't strong enough to withstand the full force of the invasion. Ferocious and devastating jungle warfare resulted in the deaths of thousands of British, Indian, Chinese, Burmese and Japanese forces. From this bitter conflict, names like Wingate, Slim and Stillwell were to become household legends.

However, by August 1942, Burma had collapsed and the whole country was under complete control of the Japanese military. Thousands of servicemen were compounded in concentration camps, and countless civilians were dispatched to refugee settlements, promptly supported by Aung Sang and his faithful comrades. It wasn't long before he realised the satanic brutality his people were subject to under Japanese Imperialism; it was far worse than under the British regime. After numerous secret discussions with Lord Mountbatten, he persuaded his ten thousand strong nationalist army to join forces with the British. They were renamed the Patriotic Burmese Forces, and together, after fierce fighting, they recaptured Rangoon on 3 May 1945, and not without the loss of hundreds of thousands of lives.

Summer had arrived; the expected sports tournament was cancelled because of the hostilities in the capital. I had already convinced myself that I would excel in the final exams, having finished in the prime position during the monthly examinations. And I did succeed. I had also structured a new-found optimism. This was coupled with vast self-assurance and delightful thoughts of receiving that present. Whatever it might be, it gave me an uplifting experience. My aunt neither encouraged nor discouraged me. All she would say was that one never knew what life had in store for us. For the present it was all excitement and good times.

My stomach fluttered with excitement on the long journey to Miss Baker's home in the countryside for my present. I kept looking at the tall trees, the ferns, and listening to the sound of the birds. My thoughts were too preoccupied for anything else to intervene as I hesitantly approached her residence. The grounds were well tended, and in the few evergreens birds flashed among the branches. I knocked at the front door nervously and waited patiently for her to appear. It opened slowly.

'Hello, Colin, I've been expecting you to call as it's Saturday,' she said, then smiled sheepishly, inviting me into her home. I stepped inside, closing the door behind me. It was a very cosy room, looking more in line with a library with all the books neatly shelved, but charming in its appearance. Despite the tightening in my stomach, I was feeling pleased with myself. After all, it wasn't something that happened very often. For a few moments, I couldn't think of anything to say or how to react. I was probably feeling a little shy.

'I'm delighted with your results, Colin, you really did surprise me,' she said, sounding reassuring.

Her comments regarding my success were received in silence through a touch of nervousness, but I nodded, still feeling a little uneasy. She left the room and returned sooner than expected. It came as something of a surprise when she handed me a beautiful little Siamese kitten.

I was delighted and overcome with emotion as I reached out to hold it gently.

'Thank you very much, Miss Baker.' I replied slowly, keeping my voice low.

'Now just you look after him,' she said, her words trailing off.

'I will, honest, I promise,' I replied and kissed him softly on his head.

'Now off you go, and I'll see you on Monday morning at school,' she said, looking thoroughly pleased with my visit.

After opening the door, she watched me leave with the kitten tucked safely in my top pocket. Outside the sun was high and the skies were a rich navy blue. However, the hostilities on the home front were intensifying to volatile boundaries. There were also strong rumours that families connected with the armed forces were soon to be evacuated. Numerous and antagonising decisions were being made instantly and with some remorse, heartache, and confusion. Many tears were to flow. Perhaps the circumstances surrounding our lives at that point made the critical difference to the festivities of 1941, so painful and unexciting. The conflict between America and Japan was now considered precarious, and reports of a possible invasion seemed inevitable. The American families employed and residing near Yenangyaung[3], home of the gigantic crude oilfields, had already begun a mass migration. Armed with the bare necessities, they left most of their belongings behind. Their country was now at war, which only helped to increase the dangers ahead.

Nearer home the atmosphere was just as explosive. The freedom and joy of a carefree life, which many took for granted, was now completely shattered. Anguish and frustration was a normal reaction. The pursuit of independence, however achieved, had become a veritable sickness, clutching at anything that moved like the fangs of a cancer. My relatives were already discussing plans for leaving, although I was never allowed to be present during these long debates. I personally found all this terribly unexciting and didn't attach any great importance to their woeful anxiety. Being still very young, I found these long drawn-out

---

[3] Pronounced *Yenangoung*.

conversations physically tiring and mentally very difficult to understand. I would sit outside waiting impatiently for them to finish, so I could be allowed back into the cosy adult company.

Because we were living under this perpetual threat of doom I needed an interim course to remove the sadness. I set my sights on another journey, one that would give me enormous pleasure and somewhere I could find happiness in spite of the dreadful circumstances. I needed a physical release to relieve some of the tension in my body and what better place than my Aunty Irene's residence, one of my usual haunts for mischief. The boys would be attending the Baptists' school, and Maureen would surely be asleep. I would use the short cut through the railway station, then cross the main intersection, which could sometimes prove very dangerous. This led me onto the road leading to her home, close to the locomotive sheds. It was a rather large building, the bottom section completely covered by black trellising. An exterior door opened into a six-foot wide corridor, which encircled two large rooms, occasionally used for children's parties and functions. An interior wooden staircase led to the first floor, which housed the bedrooms, bathroom, and the dining area. Heavy wooden external steps, protected by a sturdy banister, to the ground from a verandah at the rear.

The premises were surrounded by grassy fields and inside the hedged compound was an enormous garden to the front. This was regimentally packed with rows and rows of giant sweet peas and many assorted flowers, their soft colours paraded everywhere like the end of a rainbow. At the rear, where the land was greener, there was an added assembly of poultry, geese, ducks, and chickens. Outside the complex, the flatlands were a perfect sanctuary for her many cattle and goats, protected by dense woods. My enthusiastic arrival wasn't always greeted with favour and passion. The immature side to my nature kindled in me a tidal wave of active hysteria. With a huge sense of relief, I would launch myself forward to torment the cattle and scatter the poultry in a flood of frenzy, very much to her annoyance. My impish attitude would create a storm of protest from the servants, who would repeatedly complain to my aunt about my ungainly behaviour. Suddenly a harsh voice would bellow from an open bedroom window, 'What on earth is going on out there?' For a few moments there would be a definite silence. Her voice would return again. 'What are you doing, Colin?' She was already aware that I was around. 'Nothing, Aunty, honest,' would be my shifty reply. But with a note of disbelief in her voice she would say, 'Not according to what the servants have just complained about, it's no wonder the chickens aren't laying. Will you please leave them alone. If you can't behave yourself, off you go before Uncle Dick comes home from work.' I would nod, feeling ashamed of what I had done. However, that would be enough warning for me to leave quickly. I would be more frightened than excited and would make a rapid exit. Although he had a gentle nature, he was quite a dominant man with a rough streak about him. He was very strict, and there would be the sound of hurrying feet long before his arrival.

I would then seek pleasure in my Uncle Stan's, another favourite attraction. His home was small and compact, and he was usually at work when I called unexpectedly. Aunty Eileen would be there with a smile of welcome lighting her face. She always appreciated my visit and enjoyed my impish brand of company. There was a sort of mutual fascination between us which, in a small boy's eyes, could easily throw up a love affair. The age difference probably added to the mystique. My basic source of happiness and mischief was to chat away merrily, and she enjoyed listening to my stories and fantasies, with enormous pleasure and total harmony. They had four children. Peggy, the eldest girl, was a little younger than myself, Peta was eight, Leon, the elder of the two boys, was just four and the youngest, Robert, was barely two years old.

No excuse was too small for my visit, and her giant aviary was an inspiring fascination. It was a huge chain link structure connected to one side of the house. Enclosed were numerous fruit trees that spread over the dry ground, the branches bending silently and dipping into an attractive shallow pond. I could feel the immense delight, as we strolled through the enclosure discussing her exquisite collection of fantail doves. She admired them with justifiable pride and affection. There was once a gruesome moment during one of my previous visits, which happened with such swiftness on that particular day. The trees were bursting with green, the earth was dry and covered with the easily ruptured skin of topsoil. Aunty Eileen had placed a decorative coir mat on the ground near some bushes, directly under a huge circle of trees, which shaded the boundary of the gardens. She knew how to administer affection very easily, it was part of her make-up.

'If you and the two girls sit down quietly and behave yourselves, I will bring out some watermelon and cold coconut juice.'

We flocked together in perfect harmony. There was a flutter of laughter and a forum of indistinct idle chatter. We sat down cross-legged on the pretty mat, peacefully engaged in childish laughter. Suddenly a huge bump appeared underneath and slithered in an erratic rhythm. My body shook instantly. Peggy and Peta let out a terrifying scream and disappeared into the safety of the house, leaving me trapped in a vale of desolation. My eyes rolled open, then shut with frightening slowness. Aunty's gardener, attending to some firewood nearby, a chore that was part of his many duties, rushed towards me. I watched in silent horror as he stood before me wielding a huge axe. The blade glistened feverishly high in the humid air, like a finely balanced tightrope walker, before it came whistling down, flashing past my face and thumping the ground with a thundering blow. For a brief moment my eyes flickered as it glanced off the hard surface. Then it was raised sharply once again, the naked blade silver in the day's hazy light, before it whistled through the air once more. This time it went where it was supposed to go; suddenly there was a hushed silence. Lifting me away, in my state of paralysis, the gardener then removed the mat only to uncover what was left of the giant lifeless body of a king cobra, measuring almost twelve feet. Everything seemed to happen in a matter of seconds. The horrendous screams brought my aunt crashing through the screen door, her always pale skin now deathly white. Her wide-open eyes rolled slowly round to gaze uneasily at the earth.

'My God, where on earth did that creature come from?'

She had turned ice-cold, looking for a reason but there wasn't one. The gardener then took the sordid remains to a small fire at the end of the garden. A sense of relief that no one had been bitten flashed across my aunt's face. She blessed God, and soon regained control of herself. We all scampered inside, still shaking from the traumatic experience. Any direction away from the garden pleased me. We tried to disguise the reality of what might have been and the fear that remained within us. I soon realised that any courage that I might have had had soon disappeared; my legs were rubbery and my body still trembled.

Chapter IV

January, 1942

The years passed, and I didn't grow much taller but older. This bothered me and I needed a reasonable explanation.

'Aunty, will I grow big like Uncle Leo one day?' I asked looking wistful.

'Only if you eat all your vegetables and tell the truth more often,' she replied with a wonderful smile.

I studied her words carefully before answering, with a sense of innocence, 'You're fibbing, Aunty. I believed you when you said there was a man in the moon. I also believed you about Santa Claus. You said that "please" was a magic word. Can I go to the flicks tonight, please?' It was a childish urge to retaliate.

'We'll see how you feel after completing your first day back at school,' she said, with an imploring look.

It had been a restless night, but I woke early and prepared excitedly for my new term in the fifth standard. Now I felt a little sadness with me, having already spent two pleasant years under the capable expertise of Miss Baker. My new teacher was Miss Doyle. She was very attractive and strikingly tall, slender with fair skin and a sharp nose, beneath which was revealed an infectious smile. Her doe-like luminous eyes were darker than her hair and, going by her dress sense, she was in her late twenties. The first day was interesting but very formal, and mostly occupied with the introduction of many advanced subjects. There seemed to be a mountain to climb, as I shuffled into our comfortable living room. The sound of a horse-drawn carriage coming to an abrupt halt outside the bungalow interrupted the casual conversation that I was having with my aunt. There was a feeble tentative knock at the front entrance. Tye promptly unlocked the door, then opened it.

'Mrs Townend,' she said unexpectedly. 'Please do come

inside.'

There were looks of total surprise, and silence fell, as soon as my mother entered the lounge, her immediate presence silencing the blissful chatter in the blink of an eyelid. It was also noticeable that she had changed quite a lot during her long absence. She was definitely larger than I imagined her to be, and she was wearing one of those maternity dresses that clung to her shape. A parade of pale blue and pink hearts was stamped on a white silk fabric. Quite pretty, I thought.

For a few moments neither of them spoke; there was a distinctive silence.

'Hello, Iris,' Mother said with an air of authority about her, as she moved towards the polished table. She then glanced at me and said, 'Hello, son, how are you?' Her tone spoke of formality. I couldn't speak but stared at her, feeling a little embarrassed. My aunt kissed her on the cheek with a fervour lacking affection.

'Gwen,' she said in a tone far from sincere, 'Fancy seeing you after all this time.' She glanced at her with eyes clearly betraying her annoyance. There was a slight hint of disapproval. Although there was a close family unit, the relationship between them had been rather strained for a number of years. In 1940, my mother had married a Sergeant Arthur Townend serving in the King's Own Yorkshire Infantry, who were stationed outside the town, a British regiment acting as a protector of the colonial system. At the present time she was also pregnant. They were living in private residence on B Road, in preference to army quarters.

'There are certain things that we have to talk about as soon as possible, regarding Colin's future,' she said with a forceful attitude. Their faces were close together, almost touching, as she continued, 'We both have an important role to play, although we don't necessarily agree with each other. You are already aware of the delicate position the country is in, especially with the recent hostilities over the border.' I glanced up at my aunt, who looked calm, waiting for the next remark. 'My husband, Arthur, has agreed to take him on the army strength, accepting full responsibility for his future. The relative certificates have been signed and documented.' She paused, casting a quick glance in my direction. 'The military are evacuating all the families attached to the forces within the next few weeks, so he will be travelling with me. We do have to consider his safety and future, don't you agree, Iris?'

It was a conversation designed to irritate. Aunty Iris stared at her with unconcealed interest and listened motionless for a few minutes. She tried desperately to avoid a slanging match, knowing of my mother's vulnerability due to her physical condition. But any harmony they might previously have had was instantly blown away. Her composure went up in flames. 'No, I'm not at all happy with your comments,' she said, her eyes blazing. 'You are in no position to demand anything, and I disagree with everything that you have suggested. We are a family unit now and I want him to stay with me.' Her eyes filled with tears. I watched in silence, as one spilled down her cheek. Her mouth was quivering as she tried to control her feelings, then she burst out, 'I hate all this, Gwen. Why did you have to come here tonight? For God's sake, Gwen, why can't you just leave things as they are?'

Aunty Iris was heartbroken, knowing deep inside there wasn't much that she could do, and she had to concentrate hard to find the correct words. There was no way to argue against her, she was right of course.

'You do not understand, I know that,' she said, her voice shaking with emotion. 'But you will before I'm finished and before you leave this house. I promise, you will understand everything.' She hesitated briefly, fuming with impotent rage. I was surprised at the tone of her voice. 'All this sudden concern, you don't really care, it's just some fake show of interest you've conjured up. I've been his guardian since he was barely out of nappies. I've clothed, fed, educated and nursed him through all illnesses without any assistance from you. Now you have the audacity to come here and ask for his immediate return. Personally I've no intention of letting him go.'

I listened, trying to think what all this meant, my thoughts in total confusion weighing heavily on me. She was a little calmer now, her anger and nervousness had passed, and her face was damp with tears. Mother finally stood up to withdraw from this heated atmosphere, losing none of her composure. Her face flushed with anger, as she left, her well-chosen words to sink into my aunt's thoughts.

'I will be seeing you again very soon,' she said. 'Only the next time the army will have something to say; he is under their jurisdiction now.' Then she walked out of the house to the waiting carriage, her footsteps promptly disappearing beneath a sky sunk in darkness.

Reflecting back through my thoughts, I recalled that the previous summer had been a dismal one with the cancelled games. The spreading poison of war constantly hounded our lives and formed a huge trough of depression throughout the country. A storm was brewing and it could be felt.

Now two weeks had passed since my mother's visit, but there were still clouds of anxiety hovering in the atmosphere at home. I was reading, when there was a soft knock at the front door. I turned with a distracted look and went to open it. My mother was standing there accompanied by two men in military uniforms, carrying briefcases.

'Hello, son, can we come in?' she asked politely.

I felt nervous, scared. I didn't speak but swallowed hard and stepped aside as they entered the lounge. My aunt and uncle were sitting at the table discussing future plans, with a look of anxiety floating across their faces. After the introductions, I ran off to my bedroom. I could faintly hear voices drifting in from the lounge; they were urgent, imperative, persistent voices, a mangled contradiction designed to upset rather than resolve. These were long discussions; the voices went on and on while I strode angrily around the room. I sat on the bed and listened to these heated arguments, which appeared endless, and felt like a homeless waif. The hours that passed seemed like a thousand days, until they finally left, with the sound of their sharp footsteps hurrying out of the house.

Although it was very late I crept into the lounge quietly, my heart pounding and my skin freezing with fear.

'Sit down, son, I've something to say to you,' my aunt said softly to me.

Uncle Leo looked disgusted, feeling pressurised.

'I'm very sorry to have to tell you this, but you will be

60

returning to your mother's home at the weekend. The military are evacuating all the families attached to the army shortly, and it will be much safer for you with them,' she said quietly.

I listened with a blank expression.

'Hopefully,' she said, 'I will be leaving myself very soon but I don't exactly know when, so it's better that you go on ahead. Besides you will be so busy packing, and there will be no more school. Now go to bed, it's very late.' Her dark eyes showed panic, agony and fear as she ruffled my hair.

With the hostilities raging in the southern regions, the day finally arrived for my departure. I sat nervously close to my aunt in the lounge, with my cases neatly packed and the kitten on my lap. Aunty Iris looked terribly upset, we'd shared so many happy times together, now it was all over. Strictly speaking, she had embroidered the truth to please me; it was no mystic decision, my safety was very important to her. I realised that this simple act of surrender was more essential than the intention itself. The overcast sky suddenly grew bleak and dark clouds swelled with the threat of a storm. With the worsening weather the knock that finally came on the front door echoed like a huge roar of thunder. When the door was opened and I saw my mother, I felt as if my insides had turned to shattered glass. She walked briskly into the lounge, and it was obvious from her expression that she approved of what she saw, my readiness.

Since I was used to obedience, I listened carefully to all her suggestions and tried to understand all her reasons. Somehow I felt that I was now growing up, with both feet firmly on the ground, at a time when many young people knew absolutely nothing of the historic upheaval that was to come. It was impossible to describe the conflicting emotions that swept through me, confusion, gratefulness, pique, yet the most divine was the love which surged through my body as I clung desperately to my aunt, who kissed me on my forehead. For that moment my world seemed cupped in a silent pall. I left my home slowly, with my pet tucked in my arms, and entered the awaiting horse-drawn carriage. I waved goodbye to my aunt and my faithful companion, Tye, whose elf-like image and appealing grace would always remain submerged in my memory.

It was going to be a heart-rending journey, and I was intimidated by the thought. We headed east away from the lodge, through narrow streets. Houses straggled one after another, divided by empty fields. Within fifteen minutes we had arrived at my new home, which was situated at the end of 'B' road, from which there was no further main exit. A narrow footpath from the front entrance led to a bridge, which spanned a small stream. The rest of the outlying area was grassy meadowland. Perfect for games and flying kites in the summer, I thought. Here the path continued, passing the rear of the school where my aunt taught. Then it joined the main road, with the Railway Institute and station on the opposite side.

My brother, Trevor, was waiting to greet me, his hands deep in his pockets. He was accompanied by the cook. He was only six years old and looked more like a girl with huge ringlets dangling from his head, but feeling absolutely thrilled to see me. Although the strangeness was visible, he ran up to me and clasped his small arms around my waist, then asked, 'Are you going to stay with us for ever, Colin?' I nodded, showing a little disinterest. Then I scanned the garden, and the only thing that moved was a cocker spaniel called Dinky. He barked a couple of times, then approached me, wagging his tail. He wasn't very old but we became good friends instantly. The cook was already taking care of the kitten for me. Maybe I could try and settle down with my younger brother; he did have a smile that surprised you.

It was a yellow semi-detached bungalow raised slightly off the ground on thick wooden supports. From the road, a rough path turned sharply inside the hedge and led to the other premises. A lady came out to chat with Mother. She was short, slim and pleasant-looking and dressed casually, but her carriage lent the inferior clothes elegance. She walked with a slight limp in her left leg, and assisted herself with the aid of a walking stick.

'Hello, son,' she said politely.

I replied at once in the same manner, not knowing her name. Suddenly two girls came from behind the house. I recognised the taller one at once.

'Hi,' she said smiling, 'I'm Gloria.'

I looked closer then replied, 'I know. We were in the same

class at St Michael's.' I felt happy that we were of the same age. She was fair and quite pretty.

'I thought that I had seen you somewhere before,' she said, feeling pleased about our sudden meeting.

Her sister stood behind her, looking a little timid and clutching a rag doll with plaits. 'My name's Theresa,' she said shyly, blinking her eyes. 'It's my birthday today, I'm eight years old.'

'Happy birthday,' I replied quickly, feeling a little sorry for her, noticing her torn dress. 'See you later on.'

Then I left them to climb the four steps onto the verandah, where a large barred window allowed the early morning sun to pierce into the main bedroom. Directly to the right, the front door led into the lounge where an archway opened into the dining area. The two large bedrooms occupied the left side of the house, with a reasonably sized bathroom and an extended kitchen towards the rear, where a compact little compound cradled a swing. In the front garden three huge fruit trees, guava, apricot, and plum, hovered over the main entrance, which had no gate. A small, neatly cut, plush green lawn surrounded by an assortment of pretty flowers presented some elegance. The chirping of small birds, blue jays, lal rajahs, rani peelahs suggested some form of tranquillity.

When I entered the impressive lounge, the atmosphere was intimidating. The furnishings were of the highest quality, and an imposing burnished desk dominated the room. There were teak units and chairs, all of them expertly hand carved. The brass stands and tables glistened like crystal, displaying a menagerie of ivory. Even the floor, although uncarpeted, was highly polished, and I felt as if I were walking on a mirrored surface. Squat in the corner near the front door was a set of elephant's feet, clustered with an assortment of coloured oriental parasols.

On the white wall beyond the desk hung an octagonal mirror. Carved on its surface was a panoramic engraving of Mount Fujiyama in breathtaking colour. The instant sight of this sent chilling shivers spiralling down my spine. I ignored its very presence and quickly turned away, unable to disguise this intense hatred that I felt burning inside of me. I then glanced eagerly at a draped portrait of a young man's smiling face. I gazed at it gently, uncertain, thoughtfully. I even felt a kind of recognition, excitement, yet I had never seen this face before. His features appeared strong, clean, with a charismatic look flowing in self-confidence. For a moment the room and its endless silence cloaked me like a glass cage.

'You seem to be very interested in that picture,' said mother unexpectedly, placing a reassuring arm on my shoulder.

I nodded, my eyes still glued on it with curiosity. 'Who is it?' I asked.

'It's a picture of your father, taken shortly before we were married,' she said, with that faraway look in her eyes.

'What happened to him?' I asked quietly, sensing something was missing and desperately wanting to know more.

She looked wistfully at the picture several times before answering very softly, 'Love is priceless.'

She seemed to open a tiny corner of her past, revealing a secret grief. She appears so humble on the outside, yet so full of mystery underneath, I thought. Suddenly her smile faded, and a barb of unpleasantness impaled her inner thoughts.

'We'd only been married three and a half years, when he became very ill and was admitted into the hospital, suffering from a serious illness. The doctors said that there wasn't really much hope for him,' she said and turned to look at the picture again. 'He endured a lot of pain before he finally passed away. Your Aunty Iris kept a constant vigil over him towards the end. I couldn't bear to watch him wasting away. He died shortly before your second birthday.'

There were tears in her eyes now; it was the first time that I had ever seen my mother cry. There was compassion in her voice and sorrow in her face. I didn't feel embarrassed, so I questioned her again, 'Why did you leave me with Aunty Iris?'

She looked a lot more serious this time, then touching my face gently, she replied, 'I suppose I should be grateful, thinking back on the few years that we shared, the happiness, the joys and the sorrows. Actually, son, we were really good friends. When I lost him I made a commitment to myself never to allow a personal tragedy to destroy my life, and I know that is what he would have wanted. That was the main reason why I left you with Aunty Iris, knowing that she would take care of you, and moved away. Besides, the lodge was a constant reminder.' I felt a cold shudder before she spoke again. 'The past can leave a scar that can hurt you so much you do not believe in anything, then there is no major sin you wouldn't commit just to exist. Suddenly you wake up and step beyond that line and become human again.'

At the mention of the lodge my ears cocked, my brain raced, turning revolutions. I even heard a voice in my head asking for some answers. 'What's the lodge got to do with all this?' I asked.

She looked at me with agony in her eyes this time, silent for moments, before replying, 'Your father was a Freemason.'

'What's one of them?' I quipped, with my eyes wide open, feeling excited.

There was a long pause, as though she was reluctant to answer, then she spoke nervously. 'He never really discussed it in depth, so it always sounded far too complicated. It was some sort of cult, a brotherhood, a fellowship, a secret fraternity for mutual help. There is supposed to be something noble, something worthy of the dignity of a man who is a Freemason. Freemasons are collectively known as the great architects of the universe. Anyway, I don't expect you to understand all this.'

I listened, open-mouthed and deeply interested as she continued.

'When your father died they held the service in the lodge, this included holding a wake.'

'What's a wake?' I interrupted her once again, sounding more curious than before.

She went on speaking very quietly, 'Well,' she said and cleared her throat, 'as he was a member of the Masonic lodge, the burial service was performed by the Masons in their chapel. They placed the open casket at the head of the main table, while a banquet was held, followed by a toast. This was all very eerie, as only the Masons were allowed to be present. They attended to all the arrangements and also covered the funeral expenses, for which I was eternally grateful, but for me those were really traumatic times. When it was all over I needed to get away and to resume my work again. You know the rest.'

I swallowed nervously as I touched the photo gently.

'People have to forgive themselves, before the hurt can really heal,' she said sadly.

'How did my father die?' I asked prudently, feeling that I wanted to know the circumstances.

'It was tuberculosis, son. Those two little girls who live next door also lost their father with a terrible illness a couple of years ago, typhoid. It probably all sounds very strange to you, son, but you are still very young and that's all you need to know for now. Sometimes, if you don't make up your mind in a hurry, you never get the second chance,' she said softly, then turned and walked towards the bedroom, holding her back. She was probably feeling thoroughly exhausted with the day's proceedings. I stood there mystified, after listening to everything that she had to say, and feeling vaguely comforted.

The pieces of the jigsaw started to fall into place as a strange pattern emerged. The mystery of the lodge and its haunting attraction, the strange voices, the bad dreams and the ghostly atmosphere in that bizarre house and finally the warning about that damaged step from the faceless man, who, shrouded by a radiant light in the darkness, came to warn me in hospital. My eyes locked on the portrait with a quiet severity, glaring at it as if they had just seen a vision. My thoughts became cloudy, deeply confused. I was now shrouded in a darkness by an unseen power, which did not permit a clear image of that faceless man, whom I'd met some years ago. That unmistakable power was Death and I respectfully accepted that portrait of my father whenever I thought of him. I now know that I had truly lost a very good friend.

February had arrived; the past month had been an agonising one full of confusion. My brother and I hadn't ventured too far away from home because of the expected air raids, but the sound of a motor vehicle, droning, before coming to a halt outside the entrance, drew my immediate attention. When two army officers, whose faces were familiar to me, strode smartly towards the front door, my heart pumped with excitement and I changed into a victim of curiosity. I grabbed Trevor's hand and, without a moment's hesitation, raced homewards on the hard surface with a new-found energy. His small frame convulsed with the momentum. Our unexpected noisy scramble into the dining area was greeted with a hostile silence and raised eyebrows from the private meeting. Mother turned sharply away from the important discussion she was involved in, and looked harshly at us with startling rapidity. My heart fluttered before she spoke.

'Outside, the both of you,' she said angrily. 'This conversation doesn't concern either of you, and remain there until I decide otherwise.'

We went back outside into the sunshine and wandered around the garden aimlessly, waiting for the visitors to leave. Over the broken fence in the garden next door, the two girls were noisily playing with their dolls and trying to attract our attention.

'Are you coming over to join us?' asked Gloria eagerly.

'No, we can't, we've got some important visitors from the army,' I replied, trying to sound mysterious.

The meeting seemed to drag on for hours, and I was getting bored. There was a feeling of inquisitiveness. Suddenly Mother's voice sounded from the lounge window.

'Both of you go into the kitchen and ask the cook for some tea and biscuits, it's four o'clock.'

'I'm not hungry,' I shouted back, feeling fed up with all this waiting.

'Do as you are told at once! Dinner could be late tonight,' she replied.

Grumbling under our breaths so as not to be heard, we trooped inside for a quick snack without arguing. Time passed slowly and when the clock chimed six o'clock, our privileges of recreation seemed to have lasted much longer than we were normally allowed. Finally, we watched from the back garden as our uniformed visitors left after the usual handshakes and smiles of general agreement between everyone.

'Come inside, both of you,' Mother called again. 'This time wash your hands. Dinner will soon be served.'

They hadn't been gone long when my stepfather arrived home. He sat down by the rear door and removed his boots and gaiters, looking somewhat fatigued after being involved in some kind of jungle manoeuvres. Mother covered her annoyance by presenting him with a warm embrace, giving no visible evidence of her tiring afternoon. As he dropped heavily onto the chair at the table, he glanced at some of the literature the visitors had left behind.

'I see you've had company again, Gwen! Was it the army authorities as usual?' he enquired gently. She looked at him as he started to sip his soup.

'Yes, but I'm no wiser. There was no clear indication or any official information about the evacuation. They couldn't even hint about how much or exactly what we would be allowed to take with us.' She hesitated slightly. Plans were being implemented rather quickly, but it was all rather confusing. 'The army appears to be more concerned about my health and present condition, or when I expect to be admitted into hospital.'

For a soldier my stepfather had a voice that was surprisingly soft and pleasant. His fair hair was thin but well combed and parted neatly on the right side. The sharp features made his face look narrow, with blue-grey eyes and a straight nose. There was an air of dignity about him. His khaki uniform was tidily pressed making him look taller than he was. A wide smile appeared to be his usual expression, and he looked imposing enough to give people pause. He was my idea of a typical British soldier.

After we had finished, Mother put her hands on her stomach, stood up slowly, left the table then walked over to the window. It was painful to watch her holding her back as if in considerable discomfort. She stood with her eyes looking up towards the now darkened sky. Tears were streaming down her cheeks, her face cramped with pain. Thoughts of having to leave her home, and a baby due shortly, meant that life was going to be very difficult for her.

'I don't need all this,' she said, and sighed in disgust.

Watching her, I could see the sadness and I could hear the sound of her breathing; there was a tenseness in it. She was looking tired and old for her thirty-nine years. The pressure of being catapulted into all this confusion and trapped into this insanity could have disastrous effects. She appeared to be contentedly married with the third child soon to be born, and so far nothing had gone wrong yet.

The sky was perfectly clear now and much to my surprise and delight Aunty Eileen arrived with her four children. Uncle Stan dropped them off at the gate from his old Buick before continuing on to work at the sheds. 'Hello, Aunty,' I shouted, running over to give her a huge kiss, thinking how pretty she always looked and secretly wishing I were much older. She flattered me with a gorgeous smile, then touched my chin with her fingertips, instantly dismissing all my gloomy thoughts and relieving some of my sadness. As expected, she went straight into the house with the baby, Robert, leaving the other three to play with us in the garden.

Peggy was ten years old. She had a mane of blonde hair, which curled, under her ears, nothing like either of her parents, dark, almost black eyes and a very pale complexion. With her sweet soft nature she was easy to like. We played endless games during our recreation periods, and had a lot of imagination. This brought us very close together, sharing everything that was available. She was quite grown-up for her age in a motherly way and certainly cleverer than I was.

'Have you heard when you will be leaving, Colin?' she asked in a dejected voice.

I looked sadly at her face, a mask of gloom. I waited for a moment, trying to think of something to say, considered fibbing but hesitated. 'I've really no idea,' I answered. 'I suppose it could be any time.' I was feeling a little upset myself but tried to console her anguish, by explaining that we probably wouldn't be leaving for quite some time anyway. 'Do you know when you will be leaving?' I asked her, glancing at her eyes.

She seemed to be close to tears, so I really didn't expect a proper reply. She considered what I had said for a moment, then shook her head.

'My dad is looking at all the choices that we have. He says that, when you have all gone, we are hoping to travel up to Myitkyina[1] in the car, and that we will probably get a flight to India very easily, especially with a young family,' she replied, trying to smile.

I felt very sorry, sensing her world inhabited by fear and

---

[1] Pronounced *Mitchinah*.

doubt. For a few seconds there was absolute silence, as I tried to think of something pleasant to say to her. My stomach was churning over, so I tried to inject some pleasure into my tone, then smiled. 'I hope so because we are going to India as well,' I replied. 'It would be great if we could meet there.'

She seemed a lot happier now. 'You've got a clasp just like mine,' she said suddenly and excitedly, pointing to the one fastened onto my shirt pocket.

I glanced down, admiring it myself.

'Where did you get yours from?'

I looked at the red, white and blue V-shaped clip, which was slightly covered by a piece of lace on her dress. I had not noticed it earlier. 'Oh, Aunty Iris gave it to me before I left the house,' I said. 'Shall we exchange them for good luck?'

She immediately thought that that was a good idea and we quickly swapped them over, feeling quite thrilled with the exchange. Now we were happy, the babble and the warmth of our voices creating an atmosphere of children enjoying themselves. The sun had dipped below the trees and it was now time for the visitors to leave. Walking slowly to the front entrance, we waved our goodbyes, as they set off on their short journey home, knowing that we would be seeing them again shortly.

The next morning a second surprise arrived in the shape of a tubby woman who swept past me, carrying two small suitcases. She smiled aggressively and entered the house without hesitation to a welcome of open arms and hugs from my parents. I frowned, thinking hard. I had a strange feeling that I'd seen her on at least three separate occasions some time ago. It took a few minutes for the name to click as I tried to turn back the pages in my mind. It was Mrs Harniss. She was married to a soldier, who was serving in the same regiment as my stepfather and, as far as I could recollect, they had no children. I don't quite understand what she is doing here, I thought to myself. I was worried and it wasn't long before I was to find out. Within minutes of her arrival, an ambulance drew up outside the house. I ran inside to find my mother preparing to leave for the hospital, supported by my stepfather. I could feel my stomach churning over and over as she turned to speak to me.

'This is Mrs Betty Harniss, Aunty to both of you. She will be looking after you whilst I'm away, so behave yourselves. I want obedience.'

She spoke her words sternly as she left the house. We stood in silence and watched anxiously and waving, as the ambulance drove away, occupied in our own thoughts.

Our guardian was short and plump, shaped like a beer barrel, with powerful arms for a female. Raven-black hair and deep-black eyes sat well back in her face, which was lodged on a thick stump of a neck. She didn't speak English fluently, her ancestors being Gurkhas. She was a bubbly jovial character with an appealing smile that stretched across her face like elastic. Her explosive laugh could pierce concrete. I had been warned that crossing her was like holding a rattler by the tail, so while Mother was away we would definitely be on our best behaviour, or suffer the consequences.

About five o'clock the following evening, 19 February 1942, came the third surprise. My brother and I were playing on the bridge as usual, our laughter carrying down the stream, and our new-found friendship belonged there. We were watching the circles twisting and turning in the water, although there was really nothing to see but the restless moving humps of froth, topped by delicate crests of foam, gliding underneath in endless motion. There was a stillness in the air as if life itself was suspended. Suddenly, Aunty's voice, calling from the verandah, signalled our immediate attention.

'Colin, Trevor, come inside now! You have to get washed and changed as we are going out.' Her voice was crisp and calm, but there was urgency in it.

'Where are we going?' I asked eagerly.

'To the hospital,' she replied quickly with a smile. 'You now have a baby sister, so please hurry.' Her voice was surprisingly soft.

We soon arrived at the hospital vaguely silhouetted by the poor street lighting, and made our way through to the maternity wards to check in with the sister. She introduced herself, then escorted us to the correct ward, where a number of women were chatting to their husbands sitting by their beds. A slow hum of conversation and gentle ripples of laughter filled the ward. We took up our place alongside my mother's bed and sat on the empty chairs. On a table close at hand some flowers glowed in a decorated glass vase. She looked happy to see us but spoke softly so as not to wake the baby, who was sleeping soundly almost buried in the covers in the cot beside her bed. I looked around sheepishly at the other women in the ward. Although the ward was small and cosy there was a bright line of urgency and regimental command running through it.

My parents had already chosen a name for the baby, Marjorie Rose. The minutes ticked away slowly and the time came for us to leave. I gently reached across to lift the covers off and experienced a sweet sensation as I touched her tiny hands, like a little doll's, yet soft and real. Aunty Eileen arrived as we were leaving, with a cool reflective smile on her face and her eyes sparkling. She was holding a beautiful bunch of flowers in her arms; the children were at home with their father.

The next morning my mood was joyful, so, shortly after my breakfast, I decided to take my brother for a walk to Aunty Irene's with the delightful news.

'Can we go and tell Aunty Irene and Aunty Iris about our baby sister?' I asked politely.

'Yes, providing the both of you behave yourselves,' she replied.

'I promise that we will,' I said, knowing that we had to or else.

We planned to visit on the return journey the school where Aunty Iris was teaching. We strolled casually on the rough path through the grassy meadow, struggling with the heat, then the sun ducked swiftly behind the trees in a glorious purple haze. During these quiet hours the war seemed remote and I felt it could never affect us directly. We walked past the school towards the railway station and the marshalling yards, away from the main line.

It was the middle of the morning and the sun seemed to slip down from the sky. Aunty Irene was busy making my favourite pineapple jam plus some pies. She looked very surprised but equally pleased to see us. Her eyes grew bright as she spoke. 'Hello, you two, so what brings you here?' she asked quietly, turning away from the baking table and removing her smock. She was a tall slender woman with sharp features and a gentle mouth, deep, intelligent, dark eyes and black hair braided traditionally into a bun. She was wearing a pale-yellow dress and open white sandals. A pleasant smile shifted across her face when we sat down to chat.

'So why the surprise visit and both of you as well?' she asked, her cheeks brightening.

'We have a baby sister, Aunty Irene,' I replied proudly, with a gleam in my eyes.

'What delightful news! I was wondering how things were with your mother. I am so very pleased. It's a pity that we have all these problems at this moment,' she said, with a little sadness in her eyes.

Uncle Dick was away at work, the twins were at the Baptist Missionary School and little Maureen was enjoying a peaceful nap upstairs. The room was calm and peaceful, so our chatter was relaxed and easy to sustain. Any indication of having previously been a schoolteacher was non-existent in her attire. Her English was extraordinary; there was power in her words and expressions, and something of the bygone wisdom in knowledge lingered behind the mask of motherhood, and it showed in her stature. She had many attributes but being a gourmet was her speciality. The redolence of freshly baked pies soon found a small empty space inside of me.

'A baby sister, how lovely for the both of you. I hope that you are going to take care of her. I will try and visit both of them tonight,' she said. 'Now sit down and enjoy this.' She casually handed us a cool drink and some of her special Indian sweetmeats, the smell of which had already roused my voracious appetite.

We left shortly afterwards with our stomachs satisfied for the journey home, her persistent words of warning following us down the garden path.

'Just keep off those railway tracks, especially you, Colin,' she said, glancing at me with a small frown of warning. 'Now don't forget, no more of those stupid antics,' she continued with her warning.

My mind went back to that day when I was sauntering along

on one rail and balancing with arms outstretched. Unfortunately on that occasion I had slipped on the greasy rail, severed the lid of my left eye on the line and, but for her integrity and quick reactions in getting me to the hospital quickly and having the wound stitched up, my eye could have been severely damaged. I shook my head. 'I won't, Aunty Irene, I promise,' I replied in a voice just loud enough for her to hear me. This time I listened to her advice and behaved myself.

It was mid-afternoon now and the sun had risen steadily high in the sky, presenting a vast expanse of blue. Somehow we seemed to have chosen a day when the temperature was slightly warmer. We crossed the railway lines quickly and were well clear long before the express train had us coughing in the swirling dust. Then we deliberately turned off the main path and headed towards the school. As we approached I felt a slight heaviness of my heart. Then I got a tremendous thrill when I peeped through the classroom window and saw my Aunty Iris chatting eagerly to her pupils. My sudden appearance promptly led her to dismiss her class, and she was unable to conceal her obvious delight as she rushed outside to greet us. Then she almost bowled me over with a blaze of hugs and kisses, which made me feel slightly embarrassed in the presence of my younger brother. He didn't share the warm attachment that had formed between us, and found it all very amusing. I was overjoyed with her affection and felt a strong feeling of genuine relief.

'What are you two doing here at this time of the day?' she said, smiling softly. The calm stillness of the day gently coiled out the message.

'We have a baby sister, Aunty Iris, and we've just been to tell Aunty Irene as well,' I replied, feeling thoroughly pleased with myself.

'That's marvellous news; she will be getting some extra visitors tonight,' she said pleasantly, then ruffled our hair. She was delighted, yet appeared a little worried, being less enthusiastic in her reaction. 'How on earth is your mother going to manage with a small baby?' she asked, her voice quaking.

On hearing her touching remarks, I felt that she felt no malice but more deep concern, judging by the worried look on her face.

The question seemed to linger in my thoughts.

'Now that you have told me the good news, get yourselves home quickly and no playing around.'

Her spoken words sounded unreal on impact with the silent air, but her voice could not have been more tender. She kissed us on our foreheads, but it was one of those strange moments in my life when I lost my composure. I started to cry but tried to force back the tears of emotion, and felt a little ashamed in front of my brother. 'Don't cry, son,' she said and put an arm round my shoulder, patting it.

I wanted her to comfort me and there was a return light of solace in her eyes. We set off, treading the narrow path towards the bridge, waving to her. I started singing a melody I had heard at the cinema. It was from a gangster movie, and sung by the Bowery Boys in the film, 'If I had the wings of an angel / I would fly to the end of the world / I would tell you a very sad story / a story that's never been told.' Trevor started mocking me, and we both started laughing. Even the earth seemed to tilt and swing under the unbalanced rhythm. Suddenly there was a heavy drone coming from above. I glanced up at the sky, but there was only a vast expanse of blue, allowing the blazing sun to show its sinister face. We continued towards the edge of the field and the wooden bridge beyond it. An old Chinaman, with a spiked beard, and a coolie hat perched on his head, hobbling behind us, shouted, 'Japanese!' then pointed to the area of bright sunlight. I glanced back at him, but it took a while for me to grasp what he was trying to tell us. He ran past, heading towards the bridge, and screaming in a language that I couldn't understand.

It was so bright that at first I could see nothing at all in that area, even though I strained my eyes to the full limit. Almost immediately strange aircraft flew low across the field, heading straight towards us. For a moment we stood there motionless, staring in complete horror. The thunder of their engines was infernal, the roar seemed to pass close over the top of our heads, and the sky appeared to split in different directions. From the speed the aircraft were moving the air shook and the ground vibrated. It sounded as if the end of the world had come. Trevor started crying, the tears running down his face and dripping from his chin.

'Come on, let's follow him,' I shouted with some urgency. Then I grabbed his hand and ran, with fury in my brain, in the same direction as the Chinaman. I sensed danger circling at the back of my head. There was confusion, anxiety, and the safest path was forward. I knew that the water under the bridge was very low, due to the dry season; that was why the Chinaman had headed that way. We kept stumbling, gasping for breath, then stumbling again on the uneven surface. The bridge wasn't too far away, but the distance looked enormous, almost out of reach. We ran without stopping, as the aircraft banked upwards, then returned, maintaining the same height as before. The fear raced through me like a convulsion, shivers traipsed through my body, and I started to freeze with the conviction that we were doomed. I'd heard all the terrifying stories about the Japanese fighters that had decimated the city of Rangoon on Christmas day. They flew at treetop level, and strafed the children as they ran out to catch the balloons that were dropped from the sky, on a day that was supposed to be celebrated with thanksgiving, joy and goodwill to everyone. Yet the brutal carnage and unspeakable slaughter they left behind was beyond description. In the effort to get to the bridge, Trevor kept falling down and I had to stop to pick him up. One of the aircraft came so close above us I thought he was going to crash into the houses that were on the other side of the stream. He tilted sharply, and the engine screamed as he flew over the rooftops and released a plume of black smoke. When we finally got under cover, the area was cramped, stuffy and smelt of stagnant water. Trevor was still sobbing and shaking.

'I want to go home,' he cried, with tears running down his cheeks.

'We will in a minute,' I replied, putting a consoling arm around him.

We remained motionless, swallowing hard and fully aware of the hideous menace outside. Despite our sense of foreboding, for a brief moment we felt safe. Yet my chest seemed to be expanding, and I was filled with such a burning sensation that memories flooded in on me. My relations, school friends, the festivities, and my pets were suspended in time. The danger outside gave me visions of bombs and bullets and destruction everywhere, snaking across the field that surrounded us. Although afraid I was consumed with a deep hatred.

For me everything seemed unnatural, macabre, yet the sunlight shimmered on the green meadow. Even the trees cast glistening shadows across the rugged plain. It gave me a creepy feeling, not being able to see all the confusion outside our hideout. I tried to think of what I could do, but couldn't come up with anything. I wanted to shut my eyes but did not dare, and my body ached with tiredness and fear. Suddenly the droning died away, so I peeked up from under the bridge, thinking there might be a chance to leave this sticky area. I found it difficult to keep my eyes from wandering, especially from looking up at the sky. I glanced at my brother, thinking for a moment of what to say to comfort him. He was still crying and shaking. I grabbed his hand, and hiked straight into the meadow, heading for home.

By the time we had reached the steps leading onto the verandah, our guardian was waiting for us with a look of cold steel. I realised as soon as I spoke, it was like talking to my mother. It was a bad sign; her averted eyes meant we were in trouble. I tried to decide quickly which was the best excuse for my stupidity, and my forgetfulness.

'Where have you two been until now?' she asked angrily. 'Your mother would never have forgiven me, if anything had happened to either of you,' she continued in disapproval, looking extremely upset.

There was a brief silence while I thought of what to say, feeling hurt by her anger. All I really wanted to do was to go inside and get something to eat. Finally, in desperation, I just said, 'I'm very sorry, Aunty, but I promise it won't happen again.'

We stepped inside the house and were shutting the door behind us when a thunderous noise exploded outside once again. Aunty immediately bundled us into the dining room, where we all crouched under the table and waited. After a seemingly long period the noise subsided, and we moved restlessly about the house, glancing through the windows at the sky. The enemy, who had come very close, suddenly vanished. The events that took place were far beyond my control, and I felt torn between curiosity and fear in the prevailing silence. This was the first taste of a war that I would never forget as a child.

The days that followed this incident were like a recurring nightmare; there were no smiles or recreation. Everyone was praying for an early departure from what now seemed an invincible foe. The rumours of Japanese conquests throughout the Pacific and weakly defended areas spread a paralysis of fear. Now convinced that there would be a large-scale invasion, the prevalent topic of conversation was to leave as quickly as possible by whatever means. The delirium of tension and terror was unmistakably clear on the faces of everyone. Any concept of being held in human bondage was something that nobody was prepared to accept under any circumstances. For the local inhabitants this was going to be a complex and very difficult situation. It was the usual practice and common knowledge that families connected with the armed forces were given priority in the evacuation. Those, who were fortunate enough to have the financial resources and were quite capable of affording the exorbitant black market prices, had the privilege of travelling either by air or sea to safety.

For the remainder, the choices were few. They could remain behind in the hope that the Allied forces could repel the enemy's advance, which at the present seemed very doubtful, or make a serious attempt at the hazardous journey on foot to the Indian border some hundreds of miles away. Many were to choose the wild dive towards the latter; some succeeded in making this forbidding and threatening journey. There were thousands who were not so fortunate, as their passage ended, with them deprived of human dignity. Men, women and children of all denominations were soon to realise the futility of this suicidal attempt, a result of sheer exhaustion, inadequate food, insufficient medical provisions, combined with the intense heat, which felt like a fatal disease draining away their strength. Then there was the formidable terrain, raging rivers, swamps, mosquitoes, flies, and snakes, which turned the overwhelming jungle from the friend that they hoped for into their enemy. Many of those who found deliverance from the hordes who hounded them travelled in the darkness to escape the eyes in the sky above, but never recovered from those days of enforced humility.

One day shortly before noon towards the end of February, I was sitting on the verandah enjoying the comfort of a lazy day. Mother suddenly arrived home, cradling my baby sister. I rose to my feet quickly and ran to them. It was such a pleasant surprise and so unexpected that I blurted out, 'Are you coming home for always?' She smiled and nodded at my obvious concern and joy, and my spirits lifted when a beaming smile spread across her face. She was slimmer and physically more alive, although her reply was what I expected. 'I just hope that you two have been behaving yourselves during my absence, else there will be the devil to pay.' I paused for a second and my thoughts strayed for a while, unable to clearly understand her strange remark. Then I replied brimming with confidence, 'Yes, we have, honest, Mum!' Then I stuck my chest out with enormous pride, although feeling a little uncomfortable about the recent events. However, she accepted my answer as truthful and went straight inside the house.

The following morning I awoke early and felt a little aggravated, which seemed unusual for me. I decided to question my stepfather over breakfast about the war and the strength of the British forces operating in the region, before he left to join his unit.

'Uncle,' I said, having been told to address him in that manner, 'do you think that the British and the Indians can prevent the Japanese from invading our country?'

He looked rather surprised at my remark but remained quiet and listened. Then with kindly eyes and a natural smile he leaned across and replied seriously and thoughtfully, 'I don't really know, son, but let me put it this way. Britain has the finest army, navy and air force in the world, so I really wouldn't worry too much about it if I were you.'

My eyes blinked in astonishment. I'd never heard those powerful comments before, and finding his words very encouraging, I relaxed immediately.

'Now eat your breakfast quickly and run along outside.'

I think he sensed the fear that was circling around in my head. So I swallowed my food and rushed out onto the verandah and sat down on the steps. I thought of all my relations who lived here, troubled that tomorrow we might all die and never see each other again. I thought of my pets, and who would take care of them. I thought of all the wild animals and birds that sung sweet little melodies, and I thought of all the suffering that those horrible little invaders would bring to this earth we all loved.

With a little difficulty, my stepfather brushed past me, dressed in his khaki uniform, gaiters, polished boots that shone like glass, and the rifle hung from his shoulder, on his way to the barracks. He turned sharply to speak. 'When I come home tonight, I shall write you a poem about the "Red, White and Blue",' he said cheerfully, then left.

Shortly before midday the army authorities paid us an unexpected visit once again, expressing their apologies to my mother for returning so quickly. They entered the lounge discreetly and sat down next to the brass table, where they unzipped their portfolios and produced a string of documents. From the dining area, I listened to the captain's remarks with a little curiosity as he skimmed through the files. He looked straight at my mother and spoke rather tenderly for an officer.

'I do not want to impose on you any more that I have to, but this is the present situation,' he said. 'Because of the recent hostilities in the south, the evacuation has been brought forward a few days and, in view of your current position,' he added, pointing towards the baby, 'your family will be included in the initial batch leaving this town on Monday, 2 March.'

Her expression changed from understanding to disbelief and horror. She stood up at once, hugging herself and looking extremely upset with everything. 'We'll never survive this journey,' she moaned. 'It's too much to ask of us,' she whispered, it was so low like echoes of silence. But there was to be no denial, no demonstration, she had to maintain her sanity and she certainly wasn't going to be intimidated by the forthcoming events.

The captain continued, 'I shall be visiting you again very shortly with more detailed information. I am truly very sorry. Unfortunately, that's all the news that I have for the present.' His tone was neutral and his eyes were full of compassion, prompted by a certain sympathy for her. He got up to leave, sensing a flood of tears, which was straining to fall down my mother's face, but fortunately didn't. It had been a traumatic day and the late afternoon sun had pierced the earthen ground and grassy meadow, braiding an intricate pattern against a blue eastern sky.

The morning of Saturday, 28 February 1942 soon dawned, and my eyes burned with a fanatical gleam when I noticed an army vehicle parked outside the house. Mother suddenly appeared on the verandah.

'What is all this about?' she asked firmly.

'It's about the evacuation,' replied the captain. 'Please do forgive me for calling at such short notice, Mrs Townend, but it's orders. Advanced circumstances have made plans very difficult,' he said apologetically. His voice was calm but he looked more serious than ever before.

Mother went straight into the lounge, followed by the officers, who were speaking to her as they walked. Their tones were warm and friendly, which appeared totally out of character with their previous visits. I also detected a note of anxiety in the captain's voice when he spoke, partnered with a little uncertainty in his mannerism, as if he expected some kind of reprisal.

'Orders have come through regarding the evacuation,' he said. The urgency showed plainly in his eyes when he produced quite a collection of documents from an attaché case.

'When?' she asked solidly, emotions gathering in her eyes like storm clouds.

Speaking explicitly, he said, 'On the morning of second March between 3 a.m. and 4 a.m., an army convoy of six vehicles will be transporting some of the families to Magwe aerodrome on the outskirts of Yenangyaung [Yenanjown]. Your family will be expected to join that group. Further instructions will be given upon your arrival, that is all I can say for the present.'

My mother interrupted him immediately, feeling very annoyed with what she had been told.

'Excuse me, Captain,' she said, deliberately trying to conceal her aggravation. 'Where are we supposed to join these so-called trucks and what are we allowed to take with us, such as food and clothing. I have three children and one of them is a baby girl as you are already aware.' Her face clouded over. After a short pause he answered, and his reply was comforting and reassuring, considering our uneasiness.

'They will pick you up outside your front gate, Mrs Townend, so you won't have to travel too far.' Then he handed us some small kitbags. 'These are very light, sturdy and easy to handle; they will hold the clothing and any essentials up to the limit of forty pounds. Nothing else will be accepted, although you may carry some personal items.' He spoke cautiously.

There was a hushed silence. Mother covered her face with her hands and sobbed as the whole atmosphere changed to one of intense pessimism. I watched and listened with my brother in stunned silence. The sombre mood was interrupted by my stepfather's arrival. He looked terribly upset.

'I've seen the official bulletin about the advanced evacuation, Gwen, so we've been granted compassionate leave because of the endless rumours,' he said nervously, his voice almost a whisper.

'Excuse me, Captain,' Mother said anxiously. 'Can you please explain to me, assuming that my husband will be away involved in the conflict, what will happen to my home and all its furnishing, not to mention our belongings? Surely you don't really expect me to just walk away from here, and leave everything behind at the snap of a finger, it's ridiculous. In fact, it's utter madness.' Her words were drowned by sobs. The conversation was awkward now, the atmosphere strained.

The captain looked very concerned, and feeling a trifle embarrassed, he then replied. 'Mrs Townend,' he said firmly, 'I do have a deep regard for your concern and I don't want to appear disrespectful, but I do have my instructions and this is not a request but an order. I am certain that there will be other married women who share your thoughts and will no doubt be suffering the same torment. There will also be many others who would gladly exchange places with you, under these insane circumstances. What possible excuse can you have for staying, knowing of the impending danger?' He sensed what others might be thinking and seemed to possess an explicit knowledge of what they might do given the chance.

The anger faded from her expression.

'He's absolutely right, Gwen,' said my stepfather, offering the officer some belated congenial support. 'War is a crime against humanity and in a couple of days you will all be safe and away from this madness.'

She hesitated and shuddered briefly, then agreed with everything that was said as if a lightning spirit had flashed through her. She was quiet for a few moments and in her thoughts she felt a flood of remorse.

The captain's reactions were slowed by tension, before he spoke again. 'It would also be advisable to take with you some sandwiches, flasks of tea or coffee and some water for the initial stage of the journey to Meiktila[2], an overnight stopping point. Upon your arrival you will be met and assisted by the Red Cross. Food and accommodation will be provided for that night and army intelligence will advise you further.'

The officers then stood up to leave and apologised, their voices drifting away. Looking harassed and emotionally disturbed with the proceedings, Mother now resigned to the irrevocable mandate, which had been confirmed, thanked the soldiers for their exemplary kindness and fine manners. She felt a swift rush of sympathy for them and smiled engagingly.

'I'm terribly sorry for being the bearer of such depressing news, Mrs Townend,' the captain said, looking disconsolate himself. 'I'm quite sure that now you will understand the urgency of this situation. May I wish you all farewell and a safe journey.'

Mother then returned to the chair, her motions slow and deliberate as she shifted painfully in it for some comfort.

After they had left, the room felt like a graveyard, cold and forsaken. I remained motionless and swallowed nervously. Mother broke down, rose steadily to her feet and went straight into the bedroom, where she cried for quite some time. Despite our general unease and disillusion we knew that we had to go; the looming disaster was inconceivable to us. Life now was far from perfect. I can't say that I was happy; I can't even say that I felt sad. Like everything else in life it was somewhere in between. If you had to design a worse situation than this, it would be an impossibility. Even today, those who survived must find it very difficult to accept all the facts.

The following morning as an early dawn entered the garden, I

---

[2] Pronounced *Mektilla*.

was passing time with some tree climbing near the front entrance, Mother's urgent voice called from the bedroom window.

'Colin, what are you doing?'

My brother was waiting anxiously at the bottom of the tree that I was climbing.

'I'm looking for some bird's eggs in this nest,' I replied eagerly. Unfortunately they had flown the nest, much to my annoyance.

'Will you please go to Aunty Irene's with this note, and take your two pets along with you. She has agreed to look after them when we leave.'

With my arms festooned with scratches from the dry branches, I scampered down without hesitating.

'Yes, Mother,' I replied, then made a determined effort to collect the pets. Somehow it all appeared a trifle too easy as they appeared to be waiting for me. I walked slowly with my two friends through the meadow, overcome by a little sadness. High above us the limitless sky held all the assurance of imminent danger.

It seemed like an endless stroll; there was no sort of activity anywhere, only the soft flow of a warm breeze strafing the grass. I quickly crossed the marshalling yards while the tracks were clear, and soon approached my aunt's home. My heart soared with delight, almost reaching saturation point, when I saw Aunty Irene in the garden. She was busy snipping off some of her delightful flowers, and picking her way through the rows that were still in full bloom. Suddenly the feeling of a desperate need to unburden all my sorrows and empty my mind onto her hit me. She was somehow startled by my unexpected arrival.

'Hello, son, what brings you here and not by yourself I see?' she asked kindly, glancing across at the pets. Her voice was clear and full of warmth.

I shook my head wearily, handing her the letter, 'I think Mother wants to see you now,' I replied, feeling weak and shaky as if I'd run all the way. 'She also said that you would look after my two pets, so I brought them along.' I spoke as casually as I could.

She could sense the isolation that traipsed through my body.

'Yes, son, I certainly will, and don't you worry about them,' she replied, gently handing them over to the servants, but looking slightly bewildered by this sudden change of events. 'How are your mother and baby doing?' she asked, showing deep concern as she opened the letter.

'They are both fine,' I replied, trying to sound at ease and in control. My stomach was tight with tension and I'm sure she understood how I felt.

'I'll go and wake Maureen up.'

I paid my final visit to the open range at the rear of the house, where my mischievous antics had given me so much pleasure in the past. Some of the cattle were grazing whilst the rest were strolling around nonchalantly. On the flat dirt stretch of ground the poultry were scattered everywhere. They clucked and strutted as they watched me cautiously and ducked away from my approach. They were all very active and restless. I wish that I could have explained to them this awful situation that I was caught up in. I tried to tell myself that all this wasn't true and it was only a bad dream that I had to forget, but I was wallowing in a trough of self-pity and I knew it. This short-lived period of self-indulgence and brief silence was soon broken by Aunty Irene's strained voice.

'Come in, son, we have to be leaving soon,' she said impatiently. Then she tucked Maureen neatly in the pram and buttoned up her coat. There was an expression of warmth in her eyes. I needed no further reminder of the strange bond that existed between humans and animals. I ran frantically to my pets hugging them both with a feeling of deep sorrow in my heart. My stomach was doing somersaults, but I believed that animals do have a better way of communicating than humans. Aunty Irene by this time had left instructions with the servants, for the boys' homecoming.

It was a bright summer's afternoon. We walked at a leisurely pace under the arc of heaven in silence for a short spell. The meadow was desolate and a slight wind hurried us along, crunching the leaves that had blown across the path in mad variegated drifts. The penetrating heat was intense and the sweat trickled from our pores, much more than our careful movements could account for. It was a satisfying comfort just to reach the shade of the verandah. Mother opened the door hastily, flashing Aunty Irene a nervous smile as she did so. Her eyes widened and there was a shadow over her, as some things would not leave her mind.

'Hello, Irene, I'm glad you came so early,' she said.

It was difficult for her to hold a happy conversation, as she'd spent a good part of the morning neatly packing necessities for our journey. In a few words she told her everything that was going to happen. They trusted each other without reservation, and were bound together with a fierce loyalty. The lounge was a bustling assembly of relatives in a flurry of activity and most of the tables were occupied. Some were sitting involved in deep conversation, while others were milling around aimlessly. The atmosphere was electric, as if this gathering was witnessing an enormous pain being delivered by an unseen keeper. Their faces were drawn with anguish, which showed through their tear-reddened eyes. I was in the midst of a crowd of anxious and unhappy people. I searched for something that might distract me from my stomach, which was turning over and over. It was my very first memorable feeling of being trapped in a vale of desolation.

The afternoon passed swiftly. Outside, beneath a dark sky that seemed to go on for ever, few people walked the narrow avenue. A slight breeze danced with the leaves from the fruit trees and eucalyptus trees along the sidewalk. Inevitably, it wasn't long before Mother's voice reminded me of the immediate priorities, which only made me feel worse.

'You had better get a hot bath, son, and change into your school uniform for travelling,' she said in an unsteady voice. 'There's a clean set on the bed along with your blazer, and please do try and get some sleep.'

Dredging up a much-needed smile, I replied, 'Yes, Mother.' Then, being used to strict discipline, I proceeded to carry out her instructions, although the pain of undressing almost caused me to faint. The thought of any sleep seemed a distinct impossibility at that time, even though it was getting late. The sun had already sunk into oblivion, and the night seemed silent with the tacit hush of peaceful darkness, bringing with it a sweet freshness after the torrid day. I found myself standing in a dark room and staring through the window at a sky now enveloped in a canopy of flashing stars, and with them the cold bland eye of the moon glared down on the deserted streets below. Occasionally it drifted behind a cloud and plunged everything into total darkness. I glanced at all the shadows and shapes of the houses near our home, while some of the smaller children were fast asleep, but anxiety was keeping me wide awake, even though it had been a long tiring day. The adults were still busy, conversing in senseless conversations, aimlessly discussing everything and anything about life in general. I myself, was not seriously concerned but preoccupied with my own unhappy mood and low spirits. I prayed inwardly, without reason or thought, saying anything that came into my head, yet I felt abandoned by a God in whom many of us believed.

The remainder of that night was so heartbreaking that I can only retain a confused and terrifying emptiness, which was the very essence of my fear, now a fragmented memory. I did not dream, being awake for long restless periods. When I opened my eyes the dawn was a deep blue beyond the bars and paned glass of the lounge window. The long silence was a vivid reminder of the feeling of insecurity, which becomes so pronounced, and the ability to react and function within oneself becomes limited. My idyllic lifestyle as a young boy was about to change beyond description.

Chapter V

I stood in front of the lounge window, and the early sunlight framed my shape across the polished floor, sending streams of flashes up and down the furniture. I was anything but happy, and stared intently at the movements. A special wooden box controlled my thoughts; it contained all the Christmas and birthday gifts I had received over the years. Would it be safe I kept asking myself. I had locked it up, and the key was safely tucked away in my pocket. I even tried to imagine what would happen to our home when we left. Mother had given the servants permission to take all they wanted, or would they be staying in the house. Somehow everything seemed too pitiful to absorb, too difficult to understand. I really didn't know what to think, so I listened to all the sad voices trying to console each other. I sat down next to my Aunt Iris and watched unhappy relatives moving around restlessly, still believing that everything would work out as the army planned.

The early morning had approached to the sound of twittering birds, hopping between the branches of the fruit trees and enhancing their flamboyant colours. There were a few scouring the humid earth in search of scraps and insects, as the feeble sun broke through. Occasionally they would fly off, disturbed by an unfriendly sound, then return again after restoring confidence. Somehow I felt that my comfort was being blended with too much suffering, in the deep hollow silence of the darkness.

The clock in the lounge chimed musically, signifying 4 a.m. on this Monday morning, 2 March 1942. For our family and many others who were leaving their homes, it was a day of monumental disruption in our lives. We were all feeling extremely nervous, and the vehicles, which were to transport us to safety, hadn't arrived. Now they were keeping us in a state of expectancy, for our mobility depended largely upon them. I was quietly haunted with the thoughts of what might happen should they fail to appear. We were all so obsessed with the same question of where they were that normal conversation was impossible. I did however relax for a while, but could find no comfort, only confusion. Rubbing my tired eyes I deliberately avoided looking at the light of dawn breaking over the green meadow, now that the sun had decided to show its sinister face. The weather was perfect for this time of the year, as the monsoons weren't too far away. A warm reviving breeze circulated gusts of fresh air through the hill station before the cruel heat that would soon follow.

On the stroke of 5 a.m., which could be heard distinctly from the clock tower in the market place, the street was filled with the promising sounds of combustion engines. They were so loud and abrupt that we rushed instantly to the lounge window and viewed a column of motor vehicles approaching. We immediately clambered into the front garden, and watched anxiously as the convoy neared the front entrance. With awnings concealing the brooding atmosphere within, five of the trucks halted near the main road as the last one continued towards our home. It then reversed slowly and stopped directly opposite the gateway to the bungalow. We waited patiently as a young soldier in battledress got out of the cab and dropped the tailgate. He reached into his breast pocket, where all the instructions were usually kept, and produced a military document from an envelope. After unfolding it carefully, he then nervously read out the remaining names on the list, which happened to belong to my family.

The silence was awesome and could be felt now that time was desperately short. We slowly collected our few belongings and placed them inside the truck, the floor of which was already cluttered with numerous other bits of luggage belonging to the small gathering inside. Like us, they had already been favoured for this auspicious journey. Conversation was limited as heartache choked the brain and filled the eyes with an endless liquid film. After the commiserations had subsided, Mother was helped into the truck by her husband. She was still wearing the expensive fur coat, which had been a present from my father fourteen years earlier. She certainly had no intention of leaving it behind. She sat down at the rear, cradling my sister who, surprisingly, remained asleep during all the commotion. My brother sat quietly by her side on a long wooden bench.

Finally it was my turn to climb aboard, but suddenly the strict discipline that I had been accustomed to disappeared. I trembled, my emotions fell apart into shreds. I grabbed at my Aunt Iris in a frantic lurch, clutching at her waist in desperation and cried incessantly. In between sobs, I begged, 'Will you come to us soon, Aunty, please.' I felt like a solitary figure, uncertain of my age or what was really happening. She threw her arms around my head and held me close to her bosom.

'I promise that as soon as I can I will see you all again, nothing is for ever.' She sounded solemn, her voice was shaking with uncertainty. Her startled eyes reflected fearful anticipation, and her final farewell seemed to last for an eternity. When the time came to say goodbye I have very few words to describe how I felt. Everyone was overcome with emotion, now the eternal waiting and hoping belonged to the past.

'Come on, son, it's time we were leaving,' said the young soldier who had been waiting patiently, his face now a sallow picture. I scrambled into the back end, shaking with dread, and sat directly opposite my mother. He then raised and closed the tailgate behind me. There were about ten families all crammed inside, like cattle being herded to the slaughterhouse. The little ones looked lost and bewildered as they clutched their dolls and books. Some huddled close to their mothers, who were perched on the bench that ran along three sides of the vehicle. The slightly older children squatted on the bags in the middle of the floor, which proved to be a lot more comfortable. The canopy, regarded as a necessity against the flies, dust and blazing sun, remained up. However, this only added to a fair degree of discomfort, with the suffocating heat that would result.

Within a few minutes our journey began, and as the truck growled and grizzled, then jerked forward, our arms shot out to find something to hold on to. For a moment there were no tears and no sighs, we had gone through enough already. Everyone lapsed into a moody silence, as we braced ourselves for the uncomfortable ride. A puff of dust billowed behind the tailgate, temporarily blocking my vision, and a feeling of utter desolation engulfed me as a cold shiver ran through my body. My mother looked up sharply, her expression melting abruptly into one of heartbreak. The tears sprayed out and trickled down her face, she finally gave in and wept without embarrassment. I tried to smile and returned a wave to a forest of arms raised in sadness, it was the parting of loved ones. Leaning on the steel frame, I kept my watery eyes fixed on the receding group, then burst into tears as they slowly vanished. The drone of the engines drowned the shouts of those staying behind, who could not betray signs of their heartbreak, and the goodbyes only echoed painfully in my ears. Their images faded like the haunting darkness before nightfall, and finally ceased to exist, as the convoy negotiated the main road to Mandalay. Taking a deep breath, I kept telling myself that the worst part was over now that we were on our journey. The sight of my mother weeping made me feel sadder, causing a tight movement in my chest. Having to walk out of her home must have been terrible for her. I decided that I wasn't going to cry, because I didn't want her to worry.

I thought of my aunt and of my father whom I'd never met. I had only seen his picture, yet firmly accepted the fact that the photograph, which communicated best, was the one we believed in. There were times when the pain was so intense that I felt sick to my stomach. There were also moments of despair when I broke down and cried, but everyone else was so preoccupied with their own troubles no one paid any attention as we travelled through pockets of jungle and a labyrinth of bumpy roads, which twisted and banked sharply. We then crawled through a region of rolling hills, which had their own distinctive beauty. As I tried desperately to excel in the art of make-believe, and conceal the bestial reality behind an artificial screen, many lost moments were spent gazing through empty eyes. It was also no remarkable feat of observation for me to notice that many of the women were still desperately upset by the recent upheaval. They were also finding it very difficult to govern their behaviour in front of the young audience, obviously preferring to be alone than associated with the personal appendage during this painful exodus. The heat under the canopy was unbearable, and the peaceful atmosphere inside masked a darker reality.

Some of the women discussed home and loved ones, believing that precious thoughts would provide a healing influence in this nursery of confusion. Their faces were serious, grief stricken. Others stared with vacant eyes, which glistened, but not with bliss, only desperation in the numbing harshness of this canvas archway. Occasionally their anguish knew no bounds, when a variety of soft tones begged with conviction in a religious note of self-denial, as questions floated across their faces. I kept talking to Mother asking her many questions; she listened, then nodded, as if to reassure me that she was paying attention. I could feel my eyelids drooping, everyone appeared to be tired. Suddenly I opened my eyes to a murmur of voices.

'You have been asleep for almost two hours,' Mother informed me. I thought it was longer than that.

We finally swept into the elegant city of Mandalay, with its ancient palace surrounded by a moat. Though not the capital, it was the commercial and cultural hub of Central and Northern Burma, the core, with the pounding pulse of the nation, a harbour of many races and tribes, who came to treat themselves to a taste of the big city, whose name itself evoked spice and mystery. It was designed to entice the traveller with a chaos of sound and colour, but with an incredible warmth for strangers. The convoy came to a halt outside Mandalay Hill, a beauty spot near the two huge white chinthes, those mythological figures, whose only function was as temple guards to ward off the evil spirits in that atmosphere of contrasting landscape. The city itself was crammed with beggars, palmists, fruit and soft drink peddlers lining the busy streets. I watched them all in fascination, as they viewed this strange band of military vehicles with naked interest.

Most of the women were struggling between hope and despair, sparing quick glances at the hundreds of busy onlookers gaping at the military convoy. For some of the adults there were mood swings and uncontrollable depression, as visions of a happy past danced in their heads. It took us a while to remove ourselves from the trucks. Then we were met immediately by members of the Red Cross, who soon provided us with warm drinks and sandwiches, although for most of us the toilet facilities were to draw our prompt attention. The forty miles that we had travelled had taken almost three hours, even though we had descended nearly four thousand feet. Such were the difficulties with so many small children aboard. After an hour we regrouped and returned to our transport, continuing the journey through the narrow streets to downtown Mandalay. On the outskirts, I looked back along the road as the dark forest faded in the distance. There were many ruined structures, overgrown with ivy, creepers and a multitude of small individually built white pagodas, each one appearing as if nature had reclaimed its lost legend.

Travelling at the minimum speed made us a perfect target for enemy aircraft, so we were feeling vulnerable. As we were exposed an open invitation was a distinct possibility, and we nervously assessed our chances of survival amid such serenity, although it would have been foolish to take all this for granted. However, for the present there was no such evidence, which made us appreciate the exquisite surroundings. We passed through remote villages, which bordered on the fringes, where groups of adults with small children shouted and waved excitedly, obviously feeling overjoyed at the sight of a British convoy for the first time. I immediately returned their gestures, bravely sharing their enthusiasm, but certainly not in the same frame of mind. I couldn't help feeling pity for them. We were moving away from the conflict, whereas they would be remaining behind, to face the residual backlash of a barbaric enemy.

It was a bumpy despairing ride, and I soon began to lose the significance of being in a city. I could still see the fading buildings, dominating the skyline in the shimmering heat, although it was much quieter now and I could actually hear the wind in the branches of the banyan trees, and smell the pungent dorian trees that edged the roadside. There weren't many people around, only a few strange-looking men called pongees (monks). They always terrified me in their surreal attire, the long saffron-coloured cloaks and their heads shaved to the bone. They were really harmless people, having reached the spiritual peak of human desire, by learning and accepting how much they could do without, whereas we are never satisfied always wanting and needing more than we necessarily require.

We passed several bullock carts, stacked high with Indian corn from the nearby arable land. Their owners sat astride the hard-working animals, in dowdy clothing, with baggy eyes glittering with more than friendliness on faces. Tired features depicted skins full of wrinkles under the scorching sun. There were the usual paddy fields, where the women toiled diligently from dawn until dusk, knee-high in sludgy water, set in a perennial rhythm, dictated only by the planting, growing and harvesting of rice, the country's foremost enterprise and principle diet. It was an endless tiring procession that held my mind in a whirlpool, and the only scenery for miles was a ribbon of blue sky. My thoughts were far away in familiar houses and dusty streets, filling my emptiness with my own emotion. Suddenly I was overcome with a haunting fear inside of me, which seemed scarred and etched by turmoil, sending my mind spinning backwards. I immediately pushed it away like an undesired touch of evil. Then Mother spoke, disturbing my mood.

'Open that box, son, and get some sandwiches out, you must be hungry,' she said softly. I looked at her, taken by surprise. 'There is also some pineapple juice in a container.'

I smiled timidly, then replied, 'Yes, I am,' breathing a deep sigh as I fumbled with the lid.

The war itself, whose indefinable presence we still felt, seemed to grow less savage momentarily as we moved cautiously through a small village of frugal houses. In close attendance were miniature shrines, resembling temples, secured on the top of posts. Most of them had an outer platform, and in each one dwelled the guardian of the building. These shrines were loved and venerated by the entire family and were a source of comfort and support to them through all the vicissitudes of life. Unfortunately the discarded rags and scattered cans were clear indication that the inhabitants had left some time earlier.

It was late in the evening now as a chill spread through the air, and the convoy appeared to slow down. My first reaction was that we might be approaching a large town. My mother seemed to confirm my suspicions. 'This could be Meiktila, son, our first stop,' she remarked. Her voice was quiet, even lethargic, and her face appeared prematurely aged. However, I could hear the suppressed excitement in her voice, and wondered if she felt the same shiver rising at the back of her throat as I did. Nevertheless, with the prospect of a hot meal and drinks before us, we cheered up considerably. It was also noticeable that everyone was smiling and preoccupied with optimistic thoughts as they observed that life inside this imposing town with its Spartan houses and spacious gardens appeared tranquil. We proceeded through and stopped outside an extraordinary-looking building perched high on wooden stilts, surrounded by tall rubber trees. Huge timber steps on the exterior lined their way onto a verandah, which in turn led to the main entrance. Here jaded green fern-like vines soared up the outside, and evergreen bushes encircled the front lawn.

Members of the Red Cross and some military personnel were there immediately to greet our arrival. We then slowly removed from the vehicles our aching bodies now burning with hunger. Ignoring our uneasiness and obvious discomfort, we climbed up the steps and ceremoniously filed inside the dining area. Many conveniently placed tables brought togetherness as we all squared up to a large meal. Although relatively straightforward and eye-watering, the plates were filled with intricate patterns of corned beef and tomato sandwiches. There were dishes full of dainty cakes, sweetmeats and an assortment of fresh fruit in syrup. There was also a variety of drinks either warm or cold as requested.

There was nothing inviting about this over-spacious, gloomy-looking room, with its large windows gaping curtainless, save the tables decorated with the abundance of fresh food. A huge pile of mattresses littered one corner. With the food consumed and our appetites fully satisfied, some discipline had to be asserted for sleeping arrangements. The tables were eventually stowed away in orderly fashion, and the mattresses exercised their use as cushions on the hard uneven surface. Additional blankets were also offered as warmth against the cold and starless night outside. The room suddenly vanished into darkness, pierced only by a shaft of light through the slight crack in the roof as the moon hovered. It was just out of reach and growing brighter every minute, as sleep brought dreams of home followed by an orderly silence.

Dawn broke over the distant forests, as sunlight streamed freely through the shutters. I opened my eyes and shut them more tightly against the brightness, then opened them again and stretched out wearily. Now I was glad to be awake. With the coming of morning, breakfast was much later than expected, as some of the women had overslept, probably still feeling exhausted from the previous day's excursion. The tables were a swift replacement for the bedding materials, and the highlight of the interior was the friendliness of the people who served us with cereals, toast, and either tea or coffee.

The steady silence was interrupted once again by the military, with the usual instructions and amicable advice.

A tall, gaunt-looking officer addressed the whole congregation. 'First I must apologise for the unorthodox and rather primitive sleeping arrangements. Unfortunately I wasn't in a position to arrange anything at such short notice,' he said, smiling cheekily to himself.

A woman laughed hilariously, unaffected by his remark. 'I'm just pleased that we're not staying here much longer,' she said, in a friendly tone, 'although the food wasn't too bad and plenty of it.' She patted her contented stomach. The others agreed in unison, chuckling loudly, as the officer continued with steely efficiency.

'Your next stop will be the crude-oil fields at Yenangyaung[1]. However, it will be the last stage of your journey cooped up in an enclosed truck, that I can promise you, and I'm very pleased to inform you that the accommodation there is of the highest standard. I've also been told that the food there is excellent.' This last comment brought huge smiles of instant relief.

After finishing our meal we gathered our belongings and rejoined the convoy waiting outside. We bid our last farewells to the staff and climbed into the vehicle in the same position as before. The journey started later than it was programmed for, and the truck eventually eased onto the bumpy surface. It soon jolted into motion, rocking our aching bodies back and forth. Soon the ascending sun was already dazzling in its wake. Along the main road there were scattered groups of refugees, with prams, carts and wheelbarrows crammed full of belongings, heading north away from the conflict. Inside our make-do ménage, children

---

[1] Pronounced *Yenangoung*.

scribbled in their notebooks, some chatted, others dozed. Many of the adults were feeling reluctant to involve themselves in any discussion, feeling disorientated and fearing residual bitterness from the day before. So any conversation was spasmodic and forced. Instantly I felt a sharp tug on my sleeve; the lady sitting alongside wanted me to acknowledge my mother's attention. She had a charming smile and looked rather young for a married woman. She was slim, with long black hair, tied at the back with a tight coloured ribbon, and large, dark, almond-shaped eyes. She appeared to be travelling alone.

'Will you hold Baby for a moment? My arms are aching,' Mother asked softly. She looked at me with an expression of tenderness and love, which surprised me.

I felt a wave of happiness sweep over me, and my heart jerked with excitement as I replied, 'Yes, please, Mum.' Then I leaned forward with a blissful gleam in my eyes and reached out with both arms, gently rocking with the motion of the moving vehicle, and eagerly wanting to cradle my sister for the first time since she was born. What a place for a baptism! I thought, glancing down at her. She smiled innocently, screwing up her tiny face, enjoying the novelty of attention. She was all skinny and angelic, blinking her wide eyes at me as I held her firmly in my lap. A proud feeling of admiration and self-importance surged through me, and I allowed myself a comfortable wink, a modest smile and a flash of nonchalance. Although still young, I had grown up considerably. I asked Mother many questions about life, and the uncertainty of it at the present.

We passed through a series of low hills, entrusting our lives to the elements, but the humidity and discomfort cut us off from any pleasure of travelling as the journey unwound. Here the bark of the trees was cracked with the intense heat, as we cruised past the usual paddy fields and acres of parched land being irrigated by a nearby river, a symbol of the world we were trying to escape from, and slipped quietly through a small town named Pyawbwe[2]. My lasting memory is of smiling faces, laughter in the bazaar and the colourful costumes, although some of the buildings were drab

---

[2] Pronounced *Pawbwe*.

and dull as the sun slanted down upon a courtyard between them, overgrown by creepers and vines. As we continued on, many civilians were travelling north in the opposite direction, scrubbing along the road with their sparse belongings, all of them looking as if they had abandoned hope and no longer cared. Numerous little huts edged the roadside, the roofs supported by stakes and underneath were empty boxes which probably served as benches. Small children lined the footpaths, greedily gnawing away at large portions of watermelon with a certain excitement, while the grim mute figures of others were puzzling in silence, over the disappearing line of trucks receding into the distance.

A few miles on, cruising gently through the evening sunshine and parallel with the Sittang River, we developed a new confidence in ourselves, when suddenly we approached some huge tanks towering towards the sky. A symphony of pipelines honeycombed the surrounding area, lending the land a false hint of colour, positive indications that the petroleum fields weren't too far away. This was one of the country's fabulous natural resources, but with the absence of traffic, the avenues resembled a bleak deserted arena.

'Looks like we've arrived at Yenangyaung,' muttered the lady sitting next to me in a low voice and looking very excited. Her knitting needles flashed up and down. A tone of comfort had flowed into her speech, and a joyous smile lit her face. She was obviously feeling quite happy.

'Yes, I hope so, my backside is numb,' I replied hastily, trying to appear friendly and jockeying for a better viewing position. We then went past farming implements, bullock carts, columns of bustling villagers and street stalls immersed in sunshine. In the town itself crowds filled the roadways, strolling past the ranks of street vendors, some spilling from the shops with arms full of recently purchased goods, to join the living stream of people. Others were close to the edge of the road, as if eager to welcome the strangers who had just arrived.

Before the sun's diminishing light could pass below the horizon, the convoy halted outside some empty-looking bungalows adjacent to the oilfields. It was a pleasure to jump down onto the dry grass, when the tailgate was lowered, grateful to be on solid ground once more, and except for the sound of insects, birds, and the wind in the trees, the silence was personal. The place was deserted; that was now a fact of life. I smiled with satisfaction as I watched the others negotiate the steps nervously. We had progressed a long way without interference, accompanied by the dust, sun, flies and endured an uncomfortable ride; now this was to be our final stop. However, we were still obsessed by doubt as to what the future was, and listened to the anxious throbs of our hearts by which we lived and breathed, between hope and despair. The women of the Red Cross were there to meet us again, at their usual best, smiling and full of compassion, nothing was too much for them. We left in their company, yawning and stretching like shadows in the night. Suddenly a military car pulled up alongside, and four men in officers' uniform got out. They certainly looked considerably fresher than we felt. British intelligence! I thought.

They approached cautiously and spoke to the women.

'Ladies, please leave your belongings where they are, and follow us into the dining hall,' said one who had querulous features. His cheeks and forehead were lined and his small eyes like slits behind wire-rimmed glasses. A deep frown crossed his brow, and immediate thoughts of mistrust floated through my mind like lazy butterflies. He looked the type who relished domination. As we filed inside through an archway and tried to take everything in at once, a jumble of tables covered with blue oilcloth awaited our entrance. There were trays of shaped sandwiches, plates of meat and vegetables, salad, bread, cakes, and the elusive smell of fresh portions of watermelons filled the air. Countless fragile glasses spilt the light across the eager faces of this dreary gathering. We sat and relished everything with precious purpose, and somehow the food made my stomach dance.

Despite our tragic spectacle, everything else was presently calm, and we were eventually led away to separate bungalows. They had very recently been vacated by the American families who had been living there. To our surprise, the bungalow allocated to us had five rooms, plus a conservatory, and was painted on the outside in daffodil yellow. All the rooms looked comfortable, elegant and spacious; they were also carpeted and fully furnished. It was obvious that the previous tenants were used to a high degree of luxury; even the sight of telephones, although disconnected, left us dazzled and breathless. It was now essential to remove all the dust that had accumulated during the long journey. The necessity of a hot bath, and a change of clothing, was a pleasure that could not be dismissed. Now the warm water drummed away all the memories and cares, but it also introduced a new venture into my life – the domestic science of washing clothes, which included my sister's dirty nappies. Outside, a rising moon cast a dull shadow over the silhouettes of the huge tanks. I finally went to bed on a summery evening which drifted out over the rose garden, firmly believing that pleasant dreams would ensure a good night's sleep.

The morning of 4 March 1942, our final day, dawned as pale and as unwanted as the last morning of a convicted man awaiting execution. I certainly wasn't overjoyed at my unsatisfying sleep, and as we all gathered in the dining area, we stared at dozens of faces as drawn as our own, and although breakfast was a generous offer that day, with cereals, bacon, eggs, and plenty of coffee or tea, nobody could dispel the strange feelings hovering over them. Saturated with fear, our emotions seemed to be tangling themselves up almost lazily, as the bright sunlight fell through the windows of the room. We watched with eyes full of worried fascination on a day of soaking gloom, adrift in its timelessness. Now we were experiencing a sadness in this unaccustomed atmosphere. Everything appeared to be clouded in nostalgia, or was it a link between the present and the past? The future seemed no longer to have any significance, merely a succession of hardships growing daily less acceptable, but we were only passing through this old town, a brutal rite of passage, a sudden downward spiral in this chaotic aftermath. There was a knowing deep inside that sudden death might only be a heartbeat away from the faceless menace that haunted all of us.

After our meal the noisy conversations were interrupted by the arrival of half a dozen uniformed officers from the American Air Force. They politely removed their hats before entering the riotous dining area, and shook hands cheerfully with the officials of the British federation. Then a tall, broad-shouldered officer stepped forward, immediately drawing our attention. He paused to light a cigarette, before speaking to us in a strong southern drawl. His face was round and generous, with a rough complexion and a ready smile.

'Can I please have your attention?' he said, as the smoke curled past his mouth and drifted into the atmosphere. 'In a short while you will be collecting your belongings and rejoining the transport that is waiting for you outside. It will transfer all of you to Magwe[3] aerodrome, on the outskirts of the town. A group of B17s, or Flying Fortresses as they are better known, have arrived there from the Mariannas. They are under strict orders to fly the evacuees who are here to Asansol in Eastern India all being well. I want you all to please listen very carefully to what the crew have to say and they will look after you. I will see you again at the base.' Then he left us quietly with a brief wave.

A tremor of apprehension swept through the women, now looking cloaked with a touch of anxiety, then the room exploded into shouts and cheers. That short speech was all the heartbreak he could stand to inflict on us for a moment. Vacuous expressions flooded across our faces and voices droned across the crowded room, as we gazed at the disappearing figure. He certainly wasn't the type to accept conspicuous defeat lightly. His voice sounded good, although not too confident, but neither was there any caution in it. Now we felt powerless and our conscience was like a hushed voice from the dead. Conversation suddenly faded from the room, then the drumming of shoes on the floor broke the silence. The assembly moved forward, like mourners at a funeral procession, out through the main entrance into the glorious sunshine, and climbed into our corresponding trucks. There was now the familiar snap of the tailgate as we sat patiently waiting for another bumpy journey. The convoy lurched forward along a narrow dusty road, which twisted and turned its way over a series of woodland ridges.

Outside was more of a challenge; there the high areas were heavily wooded and a haven for many wild animals. The rest of

---

[3] Pronounced *Magway.*

this valley was ready for rice cultivation. There were numerous streams, which flowed the full length and appeared fairly deep. In all the hamlets the tribespeople sat around lazily, and didn't move beyond the borders. Then the jarring stopped as the road straightened out and the surface improved. We began to descend towards flatter country and smooth patches of ground, which seemed to stretch up to the horizon. I looked in all directions as far as I could see and observed the gathering of clouds constantly shifting and changing.

Suddenly there was a blinding barrage of machine-gun fire not too far away. The noise was deafening, and the air smouldered, thick with bitter fumes, which were hot and rich with the smell of burning gasoline. Inside the truck there was a new clattering note of voices filled with urgency, as words shuddered with excitement and faces filled with anxious anticipation. I was strangely surprised to find myself less nervous than I had been before and in comparison to what had already proceeded us, nothing seemed particularly wrong but a dart of pleasure made me shiver. After a short while we stopped and were asked to get out of the trucks. My heart thudded heavily when I stepped into the warm sunshine and saw the giant aircraft standing near the runway, looking frightening with authority and immense in stature. My eyes opened wide and glistened in the light like molten glass. Now I was curious. The horizon shimmered and danced with the vapour from the exhausts as we clustered together in small groups in this sunlit morning. The area was surrounded by huge trees; shrubs and green grass edged the runway, but it certainly wasn't any vision of paradise.

We sat down inside and listened to a short briefing from one of the officers. He was about forty years old with a bull-like frame, his face flaccid with a pallid indoors complexion. His eyes were recessed deeply behind his puffy cheeks and tough craggy jaw. He was firm, decisive and polished and spoke with a veneer of calm confidence.

'You will be sectioned off into groups, making seating accommodation a little more relaxing for the women and younger ones inside the aircraft.' He pursed his lips and clasped his hands together as he spoke. Although he sounded pleasant, he had a ruthless quality about him, more like a prison guard. 'There will be four aircraft available for this flight, which should be sufficient. Please observe the instructions you are given whilst on board, as conditions will be cramped and far from comfortable. Follow these commands and you should be all right. Before I leave, I would like to wish all of you a safe journey.' With that, he tipped his hat and left, waving a regretful farewell.

We were to be associated with the last group, consisting of the remaining fourteen families. My baby sister at two weeks was the youngest of the children, and I was the oldest at eleven years. The tension was so grim and strong among the evacuees that a local chaplain from the vicinity was asked to deliver an invocation. All the people knelt and he prayed that, whatever the dangers we encountered, to let us never be without the Almighty's sanctuary. His voice was deep and resonant, certainly not in keeping with his pale face and boyish figure. Gradually, as the entire colony went on parade, sections of people emerged from their stable positions. They moved slowly towards their respective aircraft, with a certain amount of dismay. We kept reminding ourselves that the journey had its own rewards and pleasures, with survival not the destination a recurring refrain in our thoughts.

We moved within range, to concentrate on the aircraft taking off, preferring the vast spaciousness to the inside of the confined building. Within minutes they were speeding swiftly along the runway with tremendous power, then surging upwards like giant birds of prey, leaving a fluttering of debris swirling in their wake, like a cloud's shadow changing shape and movement. It was nearly 10 a.m. now as the sun hung over the western side of the woods. Our group remained silent for a few moments, being the last of this batch of evacuees to climb aboard. I felt a sudden urge to run away from this place, and my heart started to pound in slow painful thuds. There was no ignoring the feeling of adversity in the atmosphere. However, it was too late now. The captain beckoned our group to move forward, towards the aircraft waiting for us, shimmering in the sunlight like some mirage or vision. Members of the crew then started assisting the women and children, along with their books, dolls and baggage, up the short flight of steps that hung from the fuselage. They were speaking and smiling to them reassuringly, trying to provide a pleasant exhibition of compassion.

As I approached the steps, my attention was immediately drawn to a dazzling painting on the fuselage. It was of a gorgeous woman in transparent silk lingerie. Next to her picture, the name 'Mary Jane' was inscribed in flashy italics. I couldn't help secretly admiring their seductive choice. The elegant profile certainly implied a positive closeness to my youthful innocence.

'Looks like you're the last one, son,' said the airman, smiling as he helped me up, then followed behind. Once inside he handed me back the bundle I'd been carrying, removed the steps and closed the hatch tightly.

We were leaving behind a strange disturbing world, with a feeling that the journey seemed set for a nightmare.

For a few moments the interior of the plane was terrifying, and my body whirled violently, like a toy boat caught up in a whirlpool. I'm positive that the others must have felt the same. The atmosphere was suffocating, with nothing but weapons and ammunition everywhere. A thoughtless bang could end the whole crusade. Space was so limited it was impossible to move around. The women sat on make-do seats, and the children huddled close together, pressing themselves in fear on the bags on the floor.

'Will you go to the far end of the plane?' the airman said, pointing towards the rear. I nodded and crawled on all fours until I reached the section of the rear gunner. I then sat up facing a young man, who didn't look much older than myself. He was small with a sallow face but pleasant. He smiled and offered me some chewing gum, which I accepted gratefully, thanking him in return. He was crouched opposite me with his knees drawn up, his eyes wide and white. He looked an ideal companion for a trip like this, boyish and sensible. There was a long pause before I spoke, trying to imitate adult behaviour.

'Where do you come from?' I asked more out of curiosity than interest.

'Good old Montana,' he replied, with a huge beaming smile. 'Cattle country,' he added breezily, then released a nervous laugh. In his voice I could sense an honest note.

My immediate thoughts were films of cowboys and Indians,

Custer, the Little Big Horn and Crazy Horse, all of which seemed quite natural at the time, but for the present we were a little short of words. We seemed to have been kept in a state of prolonged tension, as the waiting appeared endless. Everyone stared at each other in a kind of stupefied silence, feeling trapped in this long, narrow, metal tunnel. Like almost all the young people, I had done average work and had average intelligence. I had studied hard and asked many questions about the things I did not understand. I also had a free-running sense of humour and a cheeky streak of individualism that sometimes irritated. However, at this moment, my temples throbbed and my body was taut, ready for whatever might be necessary. I kept shutting and opening my eyes, and staring through the small square windows above the gun sponson. All that was visible was a pale-blue sky, in which there was the familiar sound of aeroplanes.

I pulled myself up slowly after an endless struggle with fatigue, and stood shakily on two weary legs, supporting my body on the inside of the fuselage with my hands. There were numerous cables and wires stretching all around the interior and a horrible smell of oil and grease. The crew were moving around ceaselessly, attending to the customary procedure required inside a bomber of this size and power. Something seemed to be happening outside, although unseen from where I stood eyeing everything with puzzled thoughts. It was heavy and electric, as a silence descended on the inside like a blanket. Suddenly, in the midst of all this peace, we were disturbed by a crescendo as the four huge engines started up simultaneously. The commotion frightened most of the smaller children who began crying. It was thundering and penetrating, and I thought that my eardrums were going to burst. We soon lost any hope of attempting to daydream. For a while the ritual continued, leaving me feeling frozen by the encounter and trapped in a pocket of fear. From above the commotion came the same friendly voice. 'Sit yourself down on my kitbag, lad, then you will be able to see through these windows.'

Beneath the friendliness, I noticed that there was a smooth and placid tone of command and sympathy. I swallowed hard, to ease the tightness in my stomach, and delight paraded across my face.

The light had slipped across the airfield, and the breeze seemed to whistle. It was a beautiful summer's day, crisp, dry and filled with glorious sunshine. Through the small panes I could just see a group of men in uniforms, officers judging by their insignia. I looked around for something that might produce an instance of pleasure and distract me from my nervousness. The young airman moved the gun sponson repeatedly from side to side.

Finally the aircraft started to move very slowly, then turned, and the drone increased. Several frightened pairs of eyes looked in all directions, faces drawn with fear. I could feel every bump as it sped along the runway, instantly gathering speed and leaving gushes of dust and dried leaves in its wake. It was a magic exciting moment as it slowly lifted off the ground. The men were waving and holding on to their hats, their clothing fluttering with the draught. Trees and bushes were swaying as we moved swiftly along the bumpy surface. Everyone was bouncing up and down as the whole aircraft shook vibrantly. Some of the smaller children were sick, others were crying. My insides turned somersaults and my heart was pumping so hard I could feel it in my throat.

Suddenly my whole stomach felt like a vacuum, as the mammoth craft angled upwards, passing the level of the treetops. The ground seemed to drop away and looked very romantic as it disappeared from view. All that was visible now was a clear sky with the occasional puff of white cloud. Gradually the speed accelerated, and we banked north-west over the Indian Ocean, leaving a contrail etching across the eastern horizon. We all settled down to a warm drink and some sandwiches as the crew moved around. For everyone there was only limitless space, and there was enough heaven around us to compensate for the hell. Our awareness of everything seemed divided; our thoughts, like our eyes, couldn't settle on anything that appeared real. Maybe we were so exhausted that we didn't care any more. The last few weeks had taken their toll, and absolutely nothing could stir our emotions. The air inside was heavy with sorrow, angling its weight on many of the adult faces. I soon learnt that children weren't the only ones who cried but with the absence of adequate lighting this wasn't a drawback for those concerned. Although my new friend and I hadn't been together very long, his companionship was of great importance to me. These were anxious moments.

Soon many of the children had fallen asleep. Most of the women were absorbed in their own personal feelings. This was a final goodbye to their homeland. I just kept on wondering where I could find new dreams to replace the old ones. These were anxious moments and the entire fuselage looked like a dimly lit corridor, filled with mental emptiness. When thoughts did attempt to appear, they were blocked out by a featureless wall of fear. Time, at the present, was just an endless flow of senses. As the minutes ebbed away, so did the movements of shadows along the floor of the aisle, interrupted only by the sun passing across the barren sky. Occasionally there appeared a dull reflection from the gun barrel and, like shadows, a noiseless uniformed movement of personnel.

For a while all was peaceful, then a rumble of voices from the opposite end flooded the metal tunnel. The sound of a shattering exploding noise ripped through the inside.

'Sit down on the floor behind me and don't move,' my companion shouted, his voice wavering, his face taut. He looked more like a pioneer without a frontier than a protective guardian in ruffled clothing. I sat perfectly still without hesitation, masked in a jagged ball of foreboding governed by the events. The sense of horror and expectation of dying must have been torturing everyone, as the sound of gunfire echoed through the passageway. I was also experiencing something that I had never encountered before, a kind of mindless barbarism. Agonising images of flames bursting out everywhere filtered through my head, the aircraft screaming into a nosedive, twisting and turning into a continuous spin, women and children shrieking and shaking with fear. My brain was in turmoil, but images of fear are seldom products of the brain.

Suddenly there was a vivid flash, followed by brilliant lights in the sky. A thundering of incredible force shook the plane, and it rolled about. I forced myself against the metal frame, constraining my eyes to watch the brutal contest between the enemy and a friend. There was a staccato chatter of machine-gun fire, which was deafening. Empty shells were falling all around me, as the sponson swerved violently from side to side carpeting the floor with metal containers. The fuselage was oppressed by pain and fear, by hate, anger and retribution. I couldn't stop or hide the tears streaming down my cheeks.

A few seconds of calm soon followed, as the fortress swayed effortlessly again, then up and down in a desultory lull. Then more vivid flashes screeched down the fuselage with deafening noise, as the enemy plane approached, carving its path of destruction. It flew past, banked away to gain height and return for another encounter. Some of the smaller children had already started crying and shaking with fear, the girls clinging to their dolls for support, while others cradled the kitbags loose on the floor. It was the first time that I'd seen so many women cry. There was something wrong, something to do with that dark outside. I closed my eyes, behind the lids – darkness. I could hide myself from the outside world. The darkness would surely protect me from this primal fear. The smell inside the aircraft was choking, the air thick and acrid with cordite fumes, making breathing almost impossible and unpleasant. The enemy came again, like sadistic pirates intent on destroying their prey. Some more incredibly bright flashes filled the interior, as the noise and rumble continued with devastating ferocity. My eyes opened and closed for an instant, then opened again, when I heard the roar of gunfire strafing the aircraft, an echo of blinding sound escalating back and forth in a regulated pattern, instantly followed by hysterical shouts and screams from the terrified passengers. However, with the protective cover of the aircraft and its tremendous firepower, no one was seriously hurt.

I kept counting the seconds, but no one could hear above the noise. Something fearful was happening, something I could never have imagined was masking my tireless determination to survive. My head buzzed and roared, as the air seemed to darken with blue smoke, which rose and fell gently in circles so finely detailed and perfectly balanced. We couldn't dismiss the reality, but acknowledged that our safety and freedom was about to be shattered as more blue flashes flooded the cramped interior. The plane rolled about, then up and down, as I tried desperately to hang on with the buffeting. Suddenly it was all very quiet as we caught our breath and wiped the nervous sweat from our foreheads. The voices had fallen silent, only dismayed emotional spectators remained, feeling disorientated and full of puzzled pride. I could do nothing but watch and pray in a weak voice, to a God in whom I was taught to believe and have faith. A warm glow flowed through me as I closed my eyes and prayed selfishly, trying to amplify my stuttering feeble words. 'Five angels guard me while I sleep, two at my head, two at my feet, one at my heart, my soul to keep, amen.' This was a poignant reminder to soothe my own heart, in this moment of ultimate disaster. Our existence, our staff of life cried out for spiritual solace. Almost instantly the gunfire ceased, as if my prayers had been answered, and the smoke began to settle. Our persecutors appeared content to leave us in peace. The attack had been so sudden and overwhelming that none of us grasped what had happened now that it was all over. I felt a huge knot in my throat and the tears stung my eyes as I tried desperately to hold them back. A great feeling of hatred for the enemy now overflowed my heart.

Our journey continued without any further interruptions, and anything else that might have happened is blurred from my memory. Time had elapsed since the conflict, and we had all settled down after the confusion, but it was still a stark reminder that danger was never far away. The plane cut through the heavy clouds straddling the horizon, and we suddenly approached the airfield at Asansol. The descent felt like some kind of escape from a living hell, and our exhausted brains clung to this fantasy. The huge aircraft hit the ground with a tremendous thud, bouncing up and down along the runway. The sound of screeching tyres came swelling up out of nothing, until it filled the whole area with a hot tension before coming to an abrupt halt. We had arrived safely at Asansol Airport, north-eastern India, on 4 March 1942, a journey that had almost cost everyone on that aircraft their lives.

Every face was stamped with an urgent anxiety, as those who were responsible for getting us to our destination were already moving towards the exit. Within a short time we all dispersed from the aircraft, and the tension subsided, as we climbed down the cramped steps like the weary travellers we were. Now we were hanging on to the only living link and feeling totally separated from the bustle of life. The shock of contact with the earth made us tremble, every bone in our bodies aching from that horrendous flight. Even time and moments vanished in fragments of ecstasy. There appeared to be hundreds of people, accompanied by thousands of eyes, eagerly waiting our arrival. A forward rush of authoritative voices, all distant, distorted into a babble. The constant human traffic passing and repassing made me feel as though I had entered a beehive. I finally glanced around once more before leaving, to admire with a sense of pride this amazing giant that had brought all of us to safety. I thought of its lines as being more symbolic of strength and power, a dynamo of energy, than of grace, an armoured citadel with wings of which there was no equal.

We made our way past these broken buildings in small groups, like sacrificial lambs being led to the slaughter, but had a tendency to break up and reform through weariness. We had spent the last two days in a gloom of which we spoke very little. The sombre qualities weighed heavily on our spirits, and even the fresh air seemed laden, as we walked towards an unfashionable-looking dwelling. Inside the premises many tables were laid out, with a wide variety of food dishes and an unlimited supply of cold drinks. The interior was decorated with huge portraits of the Raj, and elaborate paintings of elephant and tiger hunts festooned some of the walls. A haven at one time or another for the aristocracy, the building was a landmark. However, we were more absorbed in the immediate necessities, as hunger cramped our stomachs.

Outside, two rather undistinguished-looking buses were waiting to transport us to a town named Burnpaur. We had already been informed of this. As we left the airport the ground appeared to be criss-crossed by a network of landing strips and runways, and the outer area and parts of the town were incredibly dreary. The earth was barren and for one hundred yards or so it was difficult to describe where the fields left off and the woods began. Even the leafless trees looked shapeless, although the birds were singing, either with joy or fury, I certainly couldn't tell which. As soon as we had settled down on the coach, uncertainty was a source of anxiety, until the courier summoned our attention. She was a pretty young woman in her late twenties, smartly dressed in a navy blue sari and a white blouse. She had a delightful smile, very full and friendly, lightly tanned skin and round cheeks and tresses of fair hair, which spilled, around her head. Raising her eyes and smiling pleasantly, she spoke directly to the adults.

'As you already know we are travelling to Burnpaur, which is in the middle of the steel industry. There's a rather large company, where most of the male citizens are employed. It also provides a decent living for families accustomed to westernised influence.'

'Who has organised all this?' quipped a couple of women, sounding a little curious.

She didn't hesitate for a second before answering, 'The army has taken care of everything, so please be patient. I do fully understand what you have all been through. Are there any more questions?'

Most of the women shook their heads, and thanked her for her honesty, while others continued discussing moments and memories that they had shared recently. It wasn't so much painful as a sort of comfort.

'For the next few weeks you will all be staying with residents working in that industry, until suitable arrangements can be made regarding your future destination,' she continued. 'Thank you for allowing me a few moments of your time, I'm sure you must all be very tired.'

The ascendant midday sun was dazzling now and making rainbows in our eyes. The air was much warmer, and the welcome breeze, which drifted through the open windows of the coach, brought in the occasional fragrance of freshly planted fields. We travelled along for several miles on uneven winding roads, which were proving very difficult to follow. The long day had so far shown no signs of drawing to a close. Suddenly, I could clearly see columns of smoke and steam belching lazily into the dark endless sky. These were surely the steel works at Burnpaur, as the panoply of colours from the furnace fires stretched a bitter

111

orange across the horizon. Here, even the air was a thick mist of blue smoke, as we passed through the town centre. The land appeared to be much flatter and the trees were leafed out, but in spite of the weather, distant echoes could still be heard. The coach finally came to a halt and the courier stood up to speak again.

'Mrs Townend, this is where your family get off, but first there are a few details that you must know. Mr and Mrs Carr will be your hosts; they arrived here from England a few years ago. Mr Carr was employed in the steel industry over there for a number of years and now has an executive post here. They have no children of their own but they are very nice people, so please enjoy your stay. Thank you once again for your patience, and do please remember that kindness should always be valued.'

There was a long hushed pause, the warm air still vibrating with the courier's short but interesting speech. We quickly gathered our belongings and filtered off the coach, accompanied by this pleasant young lady. The front door of the house stood open, our hosts waiting to welcome us with expectation and smiles of friendliness. After some hurried introductions and the usual formalities, our escort left us to continue with the remainder of her unusual assignment. Mr Carr was a tall man, who moved slowly, but his eyes were bright with an observing look. His wife standing behind him was much smaller and kept throwing compassionate glances at us, her smile built on poetry, not for architectural purposes.

'Please do come inside out of the heat. You all must be very exhausted after that traumatic journey,' Mr Carr said. His voice possessed a certain vibrant quality, and his manner was not unfriendly, as he gestured with his hands.

The house was solidly built on firm ground and maintained a stubborn silence. There were almost no trees, so there was no fencing to separate it from a gloomy stretch of roadway, which somehow appeared to be surrounded by factories and tall chimneys. Nearby tacky little streets rose out of the ground like puffs of steam, and the choking green fronds had a horrible sweaty smell. Not too far away, clouds of swirling insects clogged the atmosphere in the remote pockets of land.

At present the heat was soporific and, despite the persistence of flies, it took some effort of will to stay awake to socialise and share their enthusiasm. However, we welcomed the sight of a huge fan as it spun relentlessly from the ceiling, cooling the room to a pleasurable comfort. A light evening meal had already been prepared for our expected arrival, soup, salad, and plenty of fresh fruit, which was all we really needed. Now it was time to relax and discuss the facts and realities of our journey, which somehow appealed to their supportive nature. They asked my mother many questions, not feeling affected by the war itself, but only the sound of their voices drifted across the intervening table. The words they expressed held a very different meaning.

I awoke the following morning to brilliant sunshine, feeling amazingly good-humoured despite the harrowing journey. At first I couldn't get up I was so tired, but I finally did as my feet drummed out an urgency to discover the countryside, which was bordered by dense woodland. Mr Carr had already left for the office at the steelworks, and his wife was preparing to leave very shortly for some voluntary work, as it was her day off. She had previously been involved in the nursing profession. The servants were busy with the household chores. I do not recall much of our activities during the short stay with these very helpful and pleasant people who had offered us a temporary home.

The area was sparsely populated, and I met surprisingly few of the residents on my excursions. I spent most of my time going for long walks on my own. If I had had any concept of loneliness before, it was nothing compared to how I felt now. I felt a sense of desolation, combined with an enormous guilt and grief, with no mirror to inform my own being. I desperately needed to communicate with someone, as the damp north wind slashed the open country like a sharp blade. As I walked through this vast disused area, the land ahead was flat and featureless, a true wilderness of thorny bushes and thickets. The wind whistled as it passed through, making shadows jump across my path, and there was no sound, only that of the breeze as it coiled inside. I turned for home now that the shadows were long and the daylight had taken on a strange orange glow. The insanities of loneliness and fear had become remarkably similar, filling me with a stirring of anger, which I couldn't suppress.

'Where have you been until now?' asked my mother, in an arched tone of anxiety.

'Oh, just for a long walk,' I replied slowly, showing no immediate concern but expecting an avalanche of questions.

'Just you keep away from that woodland,' she said with an honest glare. 'I know your game with all those wild chickens but there are also snakes, I've been told, so you had better be careful.' Her words were harsh but were meant to protect.

I continued up the stairs to have a wash.

'Don't forget to scrub behind your ears,' she said, her voice drifting up the landing behind me.

'I won't,' came my immediate reply. I undressed very slowly, thought about taking a cool bath then decided against it. I had a quick wash, then jumped into the bed next to our kid who was already dozing. I looked at the ceiling, feeling alone and confused. Sleep did not come for a long time and I felt a solitary person, but the solitude did not make me eccentric, only more curious.

The next morning I started to climb a winding path through the wooded expanse, where the air was dry and cool. There were a few houses scattered on either side of the road at first, then there was nothing but scrubby bushes and hillside. I suddenly felt a contracting of my heart, as if I were walking a tightrope, a solitary being, an isolated desperate figure slowly losing my grip on life, and aimlessly digressing into a chasm of my own subconscious, an abyss of uncertainty. I urgently wanted something to improvise in the absence of my usual recreation, and stepped into the dark undergrowth, searching for the wild fowl I'd recently heard about. The path rose and fell then wound through the wooded area, and the coppice appeared a little spooky, a place of hidden dangers and, even though the birds were calling from the trees, I didn't recognise any of them.

Equipped with my new home-made catapult and a long piece of broken branch, I forged a rugged path through the trees and brushed aside the ferns. A surge of excitement and a sense of anticipation enticed me into the bushy thicket, rustling the area with a vengeance. What stupid fools the innocence of youthful nature can sometimes make of us! The place seemed to come alive with fowl of every description, scurrying in all directions several paces in front of me. Any thoughts of imminent danger soon evaporated, amidst all the confusion. Huge possibilities seemed to prevail, moving swiftly. I had never felt so strongly the presence of nature as a united force and rich with so much potential. I felt the cracking of underbrush beneath my feet, as I swayed and sobbed for breath in and out of my lungs. The wind swept through my hair like a fine-tooth comb and roared in my ears like a lion.

Suddenly I tripped and stumbled over something that moved, and sprawled full length on the ground. Something brushed past my leg and I yelped, my heart beating in my throat. Then an excruciating pain shot through my right ankle, as my body contracted with the agony. I screamed, a horrific mixture of panic, fright and distress. I was exhausted and afraid, wanting nothing more than to be away from this weird place. Picking myself up, I ran crashing through the bracken and the low-hanging branches, driving myself, simply because I was afraid. I scrambled towards the roadside, limping badly on one leg and trying to maintain some order of balance, as I began to feel a stab of penetration.

'Please help me somebody,' I screamed out in desperation, trying to attract someone's attention, then began to shudder helplessly and feel plagued with a chilling fever. Staggering and hurrying along a path, which ran out of the woods and into an open field near some houses I fell to the ground with my head spinning in a tangled confusion. Then I lost all sense of reality and looked up at the sky, watching the birds flying in the sunlight and envying their freedom.

A man, who was tending his garden at the rear of his home, shouted at me, 'What's the matter, son?' He ran to my aid when he saw me wincing with pain and struggling to stand upright on the rough ground.

'I think I've been bitten by something,' I replied, trying to force back a gentle sob and not being too certain of my injury, but the look of utter perplexity on his face was testimony to my ignorance.

'You've most probably been bitten by a bushmaster,' he replied, looking very concerned, 'but please keep very still, it's dangerous to move about because of the poison.'

I nodded, feeling the panic surging through me.

'There are quite a few of them around here roaming the north-eastern frontiers,' he said, then wrapped a belt tightly above my right knee and proceeded to carry me into his house.

'I'm sure that I can walk, sir,' I said, feeling guilty at causing so much fuss, but he ignored my plea.

'Take him into the kitchen,' said his wife, with a glance at my leg. She wasn't really attractive, but her smile was gorgeous and her surprise was sincere. God had given her that precious gift.

The man then sat me on a stool in the scullery, removing my shoe and stocking.

'What are you going to do with me?' I asked, gazing at him sadly and feeling afraid. 'I must get home, my mum will be worried.' I was trying to find any excuse to get away.

'You sit there until I get some of the poison out,' he said and then produced a small pocket knife from the drawer.

I coughed and spluttered, dreading the pain when I saw the thin blade.

'This is going to hurt you,' he said. Then he dipped the knife in some Dettol. 'Now bite on this piece of wood as hard as you can and try to be brave.'

It was the indifference in his tone that convinced me, so I carried out his advice. His wife smiled at me, and she didn't have much difficulty in placing her arms around me, as I was attracted by her physical image. Terrified, I gritted my teeth until my jaw hurt, and all that remained was the agonising wait. Then I felt a piercing jab and my eyes seemed to fall back in their sockets and roll in space. The room spun sharply and the ceiling weaved and danced. I turned my face away as the blood pounded in my veins. The pain which twisted through me, almost stopped my breathing and my tears sprayed out in a hot flood. He was right, of course, it really did hurt and I let out a harrowing scream of terror but it really didn't matter. I very soon learnt how to endure the violent throbbing, and in this stressful situation nothing really mattered.

The man smiled with satisfaction, as I watched him go to the medicine cabinet. Then he produced a bottle of iodine and a huge wad of cotton wool, as a trickle of blood dripped onto the floor.

This made me squirm and turn my head away. The comfort of his wife's arms did enhance dignity in my behaviour, and her tender smile was easy to accept, as she teasingly ruffled the top of my head.

'I'll make you a nice hot cup of tea,' she said, smiling with childlike pleasure before releasing her tender hold.

Her husband then lifted up my leg and sucked out as much of the venom as possible, before swamping the swollen region of the wound with iodine soaked in cotton wool. I had to fight off a sudden impulse to run away when it stung cruelly, but his grasp was too strong. He then wrapped it tightly with a bandage. In the comfort of his paternal influence, any fear that I might have had evaporated quickly. After putting together a jumbled story of my travels and locations, he eventually contacted Mrs Carr at her place of work. Suddenly I was shaking, coated in perspiration. The room was whirling and darkening, sending my mind tripping. I felt I was going down into darkness as consciousness drifted away.

Within what seemed an endless passing of time, Mrs Carr had informed my mother and also had me in a bed in the local clinic. Here, anti-venom vaccine was injected into my bloodstream, obviously for protection against the poison. The clinic was small and rather ill-equipped, and the wound was never stitched, being the usual procedure. However, it was sufficiently treated and was never to deteriorate any further. I lay in the hospital bed for the next few days, recovering from the fever, and listened to the intermittent babble of faraway voices. I tried to remember how vivid those sensations had been, and how fortunate I had been on that horrendous day full of unrelated and hideous incidents. I had been very sick but had survived to enjoy the location to which I was getting accustomed, and felt a wave of happiness sweep over me amid the distant murmured conversations.

We were sitting on the side verandah shielded away from the sun, enjoying a noon siesta, when an army lorry stopped outside the front of the house. Two officers, whom we had met previously, approached, carrying the usual leather satchels. My mother's smile disappeared instantly like hesitant sunlight, as she stood up to greet them.

'Mrs Townend,' said one of the officers, speaking very gently, 'I have some very important news for you. Can we go inside?'

Questions floated across my face, and excitement rose deep in my thoughts.

'Will you please be packed and ready to move in two days, army vehicles will then transfer all the families to the railway station, where a special train has been reserved. From there you will travel to Rawalpindi in the Punjab, where you will receive further instructions.'

His voice had a note of power in it. We sat and listened to all the relevant information he could offer. His tone was informal, even friendly, a procedure we had grown accustomed to and something that was rapidly becoming a habitual nightmare. Mother wore the face of a shocked survivor and was feeling morbidly suspicious about the sudden change of events.

'We'll be ready,' she replied nervously, searching her mind for further questions. 'Can you please tell me how long the journey will take.' A ghost of a smile touched her lips.

'Approximately four days, although you will not be travelling at night,' replied the officer. He was the higher ranking of the two, and appeared to be better informed. I anticipated a spectacular journey for all, believing that travel took you to the centre of yourself.

They finally stood up to leave, having numerous other points of call to make. Although Mother made a gesture of acknowledgement to them, she looked utterly dejected with the whole idea. I sat with her for a while with childlike eagerness, but her eyes seemed to lose her fear and fill instead with bewilderment. She looked at me with an expression of shock and surprise. Dusk came on suddenly after a seemingly endless day, but it remained overcast and there was no starry night, just extraordinary darkness as Mother sat and discussed the day's events with our hosts. I repeated the same chore of silent obedience. Although I still pondered the earlier discussions with great reverence and power, which controlled reality as another eventful day finally ended.

By mid-morning on the day of departure, we were settled on

the train along with all the others, each family being provided with their own private compartment and heading for the city of Rawalpindi in the Himalayas. The train moved off in a series of desperate jerks, jolting along the criss-cross tracks, ushering in a note of sadness. Now these wooden carriages would be our homes for the next four days and nights as we took with us the discomfort, the heat and the wide open spaces of the countryside where the soil wasn't as rich as it looked.

For most of this long journey, in between stops, the scenery was drab and monotonous. During the days the sunlight was so bright one could see nothing at all worth noting, and empty fields are best seen through a carriage window. There was still no news of the evacuation or the state of the war, and this left us all feeling extremely sad and nervous. Despite the resignation that had taken hold of us, we were all still feeling that irrational self-indulgent guilt. We had also experienced some of the horrors, so there wasn't much we could learn about that aspect of the situation. Our eyes had now grown accustomed to accept everything we saw without surprise. For the present, the families were absorbed in their own personal routines, which in time was to become a hallmark of their spirit and behaviour.

By the end of the fourth day, the afternoon had begun to cloud up and by the evening a cool summer rain had started to fall, after we had spent long periods of silent contemplation. In the distance, the Himalayan landscape could be seen through the rain-splattered windows, the mountains stretching across the horizon like statues pointing skywards. Now that our journey was completed, we finally opened the door and stepped eagerly onto the solid platform that had been designated and specially prepared for our arrival. Many of the evacuees were still looking vaguely lost and bewildered. Women in smart Red Cross uniforms, which were familiar to us, and numerous other officials, some in military outfits, were there to greet us. Eventually the clouds had drawn back, the light in the west was fading quickly and it would soon be dark. With the coming of sunset the wind had also died instantly but the stifling atmosphere remained in this overcrowded arcade. Even the noise was unbearable and sounded the full length of the station, with the shunting of locomotives, shouts of newspaper vendors, mailbags being unloaded. The air was crammed with strange voices as unfamiliar place names were uttered in weird accents. Discarded newspapers blew about everywhere and porters stood around like impatient gravediggers, all of them waiting for business, which always seemed probable and would come earlier rather than later.

After being shuffled around into a crowded circle, we were bitterly disappointed to hear that we would be sleeping in the same carriages for another night. However, a cafeteria had been organised where free meals and drinks would be provided. Suddenly everything seemed to move with an astonishing speed, as we ate, washed, changed and returned to our carriages for the rest of the evening, although many were not entirely satisfied with the present location, where the lack of privacy was upsetting most of the women. There were some points of interest in this old city, but the attraction didn't leap out at you. In the houses encircling the station, people were yawning, and a warm breeze stirred the trees along the highway. Not surprisingly the inmates of this particular train were soon asleep.

Dawn broke with all its richness, and after we had had an early breakfast in the station, the officials informed us that coaches would transport us to the Murree Hills in the Himalayas. Our small party, tired of lounging around, then climbed aboard with surprise and curiosity stamped on our faces. Some of the buildings we passed were coloured in washed white, others were in solemn stone and there was a pungent smell in the air of spices and oil. The streets were coming alive with pedestrians, cars and bicycles, escorted by that cloud of smoke that always seemed to hang around a city. As the engines of commerce rumbled down the highway, the avenues appeared dirty and loud with no delicacy or simplicity about anything. A quick glance put distance between us, and the view disappeared.

We continued through the mountains on a long, endless, winding road, twisting and turning like a giant snake moving with deliberate caution. The ascent was precarious and our slow rate of progress was determined by the labouring of the engines. The side bonnets covering them were intentionally left open during the persistent climb, allowing the mountain air to cool them whilst in motion. As we travelled along this unmarked road at half-speed, the forest of tall pines looked as though they were arranged in the landscape. Higher and higher we climbed, raising the dust along the road in the great forest. Pine-studded canyons ran the full length of the mountain range and fluttered in the still air.

Some of us tried to doze amidst the continuous rambling conversations of others and the jumbled voices from the smaller children, drifting through the drowsiness between sleep and wakefulness. Down below us the valley seemed to have disappeared and the gods with it. The outlying areas were incredibly dreary, crammed with mud huts, where presumably the hill tribes lived. The vegetation was cultivated along the mountainsides in layers, like gigantic steps. Tired-looking men and women handled oxen-pulled implements on the baked hard earth, which looked unfit for human habitation. It was all very picturesque, but we were far too exhausted to absorb the views with any pleasure, and even with all the windows open, the heat was stifling. As we approached, the mountain range ahead towered majestically, and as far as the eye could see the land was a carpet of velvet. The air was now getting noticeably thinner as we struggled with our breathing.

After stopping at a small village called Bunsra Gali, we quickly removed ourselves from the coaches to stretch our legs and use the antiquated latrines, which produced an indescribable stench. We also took on extra fuel, and rattled through the ancient pass towards the summit. Here the slight change in the weather was perfect, with a soft cool breeze, and this congenial transition made everything seem easier. The clouds were the colour of cold steel, hovering overhead, almost touchable as we slipped past Ghora Gali, another small village on the outskirts of our destination, where a tiny stream cascaded down the hillside. We were gradually coming to terms with the shifting landscape, as the mountain views unravelled like a ball of thread. The villagers appeared rock-hard from a lifetime of hard work and poverty, but they were ferociously patriotic, their divine faith nurtured in the grace of the Dalai Lama.

At last we arrived at our final stop, the hill station of Murree.

As we finally came to a halt, it was no surprise that we all baled out instantly, totally unprepared for all this chaos. Any hope of blending in with the crowd was soon dispelled. My eyes strayed towards an imposing white-grey building, with long projecting wings at either end. It was fronted with well-tended gardens and neatly cut lawns. Judging by the visibly depressing sights, this was the entrance to the British Military Hospital and the scale of this structure was awesome. There were many severely wounded soldiers, probably from campaigns in the Far East. Some were minus limbs, others were walking unsteadily on crutches. Many were being slowly pushed around in wheelchairs by the responsible nurses. These unfortunate beings were receiving an unparalleled sense of care and devotion available to them. Fortunately, that is the secret behind the fertile soil of the nursing profession.

The huge building had a wide balustrade terrace, with steps leading to the main entrance. The heavily glistening doors parted and a robust presence introduced herself as the matron. She was a stout English lady, who looked much sturdier than the male associate who accompanied her. There was an alien formality in her behaviour. Her features were durable and conspicuous, holding Eastern serenity with a patronising sexism. The sun was shining briefly as she spoke to the gathering with a little compassion.

'Welcome to Murree. I know that you are all very tired, but as soon as you have all been medically examined, which is for your own benefit, meals will be provided in the staff canteen. After you have eaten, those of you who wish may visit the shopping centre in town. However, I must insist that you to please return before 4 p.m., as plans have been made for your transfer to a transit camp in Cliffden.'

Many of the women shook their heads in frustration and disapproval, feeling discouraged by the constant movement.

Then Matron continued, 'The site is a few miles away to the east and you'll find it very picturesque. It's no bigger than a settlement, but tucked neatly away under cover of forests and hills. There everything is at present being prepared for your comfort. Thank you all for your sustained attention.' She spoke in a flat monotone voice, no inflections, no emotion, just plain words.

The immediate silence was ended by the onset of deafening cheers, which followed the suppressed sighs of relief from the women. Immediate thoughts of shopping spilled through their brains, coupled with the motivating hunger of purchasing various new articles. In this part of the Himalayas, in this highland of mountains, blazing with wild flowers, crisp skies, heavy snowfalls and wild animals, the air was cool.

First, the families had to parade in single file, flocking through corridors, primed with laden stretchers, to the examining rooms. But neither the slight breeze which drifted through in spasms, nor the warm air which hung in abeyance, could change the choking path of the anaesthetic that seeped through unaided. Now the discipline, which had initially annoyed us, touched everyone with intense emotion at some of the appalling sights that flooded the hospital. For many of the wounded soldiers the war was literally over.

The matron spoke again. 'Your medical papers have all been misplaced in the evacuation and, unfortunately, as yet have not arrived. Therefore you will all be subjected to further vaccinations against tuberculosis and inoculated for protection against cholera and typhoid.' The strength of power in her tone surprised everyone, as she voiced her orders and motives bluntly, adhering to them with tenacity. The adults also answered personal questions, which stirred up lost memories and half-forgotten feelings. The conclusion was finalised by the checking of our teeth and the administering of the less ambitious jabs with explosive speed and authority in textbook fashion. My heart froze in terror, as soon as my name was called, and my pulse raced tenfold, although I had no intention of showing my fears to the nurses.

Thankfully, we all ended up in the canteen for the promised lunch. Here once again the imposing stature of the matron appeared in the doorway. She spoke in a voice full of admiration and respect about another short rendezvous ahead. We listened with impassive expressions.

'There are some army personnel waiting your arrival at

Cliffden, about which you have already been notified. There you will be billeted in houses or bungalows according to your circumstances,' she said. 'Unfortunately, the road ahead is rugged and rocky and barely six feet wide, therefore unusable by motor vehicles. Therefore you will be travelling on horseback in a single column.'

There was a hushed silence for a moment.

'But we've never ridden horses before,' came the strong protest from all the women, generating an anger within themselves.

'The animals will be in the capable hands of the owners, so don't be too alarmed. You may even enjoy it,' she said, her expression and tone firm yet pleasing.

'You certainly don't expect me to sit on a horse with a small baby, do you?' asked my mother in a deep explicit voice. Her eyes were defiant and her lips firm with anger as she looked towards her.

'I'm terribly sorry, but I should have told you that the military will accompany you. Small children and babies will have a chaperon. Thank you.'

The women responded cheerfully and were eagerly looking forward to the new challenge with enthusiasm. Once we were all astride our rather unusual transport, the small caravan proceeded on its journey along the narrow path. On both sides, dense stands of fir trees lined the roadside, an endless expanse of jungle towered towards the sky. Despite the lack of any wind, it began to feel chilly, and eerie noises could be heard some distance away as the sound carried in the menacing silence which hung from the trees. However the warmth and babble of voices created an atmosphere of people enjoying themselves. We moved in orderly groups like troops on exercise, heading towards snow-covered peaks in the distance, which revealed the last remnants of winter. But we could not ignore the conscious fact of a brooding warning, which seemed to hang over the wilderness. The utter solitude of this part of the world, a fountainhead of the Northern Himalayas, broke into our vision. Suddenly another stretch of deserted track opened up as we came upon a clearing, and we could see at a glance that it was not a natural glade. To our astonishment, it was a neat and compact little campsite nestled in a rustic scene of huge pines and dense jungle, totally separated from the bustle of human activity. Yet somehow we refused to accept the reality surrounded by pine-covered hills that stretched right across the horizon.

Terraced bungalows, in sections of dozens, formed a huge square and occupied most of the initial area on the top sector, which appeared deserted. There was no movement or sound, except from a nearby single-storey concrete block where a group of people greeted our arrival. They were the well-organised army administrators. Inside the building was housed all the necessary requirements for our use, mostly tinned foods and fresh vegetables. Outside there were huge mounds of charcoal for heating and cooking purposes, and numerous drums of kerosene for use in the oil lamps. Here and there hills broke the flatness, where trees had been chopped down and taken away with their stumps to provide space for future buildings.

All the families present were accommodated in bungalows on the top section, before the disturbing darkness caved in on us. These were spacious and consisted of two large bedrooms, a combined lounge and dining area, toilet and bathroom, a tidy kitchen, plus a small verandah to the front. All the furnishings, bedding, cooking utensils and crockery were ex-army surplus. Although the fittings inside were ancient, everything inside was symmetrical, the tables with their square edges, the straight-backed chairs, even some tacky ornaments were perched in correct order. The windows needed shuttering to cut out the severity, but everyone quickly settled down. By dusk, columns of oily smoke climbed above the forest and vanished over the treetops, signs that this little hamlet was inhabited once again, its inmates hurt by solemn memories. As the wind dropped, an eerie silence closed in on this small group of houses, which looked bewitching in the snow-capped mountains and disappearing sunset.

We were informed that large groups of jackals, with their mournful cries, paraded regularly at the rear of the buildings, rampaging in the dustbins in search of food. As I looked from my bedroom window I was infatuated with the beauty and rawness. I felt that I could have stayed here for ever. This was a precious piece of mysterious wilderness, seemingly untouched by man. However this vast and violent landscape was a shadowy deformity, which instantly paralysed all our senses. Suddenly the darkness engulfed this exclusive sanctuary, neatly encircled by a palisade of fir trees, which seemed to swallow it up at night. Now the scene was of serenity and peace, as an army of low clouds like grey smoke swept across the treetops, blanketing the moonlight.

Dawn broke over the Himalayan skyline with a rage; the harsh rays penetrated through the curtainless windows, disturbing a much-needed sleep. Having eaten with a good appetite, and with curiosity being my natural obsession, I was anxious to explore the perimeter and discover this broad green paradox of secrets. We'd been informed of a small prefabricated school with four rooms, large enough to accommodate all the children. A compact play area protruded from the front, banked by staunch railings to protect the steep drop. Apricot trees in full bloom cloaked the area, generating a picturesque landscape. An adequate surgery, with a resident doctor for minor cases, could easily be converted into a chapel for Sunday worship. A local chaplain from Murree had agreed to be there as and when required. Close to the clinic, a diminutive waterfall added significant interest to a nature enthusiast. All this triggered an explosion of urgency and inquisitiveness, so I quickly scampered off to the forest of unexpected peril.

Chapter VI

The sound of a thunderous knock on the rear door echoed through the room. I hesitated, then opened it slowly. It hissed softly letting in a blast of cool air. I was stunned into silence by the sight of a huge man dressed in garments that resembled those of an Arabian genie. On one side of a broad belt hung an impressive curved dagger, the hilt studded in intricate designs. On his head rested an enormous white turban and he stood in a pair of dazzling gold and red *patans* (sandals) which curled up at the toes. His eyes were set back in a deeply tanned face masked with a sleek pointed beard. He was more arresting than handsome and I blinked at him nervously and open-mouthed.

'Good morning, little sahib,' he said, flashing an imposing friendly smile. His voice was deep and his eyes sparkled with vitality. I stepped back trembling and looking up at him.

'Mum!' I shouted, with my eyes still locked in surprise, 'There's a strange-looking man at the back door.'

Within a few seconds his whole persona changed when my mother arrived.

'Good morning, memsahib,' he said calmly, gently touching his forehead with the fingers of his hand as a mark of respect. 'The British army has sent me. I am the cook that you asked for,' he said, smiling, with an excellent command of English. Then he produced some documents from his inside pocket.

'Yes I did,' she replied. 'Please come inside so we can discuss your hours of work, wages and terms of agreement.'

I soon trooped outside, full of vigour, where a summer morning in the Himalayas pulsed with birdsong. Leaving them alone to discuss the formalities in depth, I scrambled up a difficult path, which opened up onto a grassy plateau high on the mountain top. My legs were beginning to ache a little from the steep ascent, so I rested for a while. Down below a seemingly endless caravan of camels moved lethargically along the twisting turning route to the campsite between a coppice of huge pines, their owners astride bringing with them our lifeblood, fresh food, delicacies, and heating essentials. Suddenly a hint of twilight had come in the middle of the afternoon and the wind, which had been calm all day, began to rustle angrily, threatening a storm. Time passed, however it wasn't only time, but also a relentless flow of information passing from my senses to my lucid mind. The afternoon wore endlessly on and the slow movement of shadows passed across the ground as the sun made its way, shielding the enamelled sky. In spite of the exhausting exercise, I could feel the coldness creeping into my body. I headed back down the mountain with a lively step as the sun dipped, and for the first time in a few weeks I really did feel cheerful.

A couple of weeks had now passed, and we had gradually come to accept and settle down to this new existence, when another batch of evacuees drifted onto the site. I watched them by myself through dazed eyes and in frightful loneliness. They wandered through the heights of tragedy, as the dry leaves crackled under their tired feet. I found myself harnessed in a silence, which drowned out all the commotion and left an enormous hollowness inside of me. Never before had I seen so many people struggling to uphold their sense of human dignity. There appeared to be very few children and even fewer men. It was obviously clear that under that mask of pride there was a maternal vein of discomfort. The women did not seem to suffer in a world without men, but appeared calm and relaxed, and knew very little of the madness that still festered in the Far East. Their faces seemed unnaturally cold under the pale sunlight, but the vast distance they had travelled was probably the main cause, coupled with the fallacious belief that all this would soon be over.

We had forgotten what normal was. We felt that we'd been living like this for so long that the world belonged to us only. Women from the campsite rushed in and mingled with the restless crowd, frantically questioning and demanding quick replies about husbands, relatives, or even close friends. The same questions resurfaced more than once, with heated voices, many unable to control their emotions. My mother grabbed my arm and pulled me away from the hysteria.

'Come on, son,' she said sadly, obviously feeling upset herself. 'None of our relations are with this batch. Maybe next time.'

I found myself wondering why they weren't there, and thinking there must be a simple answer. I had little interest left so I turned and walked away.

The month of June now showed, and the only respite from boredom was the forest and its inhabitants. In fact, it was amazing how peaceful the woods could be during times of stress. Saturday arrived, and although school was not on the agenda, I went to the bathroom early and washed, then quickly went out. It was a warm day, with a slight wind blowing across from the mountain tops as the dawn sun came up. The sky was perfectly innocent of clouds, and the green forest climbed the mountain like a moving carpet. We heard their voices long before we saw them. There seemed to be dozens of women and children sitting reluctantly astride their horses. Some of the men walked alongside in military fashion, although many were civilians, appearing full of muscular enthusiasm and looking far more agile than they could have imagined. Now they were driven by something more powerful than a simple lust for food and rest, a sense of pride that puffed out their chests. They approached the main entrance, moving very slowly into the compound, and were stopped suddenly and besieged by overanxious residents pushing forward impatiently in a mass, begging for any news about relatives and friends who had been left behind. When the rumours escalated that there were some soldiers amongst the group, it sent a flurry of women to the verge of hysteria. I shifted my attention to a small group that was detached from the main batch. Suddenly I saw a face I thought I knew and ran closer to the crowd. Everyone else seemed to be doing the same.

'Uncle!' I shouted in a choking voice.

The look of astonishment on my face stopped him in his tracks as he glanced at me. I raced forward and threw my arms around him.

'Uncle Ossie,' I shouted, clinging to him.

He never spoke, just rubbed the top of my head with his hand, his face a mixture of pleasure and sadness.

'Where is Aunty Iris?' I asked anxiously.

He didn't answer me again, but I could feel the urgency in his hands as he tried to steer me away from the crowds. Walking close to him was a soldier, who smiled at me. His face was so badly marked and withdrawn I hardly recognised him at first. A rifle hung from his shoulder and a small haversack was strapped to his back. For a moment a stillness hung in the air, then he put his arm around my shoulders and squeezed them before speaking.

'Where is your mother, son?' he asked hurriedly.

I knew then that he was my stepfather and blinked several times in disbelief at his poor condition. I pointed excitedly in the direction of the bungalow, where the trees of the woodland edge absorbed the heat that carpeted the dry ground.

'Where's Aunty Iris?' I repeated, fearing that something had happened.

'I'll tell you when we get inside the house, son,' he replied softly, full of sadness and depression.

Then the three of us strolled casually over as the feeling of joy and hope had begun to take hold. Could everyone be safe or was it just a celluloid dream? Still I couldn't stop the smile spreading across my face.

Mother ran from the house, with tears streaming down her face and her arms flashing around like a windmill. She threw herself at her husband and embraced him in a frenzy of kisses. Then she turned and put an arm around her brother. It was an emotional time for everyone as tears, laughter and deep sobs mixed with the pounding of heartbeats. It was getting late because the cook provided extra meals, but words weren't present at the dining table, only forced smiles. They probably sensed what Mother was thinking and tried to ignore it quietly. Not surprisingly, dinner was over rather quickly, because of the silent meditation and the occasional tears of happiness.

The next morning they gathered quietly in the dining area to discuss personal convictions and reflect on the state of our lives where memories were still engraved deep down. I stood in the doorway, not feeling comfortable in company with adults at this time, and fearing the worst. Minutes passed, and with Mother's patience exhausted, my stepfather started to speak. Glancing across at my mother he said, 'I'm very sorry, Gwen, but the news is bad. Iris is dead.'

My heart sank into the pit of my stomach. For a few agonising moments Mother did not respond, just stared at him coldly, with dead eyes. Her expression paled, then froze, as she replied with an edge to her voice, 'How can you be sure? It can't be true, Arthur. I don't believe you.'

He grabbed hold of her hand gently, and clearing his throat, he began the inevitable task of trying to explain what had happened. 'You have to be brave. It is true. I was there. I saw it all happen right before my very eyes,' he said, his voice drifting into a whisper, as the anguish on his face confirmed the poignancy of his remembrance.

My eyes were swamped with tears like a cold grey mist, and my stomach muscles tightened as I listened quietly. A silence fell all over the room, and when my stepfather spoke, it was in a voice that faltered with unsteady emotion. Mother said nothing, just stared wide-eyed into space, then wiped the tears away with her handkerchief.

Trying to stop himself from shaking and establish the mental picture in his mind, he continued, 'The wounded were transferred up north to various aerodromes, for evacuation by air to hospitals in India. It was mid-afternoon and I was among those waiting for a flight on the airfield at Myitkyina. There were literally thousands of refugees clamouring for flights, mainly women and children. The whole area was a flood of confusion and mass hysteria and the throbbing of aircraft engines filled the air. There were countless badly injured individuals accompanied by nurses. Some were strapped on stretchers and being moved very slowly to the waiting transport. Numerous others were waiting, jerking and groaning with severe pain.

'It was then that I noticed Iris deep in conversation with another woman holding two small children. Despite the heat she was wearing a corduroy skirt and a jacket. She was carrying a baby, so I shouted her name. Her face brightened when she saw me, and I immediately waved her across. They seemed to be detached from the main batch and waiting anxiously for consideration. She was shocked to see me lying on a stretcher. "What on earth are you doing here, in this cycle of destruction?" I asked her as she approached. "You need to take care of yourself." I even begged her to travel with me, as army regulations allowed a close relative to accompany the wounded. "I'd love to but it isn't possible, Arthur," she replied. "I made a promise, and I'm obliged for private reasons to stand by that now." She then explained to me that a Doctor Ranjit, who lived opposite her in Maymyo, had some clout with the administration department. He had booked and paid for a flight for her, providing she assisted his young wife and three children out of the country. It was necessary that he stayed behind, but would be travelling on later. I told her how much safer it would be with me and the hospital staff, but it was no use she was adamant. She even joked that she would be in India before me, being on the next flight. We chatted for a while and discussed many things. I wanted to offer her words of comfort but there just wasn't the time. She was under a lot of stress, with Ronnie's death playing on her mind. He had left college and taken up the position of headmaster at a school in the Shan states. However, with the conflict raging, he'd given up that post and had joined a small group of guerrillas working behind enemy lines. They were supplying vital information concerning enemy troop movements to the Allies. On one of these secret excursions the group was ambushed, and he was killed.

'The time came for her to leave and the tears welled up in her eyes as we clasped hands. Then she finally kissed me and left. Before boarding the aircraft she turned and waved excitedly, then shouted, "See you in India." I felt happy for her as she boarded the plane. Her words expressed what thousands of others were thinking.

'As soon as everyone was aboard the transport, it taxied then started the run for taking off. Just as it sped along the runway, two Japanese fighters dived out of the clouds towards that strip of ground. I couldn't turn my eyes away as I heard a muffled rumbling like faraway thunder, mingled with the staccato of machine-gun fire. I couldn't believe that sudden death would strike from the skies, as the explosion shifted the ground we were laying on. People surged through jagged openings, engulfed in a swirling cloud of dust, while others were in a state of literal madness. Terrified women were clutching their children, trying to shield them from the flying debris that was swirling everywhere. The whole area rang with screams and cries for the defenceless aircraft, as it lurched into an irrevocable spin, leaving a thick plume of black smoke in its wake. Then the undercarriage collapsed as it skidded along the surface, twisting and turning with its human cargo. Finally it blew into infinity. My heart was thumping so violently I was afraid to even look, but couldn't help it and watched the hideous execution of human life through veiled eyes. It was a nightmare, which returns in the shape of a dream, the being without a face. At that moment their fate was sealed and searing rage blazed inside me; nothing seemed to make any sense. The west side of the airfield was awash with jagged bits of metal and huge flames towered above the treetops. I closed my eyes as the planes flew directly over us, the violent noise sounding like the end of the world. Then we were engulfed in bits of grass, earth and broken branches off the trees. People were running in every direction, through the smoke. I tried to see if anyone was alive. I really thought that the end had come for all of us on that airfield. Everyone was shaking as the ground trembled, and the atmosphere was suffocating.

'Suddenly a group of American fighters ranged over the horizon, following in the enemy's tracks. For a while an undeniable weight hung over the mutilated field, a ghostly silence, a fear that things had gone terribly wrong. Distraught people ran for cover in all directions. Bewildered children were screeching as a towering inferno belched skywards. The brave ones prayed, others screamed with screams from hell. It was a volcanic eruption obliterating the sun and shrouding the entire area in total darkness. You know, Gwen, I've already experienced horrendous sights, even death, but this appalling mutilation exceeded everything. The terror of their screams filled my ears, and my feverish eyes swelled with tears, but I wasn't ashamed to betray my weakness to anyone. Although it didn't last that long, it seemed like an eternity. It's a nightmare that still haunts me, and always will. Poor darling Iris, she was so young and everyone loved her.'

There was a long pause after he had finished speaking, followed by a deathly silence. I saw the grief in Mother's eyes, her face contorted. She bore the loss with dignity, but I knew what was in her heart. My eyes could only see darkness and words describing love and tenderness had now lost all their meaning. In the moments that followed, the grief allowed me to cry and to mourn, but it did not relieve the intense pain. I thought of death and tried to analyse it a thousand times, but nothing would bring my aunt back to me. She had been the most influential person in my life.

The camp was not slow to wake, even before the edge of the sun peeped above the horizon activity had begun outside. I went from the kitchen and looked into the dining room where my mother, with worry written across her face, was talking to her husband, and the sorrow spread like a physical wave. There was no news about her eldest sister, Myrtle, and her family, although reports were that her husband had been made transport officer for the whole of the Burma Railways. He would be responsible for any Allied troop movements to the front line. Her younger brother, Leo, was attempting the trek via a longer route into Northern India, accompanied by a close friend. Her other brother, Stan, along with his family were heading north to Myitkyina[1]. Frequent news that numerous sorties were flying refugees from that airfield might prove an advantage in his favour, as he had such a young family. There was also no news about her sister, Irene, and her young family, who were left behind. This almost had her believing that only the absence of God could allow all this kind of evil to spread like a rampant forest fire.

To crown the endless toll of misery that clouded our family, my sister was taken seriously ill and admitted immediately into the military hospital in Murree. Within a few days five more babies were also accepted into the infirmary. The extraordinary scale of the admission of babies suffering from identical symptoms was devastating. I wasn't old enough to understand, but I knew something was wrong, as hundreds of confusing thoughts and pictures flooded my mind. I felt sick and depressed trying to block out the unwanted fears and images, wondering why all these awful things were happening to our family. Mother

---

[1] Pronounced *Mitchenah*.

rarely ever came home, her mind focusing only on her baby daughter, and the enormity of this sickness weighed heavily on her. The hospital staff were kind enough to provide her with suitable accommodation, and she kept a constant vigil over my sister, as her condition appeared to be stabilised. My stepfather stayed at home to care for us and visited the hospital every night, occasionally returning home very late. I lay staring at the ceiling, forcing myself to think about anything but sleep. Behind open eyes I smiled, trying to revel in the pleasure that I often felt with my sister. Then the pictures stopped and the sadness covered the smile.

In the Far East, the morning dawn had stolen through a steady monsoon rain, which was neither heavy nor light. With the disappearing showers the sun rose slowly on this late June morning of 1942. The rays cast a shimmering light over a small village with the unusual name of Myingre[2], south-west of the city of Mandalay in central Burma. The place itself wasn't anything special, except that it harboured the railway workshops, at that present time a vital lifeline of communication and transport, with a network of administration, essential for the information of troop movements. It was a vast complex assembling and repairing railway carriages and haulage conveyances for the whole of the railway system in Burma. The company also provided respectable and congenial accommodation for all the Europeans employed at the depot. Choices varied from bungalows to houses, with sufficient land to oblige the enthusiastic gardener.

The premises were situated out in the country in sheltered woodland, through which ran a labyrinth of forest tracks. Concealed in this haven was the imposing Railway Institute, where most of the families congregated in the evenings or during leisure periods for a spot of congenial recreation. The overzealous worked off their energetic appetite in a game of tennis, while others would seek a less active relaxation in a passionate game of cards or tombola, and the more serious engaged themselves in some intelligent conversation. Heavily wooded forests engulfed

---

[2] Pronounced *Mingair*.

the surrounding area, and the trees, which were mostly banyan and tamarind, rose in gentle slopes towards the north. From that point the village was not visible, only the trees, and behind the trees, the gable-tiled roof of Mr and Mrs Unitt's residence. It was located in close proximity to the railway station and adjacent to the Roman Catholic Church on one side. On Sunday mornings the constant pealing of bells and the singing of hymns could be distinctly heard, a pious reminder of blissful worship and strictly adhered to by the vast majority of the residents, when their procession slowed to acknowledge its religious significance.

The residence was a rather large and rambling-looking dwelling, peering towards the village centre and standing in over an acre of hard-trodden land. It housed four decent-sized bedrooms on the first floor, and the ground level accommodated rooms of various dimensions. The roof was steep and the eaves overhung for protection against the torrential monsoon. Huge trees fenced in the perimeter and battalions of spectacular flowers bordered the inside. Reinforced wire netting produced added strength and protection to the grounds. Here a gravelled drive led to the main road, edged by layers of green grass. From the remainder of the baked earth sprang numerous fruit trees. Apricot, plum and custard-apple were in abundance, shading the entire area like giant umbrellas from the scorching and ever-present sun.

Gently winding its way through the centre of the grounds ran a delicate little stream, where numerous tiny birds chirped and nestled in the branches that hung and dipped in the ripples below. To the rear lay an enormous duck pond, a nourishing sanctuary for the family's collection of geese, ducks and chickens. Their returnable assets were mainly a variety of eggs, and the occasional tasty trapping for the dining table. The property also provided desirable attraction to several wild fowl, doves and green pigeons, which nested in the nearby trees. Periodic visits were usually paid by the boastful barking deer and the less appreciative sadistic tiger, often lurking within striking distance of the small village, not too far away from the property. The sun shone through the open window and moments later filled the room with its intensity. Here Aunty Myrtle was sitting quietly at the dining room table, scanning the daily newspaper, now a well-practised ritual, as alarming thoughts ricocheted through her brain.

The lady of the house was the eldest of the Harding family and my godmother. She was of medium build, with short black hair, with a light crisp curl, and dark-brown eyes that gleamed with mischief. She had a delightful smile, very full and friendly, bearing an unhurried look of serenity, and she somehow always managed to achieve the effect of sheer elegance. The regular morning chat with her children often ranged from the progress reports she'd received from their respective schools to the day's recreation now that school was closed. She was perfectly content to take the girls shopping with her and leave the boys in charge while her husband was away at work. Always popular amongst the women, she had established a high position in their bureaucracy in an area where a strong identity meant everything. She lectured openly on subjects ranging from rearing children to political adventure, and wouldn't hesitate to scuttle anyone who spoke out of place.

Her husband, Ben Unitt, was tall and sturdily built, with smooth, straight, black hair and clear, blue-grey eyes. His sharp features sported a trim moustache. He had spent most of his life on the Burma railways as a traffic inspector, and the company provided him with a white carriage for his services when travelling around. It was usually coupled to the rear of the passenger train, whether it was for business or for the pleasure of his family. Now, because of the new emergency, he found himself drafted into the Royal Engineers as a lieutenant and made transport officer for the whole of the railway system. His vast knowledge and considerable experience placed a heavy responsibility on his shoulders, organising troop movements to the front line.

Five children completed the family circle. Rex, the eldest son, would soon be fifteen years of age. Deryck at thirteen was slightly older than me and both the boys attended the Government English High School in Maymyo as boarders. Hazel, the eldest girl, and I were of the same age, Joy was a little younger, and the girls attended Saint Michael's school, also in Maymyo, staying at our home during the term. Terence, the youngest at five, was never introduced to any of these schools because of the conflict, and the alarm bells that rang at his birth were intimidating. His parents were concerned about their newborn son. Although scrawny and pale, there was something more sinister about his appearance. Not being able to observe his face clearly brought worried expressions, as darkness covered his tiny features in the shape of a cowl. Curious thoughts lingered over the legend that is well known to be the tidal phenomenon of good luck, especially to nautical captains. Few doctors would argue with the spirit of superstition. On the other hand, they had an ethical obligation to protect what belonged to him.

A lattice of railway lines filed past the rear of their home, and the majority of troop trains hauled Chinese regiments. The conflict wasn't far away, and the enemy's advance was rapid. However, many of these were so inadequately equipped for jungle warfare that thousands deserted and readily joined forces with the Burmese dacoits (bandits) who ravaged and marauded the countryside. They marauded and destroyed helpless villages, murdering the occupants and raping defenceless women. There were a few British regiments, which included the King's Own Yorkshire Light Infantry and the Gloucesters, who were to eventually engage the enemy, the Gurkhas, and two Indian divisions, the Rajputs and the Bengal Lancers. There were some Burmese irregulars, but they were also badly equipped and undertrained in jungle warfare. Casualties were often horrific in a bloodbath, with very few prisoners taken on either side.

The monsoons had retreated to their own confinement, allowing the first breath of spring to hang in the air. Trees and bushes were returning to life with a frenzy, and even the birds whistled their warning. Soon the residents were to realise the strategic importance that the railways would have, in order to stem the enemy's swift and relentless advance. Suddenly the storm clouds of war gathered menacingly overhead. The sun glared from an unforgiving sky, which vibrated with the strange sound of unwelcome visitors, circling like giant vultures in the heavens above. A piercing blast shattered the stillness of the afternoon air, as they released clusters of their destructive cargo. Falling through the sky from open bomb bays, the exploding shells shredded and tore up everything in their path. The earth trembled and shook violently, there were countless fires and panic was at its worst. The acrid smell of smoke clogged the atmosphere, turning day into night with a frenzy. Huge flames rose in coloured coils pulsating into kaleidoscopic shapes, burning with a deep hunger and spreading and devouring everything in their path with an insatiable appetite. Suddenly, chaos erupted and many buildings burst into fragments; dust, debris and flames cloaked the entire area. A vast cloud of thick black smoke gushed up and spread across the small town.

After the intruders had expelled their bombs, they left like migrating birds. Almost immediately business activity ceased to exist, as the citizens scrambled and stumbled aimlessly in search of shelter and safety. They were being shaken by a bombardment of astonishing violence, and since they were unused to this sort of aggression one could well imagine their trepidation. The lazy clouds drifting across the watchful sky suddenly brightened, and there was a vastly different sound. A hum in the distance gradually increased to a stupendous roar as four P40 Tomahawks from AVG (American Volunteer Group), looking menacing, loomed just beyond the horizon. They climbed high above the intruders, then swooped down with all their guns blazing. One of the enemy's escorts detached itself from the group, but was immediately pursued by a P40 circling the rooftops and was brought down by a hail of cannon fire. People stared at the sky with ghostly faces, unable to believe what was happening. Others just glared without speaking, suffering from a belated reaction. The enemy finally disappeared with the loss of three aircraft, leaving behind them smouldering remains, and the entire surface well furrowed with craters and bullet holes.

Two of the American fighters were slightly damaged, but with caution landed safely on the make-do airstrip next to my aunt's home. Both the fliers jumped down from their aircraft unscathed and feeling delighted with their good fortune. Laughing and joking, they strolled across the heavily wooded terrain before reaching the main entrance of the house. They were very young and brash but well-mannered, generous and loyal to the cause in which they firmly believed. On this occasion chance had definitely favoured them. However, these characteristics soon became less pronounced during times of extreme stress. After what seemed like a dozen knocks, the door was opened.

'Can I be of any help?' My aunt asked in a quiet voice. Relieved to be home at last, she looked drawn and pale, and was fast approaching the limit of tolerance.

'Yes, Ma'am,' replied the taller of them. 'Is there some place where we can get shelter, a hot bath and some food around here?' he asked in a strong voice.

For a moment she lost her train of thought, and couldn't help feeling sorry for them. She considered their question, then in a few words she said, 'You are both welcome to stay here for dinner if you wish. My husband will be home soon; he'll be able to advise you further.' Her words were soft and appealing.

They were overjoyed and their eyes grew warm at the invitation.

'Thank you very much, sounds great,' they replied in unison. 'We need urgent repairs, and for fuel to be sent up from Mandalay, then we'll be on our way.'

Leaving their flying suits in the entrance hall, they followed her into the sitting room. There the children chatted with unnervingly loud voices and the gramophone pelted out some dance music. The damage to the aircraft was only superficial, and was soon repaired by the engineers from the workshops. However, they remained as guests for a few days, largely due to the length of time for the fuel to be delivered. They eventually left to rejoin their squadron.

A week slipped by and, although the wet season had subsided, storm clouds swept across the land with a roll of distant thunder. The rain fell in a heavy downpour, slanting like glistening dowels of crystal from clouds of deep purple. Lightning cracked high above and the sky was fractured, displaying bold patterns. However, the rain relieved an explosion of life, when it came with a vengeance, liberating the area from any enemy aircraft.

Most of the surrounding land and station platforms were congested with thousands of Chinese troops. Suffering from a severe shortage of military weapons they had switched from advance to retreat, and just as many were falling into captivity.

Absolute chaos seemed to reign, and abandoned vehicles were scattered in every direction, cluttering up the streets and main thoroughfares. The compound of my aunt's home was now a makeshift camp for hundreds of fleeing refugees, a conspicuous orgy of activity and increasing in numbers as the days continued. They were running away, like sensible people would, in an endless stream from a barbaric adversary. Day and night the convoy of travellers moved slowly towards Mandalay, with a spirit of optimism and ever increasing determination, without being heroic. Their few possessions were thrown into carts, traps and prams; some had taken along their pets. There was nothing else they could choose to do. This route was preferable to a cemetery enclosed by barbed wire fencing.

All the recent carnage and the sight of this human misery brought instant thoughts of leaving the country as soon as possible. Uncle Ben was already in the process of arranging immediate flights to India for his family. He glanced through the windows as, in the distance, plumes of smoke drifted in a black pall as dacoits destroyed and looted abandoned homes near the outskirts. It was time to depart and the events of ordinary, everyday life were to change overnight. Then a series of obstacles had to be surmounted, since they realised that the penalty for failure was internment or certain death. A large number of the human population had some idea of what it would be like to be caught up in this carnage where they would die without dignity.

The weather was perfect with a blaze of sunshine, and the sky overhead was cloudless. A tempting meal was made of fish curry and rice, followed by plenty of fresh fruit. My aunt suggested that everyone fill their stomachs for the long journey ahead. Anxious faces turned and scanned the crowded area as they left their home timidly; then they glanced at each other in speechless confusion, choking back the tears. Everyone was subdued on the short walk to the railway station, their thoughts were elsewhere. It was a distance that no longing, no amount of hope, could ever help them bridge again. Taking long deep breaths and holding hands, they tried to restrain their painful emotions. The hidden thoughts masked a darker reality. Beneath a deep blue sky they struggled with their personal belongings, and a remembrance of happier times. Most of the valuables were secretly buried deep in the back garden. Yet it would take a superhuman effort to turn a blind eye to everything else. Now their feelings appeared sluggish and weighed them down in a black mood of depression. It was a horror of one-way traffic, which swiftly clogged the main road leading north. Civilians were soon to find war on their streets, and expressions of frustration and distress showed on their exhausted faces.

The family stayed close together, moving through a river of uncontrolled mayhem, pausing briefly for hasty glances at disapproving strangers all around. A moderate breeze kept most of the heat away, as the temperature rose inexplicably in this path of terror and disbelief. The station had now become a busy region of commotion, on this quiet Sunday morning. Here, abnormality had secured the day of worship with a vengeance. There was nothing more terrifying than people on the verge of hysteria. Tension, frustration, even madness appeared on numerous faces. A freight train passed noisily through, but was pulled to a stop in a siding as eager eyes watched. Within half an hour all eyes peered uneasily at the great plumes of black smoke that belched out of a passenger train as it approached the platform. Unfortunately, refugees had claimed almost every available space there was. Many clung to the outside, standing on the wooden rostrum. Others squatted on the roofs of the carriages, clinging on to their sparse belongings with a grim determination. Aunty Myrtle comforted her young family with soothing conversation. Any anxious desires were tempered by an unseen fear, and visions were surrounded by an air of gloom and despondency.

Everything seemed out of control, as hundreds of voices shouted in despair. There were groans and screams of frightened people as they scrambled for places on the packed train. Within minutes, the solemn family gathering was met by military personnel who were waiting for their arrival. No sooner had the train come to a halt than they were ushered into a reserved compartment at the rear of the carriage, with their belongings. Tired with all the commotion and confusion, they slumped down in the congested area, feeling rather uncomfortable and stifled. Tension was increased by the weight of their misery. The train finally moved away sluggishly, as if weighed down by its human cargo, climbing steadily to the flat open country like a giant centipede being embraced by assailant ants. It spewed out huge black clouds of smoke and darkened the sky as it puffed its way through the wooded countryside. Families were wrapped up in their own private dreams.

Tears welled up in Aunty Myrtle's eyes and her hands were moist with sweat. Both the girls were silent but the boys were impatient and fidgety. Whatever is going to happen will happen, there is no time for emotion now, only anger, she thought to herself. Unable to stay quiet for long, the children focused their eyes through the barred windows void of glass at the open land where farmers and workers paused to watch the incredible movement of the train as it gathered momentum. Aunty Myrtle was paying particular attention to the front page of a tattered newspaper, indicating detailed reports of the turmoil in the southern regions and finding it very difficult to accept the disturbing growth of terror.

Both sides of the track, where the ground fell away, were littered with items of rubbish, old pots, ashes and vegetable waste, results of recent habitation. The heavy clouds had passed over and were heaped near the horizon, and the sunshine was now a warm golden surge as the train halted at Mandalay. This once handsome city had suffered dreadfully, and the ruins were bitter testament to the recent bombing. The entire area was swarming with soldiers and military vehicles, as a great surge of change was approaching in the shape of an intruding presence.

There was an uncanny silence as the thoughts of home clouded their memory, with a feeling of instant relief as the train continued on the last stage of the journey. It was a fine day but the sun's rays were shining through the broken window frame, making breathing painfully difficult in the intense heat and cramped conditions. The carriage was full of noise, everyone trying to forget the ghastly reality facing them. They passed through villages, where the tracks were gutted with the war and the inhabitants wore faces washed with sadness. By now Aunty Myrtle was haunted by so many thoughts she found it impossible to speak to the children. During these moments of tension, she couldn't stop the flow of tears as her heart raced wildly. Suddenly, much to their discomfort, they were confronted with some of the most hideous and appalling sights. Lying alongside the track were hundreds of dead and decaying bodies of men, women and children, who had been using the railway system as a means of direction. They had been mercilessly butchered by the Chinese deserters and dacoits for their food and priceless possessions. The cries of people touched by such unbelievable sights ripped through the entire train.

They eventually arrived at Shewbo, the final destination, and were immediately transported by the military to a prefabricated airstrip on the edge of the town, amidst an intensity of noise and a wail of sirens, which sounded like the end of the world. To their horror, they had arrived in an air raid; now they felt like all the other nomads, with no home and a questionable objective.

Here everything appeared to be badly organised. There was total confusion and chaos, as the knot of fear tightened in their stomachs. The surrounding area had become a harbour all tangled up with damaged remains, broken-down trucks, planes and army equipment. Havoc had been created by a recent air raid, and the entire place seemed on fire like a hell on earth, and the outskirts were a wilderness of uprooted trees and bushes.

Inside the damaged buildings hundreds of panic-stricken civilians cluttered the administration offices, demanding any available flights out of the country. However, unless they could account for their presence, they were removed immediately. My aunt waited anxiously with her family for official confirmation of their flight, and for the arrival of her husband. He had obviously been delayed, and would not be travelling with them. A quick glance into the main office caught no evidence of his arrival. She moved away, turning away from the intrusion of the sun's warm rays piercing through the window.

Minutes later the office door opened, and a tall impressive-looking man stepped out. His hair was a quiet grey, and he had a calm imperious face and dark watchful eyes. He viewed the heated area with authority and walked without hesitation to where she was sitting, pausing slightly before he spoke. He obviously recognised the lady with the five children.

'Mrs Unitt.'

The voice from close by startled her, until she realised it was speaking to her. She stood up instantly, tried to smile but failed miserably. 'Yes,' she replied.

'Will you step inside, please,' he said, moving towards the entrance of his office.

She walked hesitantly inside, occupied one of the vacant seats, and waited patiently for him to speak.

'The seating arrangements are typically out of date,' he said. His voice was odd, deliberate. 'I'm very sorry to have to inform you, but regretfully your eldest son cannot accompany you on this flight.'

'Oh, my God, whatever for?' she exclaimed in horror. 'This is ridiculous! What stupid law prevents him from travelling with the rest of my family?' She threw him an agitated glance and felt a little embarrassed.

'Mrs Unitt, I do not make the rules, but he is not considered a juvenile at fifteen years of age. These *Dakotas* have been compounded for use of women and children only. I have no alternative choice, and I do have my orders. I hope that you can appreciate my position.' His voice was now a whisper.

She was furious. 'I'll tell you what choice you have. If my son is not allowed to board that aircraft then we shall all remain behind until my husband arrives. We'll see what he has to say about this,' she replied, expressing her annoyance in the strongest terms. Now there was anger in her eyes.

He knew that this was going to be a personal battle, and she could say whatever she liked. He was still bound by professional rules. To anyone else those orders might have been persuasive, but he had underestimated the depth of her defiance. In the presence of high-ranking officials, she could handle herself like a veteran.

'But, Mrs Unitt, the *Dakota* taxiing on the runway is waiting for your family to board her,' he replied, pointing to the plane already full of passengers.

'I'm sorry, but I'm not leaving my son behind,' she said, walking out of the office. She wasn't one for mincing her words once she got involved in a heated discussion. Almost immediately a shouted command through the open window drifted across the compound. Another family, waiting patiently, soon replaced them on board the aircraft. Within minutes the entry door was firmly closed and the plane sped along the bumpy strip of ground.

The sky had turned a dark grey when four tiny specks appeared across the top of the hill. The air shimmered in the heat and the trees shook from the drone of the engines as they approached almost at ground level. Suddenly there was a series of cranking explosions as a cannon shell tore through the fuselage of the vulnerable aircraft. It staggered and spun relentlessly before bursting into a pillar of flames and exploding. All the passengers were killed instantly, as huge flames rose skywards. The air shook and the stench of burning was indescribable. Aunty Myrtle stared at the man in a dazed silence, without speaking. Her mood swung from fear to compassion to putting on a brave face. She still wouldn't conform to the intended pattern for evacuation and the military control of flights. His further wailing and persuasion came to nothing; she remained adamant, waiting patiently for the arrival of her husband. She suspected an unavoidable delay. Now a thousand questions flooded her mind all at once. The information about her son should have been received yesterday, not at this precarious time. Unhappy thoughts were rushing through her mind. All she could do was hope – hope was where tomorrow began. A desperate frustration gripped at her insides.

When the second plane started its run along the strip, under the watchful eyes of onlookers, who raised startled cries of alarm and horror, as another *Zero* returned, banking steadily, then levelling off above the treetops, before it approached with its guns blazing. Flames spiralled from the exposed plane, as it ploughed into the forest, like a fireball. They couldn't recognise the humans silhouetted in the inferno. Everywhere soldiers and civilians were fleeing for shelter, some dragging the injured with them amidst blood-curdling screams. During these moments of frenzy many clung to each other for compassion. The woods beyond were red with fire as machine-gun bullets fell persistently, hurtling through the grass and slithering across the baked soil like sidewinders. Plumes of fire could be seen through the spirals of smoke and dust and the earth was pocketed with numerous holes and large craters. Suddenly there was a surge of jubilation as a batch of American fighters approached, furnishing an intimidating image against the turbulent sky. They signalled an immediate reprieve for the unfortunate refugees and the badly damaged airfield, which now resembled a battlefield. Now the enemy, fully aware of the superiority of their attackers, fled under a hail of bullets. The evacuees shouted with joy as one of the *Zeros* burst into flames, the same joyful reception continued when another spun earthwards with thick smoke trailing from its fuselage.

The clatter of approaching footsteps didn't sound too pleasing. Something was happening out there that made my aunt feel afraid. The instant the door opened she realised who it was. There was urgency in his voice this time.

'All right, Mrs Unitt, please get your family into that transport plane as quickly as you can,' he said.

She listened to the intensity in his tone before replying. He saw edginess in her eyes, which appeared coldly mocking, even prideful. He pleaded with a frigid smile. She sat there for a moment as if she couldn't breathe, staring at him in silence, feeling betrayed first by his encouragement, and although her gaze was as bright as ever, there was something else in it too.

'Thank you very much,' she said agreeably. Her wishes were fulfilled. A few last courtesies and he was on his way out of the room. She didn't wait for him to repeat himself or even to change his mind. She followed him, intimating with a glance to the children that they should accompany her. Whatever doubts they had felt on this issue were immediately swept away by his enthusiasm.

A life spent in peace and tranquillity now had to be one step ahead of any conceivable disaster. The most important thing was that her husband had now arrived. She realised that all her silent prayers had been answered and that God had handed her a lifeline. No matter how dark the past few days had been, there were rays of sunshine ahead. She smiled at the face of the person she loved, and now emotions were running high. In the moment's hesitation, they didn't know which way to move or where to go. Their eyes met in a silent exchange, exciting their hearts and paralysing their insides with emotion. For a while the words of comfort and joy hung between them like an unresolved chord, as time was precious. The large sections of the damaged airstrip were being hurriedly repaired in patches and the littered debris removed just as quickly.

They spoke to one another with expressions of deep concern and mixed feelings, trying to overcome the trauma of the impending separation and the safety of the family. The area was bursting with activity now that the time for the final farewells had arrived. There were sobs, tears fell uncontrollably, words were choked and remained unspoken, feelings tore large holes in their reasoning. For all of them, men, women and children, war had become a ghastly reality. Someday she would relive all the happy memories, in times of sadness, but for the present, patience and discipline had to be prominent. They couldn't pass through the barrier without a swallow of fear. Everyone was filled with an impenetrable sorrow, wrapped up in their own private sadness and, although they were exhausted, there was no suggestion of a halt. They felt entombed in a territorial nightmare, for nothing seemed certain any more. Aunty Myrtle didn't restrain her tears, and embraced my uncle tenderly when she whispered goodbye. His voice, his features were breaking her heart. There was a last intense glance as they hurried away, waving sadly to him, before boarding the only remaining *Dakota*.

It certainly wasn't luxury in the cramped conditions inside as they stretched out, jolting about for a position on the steel surface and strapping themselves to the sides of the aircraft in an unaccustomed fashion. There was a short pause as the power of the engines increased, then it roared down the strip and climbed effortlessly into the atmosphere. Uncle Ben remained behind for a while, watching with an enormous sigh of relief as the plane flew past the treetops. Straight ahead the smoke blotted out the light and the horizon was circled with fire. Down below, the people waved, cried and prayed in their hundreds. For them, the nightmare was about to begin. This was the last transport plane to leave the airfield of the war-torn country, as the forest dwindled swiftly behind, with the trees swaying in the gentle breeze.

Inside the aircraft hideous thoughts entered their heads, with the fear that soon they could all be dead stamped on their weary faces. They huddled together in a space with few concessions for passengers, now crucified with the heat, tired and irritated. They sat in silence, inwardly facing a baptism of terror. The thoughts of all present were far beyond the Chindwin River or the hundreds of miles across the dense jungle. Some were sobbing, others were conversing in their hearts with wives, fathers, husbands, and many remained steadfast in their deep abiding faith that love gave you the strength to resist pain and isolation. They kept their ears close to their heartbeats, listening to the anxious throbs and waiting for what fate might have reserved for them.

Finally, after a few hours of buffeting and discomfort, there was a note of relaxation, when into the darkness crept streams of light. Not many moments before, the future had looked bleak, now they were descending rapidly. Brief smiles lit their tired and fearful faces. Although having more hopeful thoughts they were splintered by one more fear. After all the days of waiting and the safety they had dreamed of, the barrier between the war and themselves was lengthening. The full sweep of emotions flooded through my aunt, fusing together bitterness, trepidation, and hate. Suddenly, a bone-jarring impact with the surface of Dum-Dum Airport, Calcutta, Eastern India, as they touched down like the thin thread that wound back into the hands of God. Here the warm winds stirred the trees and the sun shone over a less hostile civilisation. Yet somehow those memories would never fade.

Chapter VII

The winds stirred in the trees rustling the green leaves gently, dislodging pieces of dead bark off the branches. The once safe sanctuary of this little hill town of Maymyo was now threatened, as it clawed at the early morning sky. Richard De'Santos kept looking towards the east from the lounge window; his face wore an expression of both helplessness and intense anger. He had become a different man, tense and tight-lipped as he assembled his family together. He waited anxiously for the orange sun to reveal itself, now that the clouds had almost disappeared.

The family owned a comfortable spacious home with room for everything, in the equally pleasant area where they lived. Towards the rear, acres of spare land spread out under a shadow of trees. The essentials were drawn out by their willingness to make it work. The neighbours were very friendly with their cordial exchange of views and welcome manners. Here they felt central to a fast-growing community, and were determined to remain in this peaceful haven for the rest of their lives. Uncle Dick shivered, cold icy flutters roaming between the blades of his broad shoulders then glanced despondently at his loving wife, Irene. Their three young children, Peter and John, the twins, just seven years of age waited patiently, and Maureen, still a baby at three, was cradled in her mother's arms.

The boys were well behaved and of average size for their age, but they didn't look alike as they each took after a different parent. Peter, slightly older than his brother, had sharp features and was slim like his mother, and had her temperament. John, on the other hand, was stocky and his precocity resembled that of his father. Both were clever at school, inspired by their mother, but they didn't entirely possess her loveable nature. Maureen was cute, with a beaming smile, and a mischievous twinkle in her eyes. Their parents envisaged an excellent career for all of them, and hoped that they would develop the same personality traits as themselves. Their father paced up and down the room, shaking his head, his face contorted with anguish and fear. They were staring at him, watching and waiting in total silence, as a burst of conversation from the servants floated across the compound.

Pausing for a moment, Uncle Dick spoke quietly to Aunty Irene. 'I'm afraid this is going to be very difficult and painful, especially for the children. We should have left with Stan and Eileen a few days ago, now it could be far too late,' he said in a soft voice. He longed for the solace of peaceful chatter, with an ache that choked in his throat. Picking up two of the suitcases, they walked out of the house together, closely accompanied by a servant carrying two more packages. If only it were another time, Aunty Irene thought to herself, then turned around for one last glance. The tears were still wet on her cheeks and at the corner of her eyes. No, she reminded herself, this can't be really happening to us. Then she instantly removed her thoughts away from the emptiness. Her voice breached the oppression, when she called out to the boys to accompany them. Now their path was equidistant, but heading involuntarily to an uncertain future. Obediently they followed them out of the house and through the beautiful garden, onto the rough stone track to the railway station. They were silent most of the way, unable to focus any attention on the few passers-by. It was all very sad and heart-breaking, as the stunned silence indicated sheer disbelief at what was really happening.

There were numerous dangers ahead with a touch of adversity in the air, but it was impossible to dwell on them. Uncle Dick was making a supreme effort to cultivate a serious understanding with his own conscience. For a moment his mind drifted back to happier times. He thought back to his wedding day, nine years earlier. How different things were then, everything so full of promise and possibilities. He was secure in a permanent job as a passenger guard on the railways. Aunty Irene, although at present committed to a motherly role, was a highly respected schoolteacher. They had spent the past few years sharing and shouldering the problems and responsibilities, which are necessary for a successful relationship. There was no apparent danger of failure or dissolution by neglect. All the pictures were leaping through his mind like a galaxy of stars, as he tried to capture just one image of the reality. Suddenly this life had changed out of all proportion, not because of his family, but because the whole world was upside down. Once an epitome of boundless plenty and garnished with rainbows, it was now replete with endless suffering and death. When time was warped with power, greed, terror, and necessity bares its ugly face, it concealed an obscure reality making freedom a high price, so each moment was precious and important.

They walked hastily in the direction of extraordinary change with a feeling of revulsion locked inside their thoughts. The boys were well behaved and enjoyed themselves, laughing and teasing each other, unaware of the mystery and confusion that lay ahead. Life for them, as for so many others, was a roller coaster of emotion, fear, and suspicion, as they filed through the narrow spaces on the crowded railway station. Here, masses of eager people hustled each other as they prepared for the imminent rush. The family weaved their way through the crowd thronging the area, and mingled with them as echoes of footsteps rose up against the low brick buildings then disappeared. They waited anxiously, knowing that the oncoming train would take them away from their home and friends. The adults talked between themselves without really listening. Now even the town where they lived seemed utterly strange and soon even the familiar landmarks would change rapidly. They would also be changing their common currency of life for a world of beyond.

The atmosphere had changed; there was a humming that was getting louder. Suddenly, huge puffs of billowing black smoke and fingers of steam scratched the silvery sky above the impressive Garrett locomotive. It came on with a vengeance, chugging along with its human burden into the station from the south, hauling behind it a column of primitive battered carriages, crammed with impatient refugees. For endless seconds they stared at the stationary train, then quickly remembered the urgency of this journey. Their attention was disturbed by some eager families squabbling for seats further away, and disobedient children ignoring parental commands. The railway guard soon recognised them and beckoned them over to the rear of the train.

A silence followed, a silence magnified by thousands of thoughts and images that engulfed Uncle Dick's mind. He shuddered as the immensity of the task he had taken on came plummeting down on him with all the impact of an exploding bomb. He then wondered, with all his power of analysis, exactly what was going to happen to them. They climbed slowly into the special compartment that had been reserved for the family. They were counting on him; his was the guiding hand and they trusted his decision. Irene hugged Maureen tightly, allowing one hand to caress her extra large handbag, which contained all their important documents and some valuables.

Slowly the train moved away from the still crowded platform. Many were left behind, complaining bitterly, with a show of waving arms and verbal abuse. It accelerated across the points, rocking as it gathered momentum, then passed some scanty villages set back and shielded by tall greenery. Here the land was lush with little traffic, a bit of nature tidied up but not defeated. The climb became steeper, there were no more houses between the trees, just acres of paddy fields. Now Irene's heart thumped heavier than ever before as the speed increased. She tried to swallow, but there was far too much dryness in her throat, and taking a cup of water she gulped it down quickly. The boys were busy writing an essay in their books; with their mother's experience it was relatively easy for them to ask questions.

Travelling through shanty towns, villages, and dense jungle, the train finally rolled into the small station of Indaw, belching out great plumes of smoke before shuddering to a stop. Aunty Irene had kept silent most of the way, her eyes flickering with thoughts as the menacing jungle flashed past. The sun set through the trees and dusk fell instantly, leaving a weak moon hanging behind low clouds. They stayed the night cramped in this small berth, at the rear of the station, in a siding near the crest of a hill. Some of the windows were left open for any wind that might blow and outside, the noise of jumbled conversations mingled with the night air, which smelled of damp foliage. They tried to sleep in the vast silence that stretched all the way to the distant woods, which looked rough and untouched, under the wide sky flashing countless stars as the night descended on the penumbra.

They waited for sleep but it seemed like an eternal wait, as it became more and more difficult to close their active minds.

Suddenly they awoke, aware of everything around them, struggling up from the depths of their subconscious. Then in a few minutes they were on the move again as the rising sun reflected for a moment on the windows. The train climbed slowly at first, then more quickly, a long black stretch, swaying as it ascended and soaking up the miles with an angry growl. Then it descended past Mogaung, crawling its way past patches of dense jungle, scattered villages and rugged mountain slopes. They gazed sideways out of the window at the vast rolling plains of bamboo forests which stretched away to a horizon full of obstacles and trees. Here the countryside running parallel to the main road looked worse and even the dirt shoulders on both sides were jammed with frightened people, thousands of them, nearly all on foot. The only transport was some bullock carts piled high with loot and luggage. Some refugees were pushing prams and cycles; others shouldered their heavy burdens on aching backs.

The whole atmosphere was eerie as seemingly endless columns wended their way up north, their feet trampling the hard earth to a fine dust. It was late in the afternoon and the sun was high in the sky and blazing down mercilessly. They could feel the weight of gloom that flickered like a neon sign in a dwindling light. Irene's tears were running freely now and she felt compressed in the decreasing atmosphere, as she watched the pitiful columns. They walked blindly, aimlessly, to nowhere, and the sense of suffering held so many memories. Then she sighed.

For those inside the carriages the temperature was unbearable; the sheet-iron roofing seemed to magnify and concentrate the day's heat. The tall trees cast long shadows as the sun dipped out of reach and beyond that the land spread featureless to the horizon. The short trip lasted for hours with halts, delays and endless stops at nameless villages en route. The train finally pulled into Myitkyina and their arrival was not unheralded in the refuge of the station, where people, who normally assembled together, were fighting an urge to run away. It was always a bustling town; now it lay unsettled under a pale sunless sky. Previously, the streets were lined with little stores and repair shops, which, day and night, were always crammed, along with the dust, noise, gasoline fumes and horse dung. Washing hung from windows on lengths of string between houses. It was still alive but now packed with grieving faces, heads turned and leering towards uniformed soldiers. To their horror the destination was a Japanese-occupied district.

Many people lined the narrow streets; once they had gossiped, grumbled and aggravated each other, now they were seething. There were huge crowds pushing forwards into a fine line between the illusion and the reality, with nowhere to go. Within a few minutes the passengers were removed from the train, sectioned into groups and herded into streets littered with broken-down carts and abandoned and burned motor vehicles. There was a madness in the air but there was a purpose behind the madness. The embittered silence was remaining longer than Uncle Dick had expected, and it couldn't be easily dismissed. For him a sense of realism prevailed and passing thoughts crushed down on him from nowhere.

Uncle Dick and Aunty Irene couldn't communicate with each other for a moment; the suppressed stillness checked them both. A restless pressure weighed on Aunty Irene, which made the air appear sticky and lie thick in the back of her throat. She felt trapped inside herself, claustrophobic, two separate people slipping apart in different directions inside her body. The Japanese officer confronted them with a harsh tone and in an alien language they did not understand. It was a stranger's face. The expression in his widely set, thin-lidded eyes was evil, as if he found these civilians barely worth serious consideration. A shiver snatched at Uncle Dick's back and slithered up his spine; he could almost feel the vomit sliding up into his throat. Now, for the first time, for his family and countless others, life had retreated into a background hum. These were overcrowded areas with frightened people, whose anxious faces bore the strain of the forthcoming captivity. In the stifling humid atmosphere, there were now mixed humanities. In full view, dirty khaki-uniformed soldiers of the highly organised Japanese Imperial 18th Army marched in double rank along the main street. They swept proudly into the town, tolerating no waste of valuable time, in the crude style to which they were accustomed. Towards the rear, some of them rode bicycles with little Nippon pennants fluttering in the breeze. The main force, who appeared to be as ruthless as they were rumoured to be, continued into the countryside where they were brought to a halt. There was something sinister about the atmosphere that settled in the air, like a touch of terror. The surrounding area was littered with waste and discarded newspapers blew around in the slight breeze.

Many civilians had already fled the country, determined to survive. Some were fortunate enough to reach safety, thousands were to perish, but for the remainder there were years of captivity ahead. Dust and debris covered the bushes and the boughs of the trees, everything was dusted with a thin layer of fine powder from the recent bombardment. Here many of the fires were still burning and Allied soldiers were helping each other to carry the wounded, while others were stumbling around in a stupor. Uncle Dick thought to himself that there was a time not so long ago when they could have got away but the baby wouldn't have survived the arduous trek. However, the real truth was that he could not afford the black market air fares on offer, even though from his earliest years he had been taught to save for difficult times. But who was he to query the ethics of usury and now sadly it was all too late. Strange though it might seem, the children gave no trouble, seemingly unaffected by the turmoil around them.

'You are now all prisoners of the Japanese Empire,' said the Nippon officer with the churlish eyes and a gun in his hand, his bright twisted teeth protruding from behind his thin lips. This formal presentation was crude and designed to fill them with fear. He shook his hand, waving the menacing revolver at them. 'You are all being transferred to the refugee camp at Samow,' he boasted, then laughed hideously, showing a blatant disregard for human life. He was physically on the small side, short-sighted and uninteresting to look at.

In the dry heat they were ushered along a dusty road out of the town and into the open country. By now everyone was feeling a little disorientated in the bustle of human traffic. The crowds shuffled endlessly in a black tide, which ebbed and flowed, all afraid of their own shadow. After several hours of this bruising struggle, ahead of them in the hazy, blue, shimmering heat stretched the mountain range. Close to them there was nothing but tall cogon grass burnt brown in the dry season. They displayed their character and emotion by obeying their oppressors, a vast army of victims suspended in the stinging heat, walking slowly through the wilderness, looking and praying for something or someone to help conquer their fear. The long journey was designed to humble them into supplication, far below the aching emptiness they felt.

Soon the roadway became narrower in the process, and the few houses, separated from each other, were divided by fields rather than squares of green lawns and flowers. Here the buildings seemed untidy and dilapidated, the inhabitants offensive and disorderly. The ascent opened up views of a vast extent but the country wasn't really featureless, forests of various trees added their contrasting colours. There were numerous mountain ranges with many streams, some of considerable size, which mirrored the deep azure of the sky. Here even the sunsets seemed to linger to get the best out of the day, with a sense of magic and mystery, which was almost tangible. However, it was also a country where there was a constant toil of field work.

Suddenly the trees vanished and the horizon widened, the view then taking on a look of dismal bareness. The air was thick with dust, filtering diagonally in this shrouded valley of tough unyielding soil. In this wilderness even the hawks moved restlessly from tree to tree, squawking incessantly as if they were disagreeing with the unwanted visitors. The soldiers hurried them in a disorderly and shambling column to a large disused field. The landscape was scrubby and there were very few trees to mark the dismal perimeter. In patches, burnt grass cushioned the lifeless, rock-hard surface, and a strengthening sun was breaking through the haze of low clouds. There was something macabre about this surreal journey; the makeshift damaged dwellings, the wrecks that littered the dirt track, and some mutilated shrines, which were a lasting tribute to those who had perished searching for an escape route. There was even the stench of death in the air.

Everyone was struck with morbid curiosity at what exactly was concealed under the three canvas coverings positioned close to the entrance. Standing to uniformed attention, two soldiers stood by each podium like creatures of habit. Now there was mounting frustration and they could feel the panic building inside them.

'My God! I wonder what is going to happen to all of us,' Aunty Irene whispered in a desperate voice, peeking sideways at Uncle Dick.

He didn't feel too comfortable in himself, and his eyes narrowed before he spoke. 'I don't know for sure, but it doesn't look too healthy,' he replied, shaking his head. There was a tightness in his voice, unmistakable proof that he was also deeply afraid.

The children stood alongside, unaware of the delicate situation. The guards were shabbily dressed and scowled at them, speaking with an occasional word of broken English that was barely audible. Activity was suddenly increased, with a wave of hysteria, by the screaming soldiers who walked beside them.

'All of you line up over there quickly and face the commandant,' shouted the officer in charge, indicating the correct area with his automatic. His prominent teeth gleamed in a sneer, under the wire-rimmed glasses.

Fear clung to all of them like a magnet, as they tried to assemble themselves into some order. It was no surprise that in the eerie silence that hung in the air many of the younger children were crying. Most of the women were now suffering from grief and anxiety at finding themselves in this bizarre situation.

They were soon to discover that hidden under the canvas camouflaged structures were some metal executioners. Suddenly the staccato of machine-gun fire opened up over their heads, the bullets slicing through the air. Dust clouds almost smothered them, when they flung themselves to the ground in a frenzy. There was complete madness, pandemonium, and cries of protest as the sounds of screeching shuddered through the atmosphere. They were crawling on their hands and knees, shocked by the violent noise that shattered the placid area. Many were so paralysed by terror that they felt cemented to the baked earth. The splutter of gunfire only lasted a few seconds, then the hideous noise ebbed away slowly into a positive silence. They were in no doubt who was now in control of their lives, as the guards watched the panic and confusion with smug amusement.

'Very very sorry for this exhibition of authority,' said the commandant, with a sardonic smile playing across his small face. Then he leisurely waved aside his own pedantic instructions. 'Now you will all behave yourselves in the camp, or there will be some additional punishment,' he chuckled with pretension.

The nightmare was about to begin, intimidation or the threat of violence was now guaranteed to work. Any doubt about which sector this officer belonged to was very soon resolved.

It was well past five in the evening when they finally entered the barbed wire campsite, tucked away in the forested hills. Others had already reached this destination, as crowds seemed to materialise out of nowhere. One minute the site was empty, then suddenly the figures converged in hundreds. The congested area looked like a railway station in rush hour, everyone standing and waiting around impatiently. There seemed to be too much noise and confusion to hear one's own breathing. There were people of both sexes and of all ages, but none of them dressed for this occasion. The mood was certainly not convivial. There were many bewildered children, some of whom carried their school satchels. There were numerous suitcases lying everywhere of all sizes and shapes and various makes, leather, canvas, and even straw and wood.

'You will stand in line and there will be no talking,' shouted the belligerent guard when some people moaned, though others remained silent. There was an instant pressure of fear and overriding apprehension. They formed a human chain inside the perimeter now caught up in a maelstrom. Surprisingly, everything was calm but the gloom was intense. There were so many people yet no one uttered a single word. The silence was oppressive.

This was followed by a long, slow, humiliating process, when all the cases, boxes and purses were opened for a thorough inspection. Even the human anatomy was meticulously searched for added pleasure; no one could grasp the importance of all this effort. The officer in control was rather small and wiry with broad cheekbones and dirty little eyes. He spoke in Japanese, giving some kind of abrupt command, all very boorish.

'Those who do not obey orders will be punished,' he shouted.

This time his English was meant to disturb.

Then everyone was expected to change places with each other, some complicated scheme to create confusion. In all the years Richard and Irene had shared together, they had never discussed what they felt and feared. However, this evening brought an unexpected change; there was a murmur of something urgent.

'I'm terrified,' said Aunty Irene in a timid voice, something she rarely admitted to anyone.

'We'll be all right here for a while, don't worry too much,' whispered Uncle Dick.

She turned and looked at him with glassy eyes, her eyebrows knitted together. 'What did you say?' she asked, feeling she'd misheard him.

'I said we'd be all right, dear, why shouldn't we be?'

She didn't answer him but tears were rolling down her cheeks. He tried to think of something to say, searching for the correct words. 'The Allies will soon be here, you wait and see,' he said, with a modest and determined conviction. His voice was composed with such sincere control that they found themselves moving forward in unison. They began to walk along a narrow path on a carpet of dry leaves. He carried Maureen, and the boys followed in close proximity. There was a distinct note of pride in their movements.

Suddenly the air seemed to have changed as they stood together watching hundreds of people undulate and pass by. The bedlam of conversation pulsated around them, and the grinding numbness of bondage showed on pale anguished faces. Blanching light pierced the darkness through the tangled uprights of the thatched dormitory. The conditions were certainly cramped with very little space between the straw mattresses. Yet they felt strangely warm in these ill-furnished surroundings, and in spite of the situation, everyone at one point seemed to think and act in a true community spirit. The boys and Maureen were soon asleep after the long tiring day. In the dim light Uncle Dick whispered to her, 'Are you all right now?' He searched his own thoughts and showed genuine concern.

'Yes, of course,' she replied feeling a stab of disgust deep inside.

A beam of starlight struck the floor and a shaft of milky sky pierced through the gaping crack in the thatched roof, as they hovered on sleep. Outside, the premises stretched out of sight to undulated woodland in every direction.

The morning sun reflected on their faces through the interstice. It had been another chapter of broken sleep with eyes full of stark hatred of the night. Now all the Japanese engulfed them like breakers on the rocky shore. Suddenly the time had arrived to face the day as survivors of an unjust world, with a feeling far removed from any concept of humanity and justice. The sun was rising higher and higher above the numerous trees, which covered the slopes running down to the camp. There were masses of coloured birds in the green belt, and somewhere in the undergrowth even pheasants sounded a lonely cry. They were roughly ushered outside by their captors, clouds of dust following them from the soil that had dried quickly, and there was an awareness in the air like a warning; it was unnatural. It was a day of apprehension as the frightened crowds assembled in front of the main office building. Here guards stood erect with fixed bayonets. The focus of everyone's attention was a small man in front of them. He had an unfriendly face and an intrusive manner that mantled the entire compound.

'You will all bow to the commandant,' shouted the officer in charge, the whole system orchestrated by soldiers pushing and shoving. They readily behaved with annoyance, jerking into position; survival was their first priority.

'How about some food?' a woman bellowed. 'The children are hungry.'

Other voices rose in heated agreement but were ignored; they even exulted in the curses that were hurled back at them in return. Outside, along a narrow path, were native huts, with thatched roofs and bamboo floors, resting on stilts. Close by, the children's solemn faces peeped out of the shadows underneath to watch in silence. It had started to rain and a downpour flattened the wild flowers and long grass into a green carpet. Everywhere there seemed to be shallow ponds forming. They felt disorientated, with the smell of damp grass and a sense of fear. Nothing but barbed wire and two machine guns separated them and the camp huts from the fields. Shrieks and sobs filled the compound. Groans, prayers and curses came from the angry crowds as they huddled together like frightened sheep. Now every face was focused on the guards, with looks more resigned than determined, looks of intense horror. Instantly the hunger disappeared, replaced with premonitory fear. They bowed their heads again, then whispered secretly to each other before lifting them and then bowing again. Some people didn't raise their heads with the others; they were weeping quietly. They had heard numerous stories of horrendous suffering and physical persecution at the hands of the Japanese.

They were all strangers, faceless victims, groups of stunted sickly people waiting impatiently for further instructions.

'You will all work. There will be no loitering in this camp. That is an order,' bellowed the commandant, his voice a whine. 'Now all of you return to your quarters.' The command was louder this time.

The commandant was a small-boned thin man with a round face, a shiny forehead and a thin-lipped mouth. His khaki uniform was perfectly pressed. No one answered him. The subsequent morning in the compound after assembly, my aunt was following some thoughts in her head, trying to rearrange things to fit this absurd existence.

'I'm a schoolteacher. I could open a small school for the younger children,' she said in a calm voice, pretending a composure she didn't really feel. It was at best an uneasy truce, but thoughts of keeping her own children close at hand were more to her liking.

'It is good of you to consider this,' replied the officer with a huge grin, his eyes squinting in the bright sunlight.

'I shall discuss the matter with the other families, they may want to help,' she said, her voice hesitant and muffled as if she were speaking to herself. Then she bowed in false gratitude with a blank impassive face. She was trembling; the only sound was the pounding of her heart as clouds began to cover the sun.

'This is an extremely good idea, you will make all the necessary arrangements,' he replied sternly, then turned to discuss other workloads with his sergeant.

My uncle made no comment, although his face registered concern. He was deep in thought, trying desperately to evaluate all the possible consequences of speaking or keeping quiet. Nevertheless they eluded him, suspended just beyond the edge of his vision, so he agreed with her. She was right, of course. It would help to sustain life for a while at this time and place. The silence was suddenly broken when four *Zero* fighters, with red circles painted on their wing-tips, zoomed across the site, commanding instant waves and cheers from the soldiers. They were flying so low that they were threatening to add the thatched roofs to their destructive cargo, swooping and banking through the air with imposing supremacy, firm evidence that the enemy now controlled the skies for the first time.

Although spread in a large rocky basin, the camp was sheltered by an umbrella of bamboo forest. The primitive living quarters were long rows of crude grass shacks, raised on wooden stilts, and secured close together denying easy access. Sometimes torn sheets were strung between tree trunks for added protection against the blistering sun. The drainage system was inadequate, allowing pungent vapours to contaminate the entire area. There was an insufficiency of food, fresh water and medical provisions within the barbed wire fencing. Because of the stifling heat, most of the women tried to wear long sleeves and full-length skirts, to avoid being bitten by any insects, although they created a feminine illusion of coolness and elegance, they proved an impediment under these sardonic and harsh circumstances.

The days passed uneventfully and 25 December came with its rites and customs. It was my Aunt and Uncle's first Christmas in captivity and the New Year also slipped by without any festivities as each day brought only sadness. For them the intensity of fear only grew, and now they lived for their dreams. Uncle Dick was afraid to think about how many other things could suddenly go wrong, and the dread of being totally separated was always in his thoughts. They had cultivated a strip of ground near the hut, growing a prodigious quantity of fresh vegetables, which were a welcome addition to their mediocre rations. Although not so many miles from home, it felt like a foreign country. They had hope; it might have been false but it was better than no hope at all.

For them three factors dominated their lives, hunger, sickness, and liberation from this humiliating incarceration.

To add to their misery, a starvation diet was dealt to anyone who appealed repeatedly for drugs or medicine, and as food became sparse so sickness spread like a fire in a dry brush. The captives soon became undernourished and, with little resistance, those suffering with malaria and dysentery died quickly. Even the slightest scratch turned into jungle sores and large ulcers, which savaged the body with an uncontrollable itch.

Very soon the days and months of uneasiness and nervous tension passed one after another. Everyone was at the disposal of the camp authorities and were soon put to work by foul-mouthed officials, who bellowed at them at the top of their lungs. Nothing ever affected the routine of the camp. Even when they returned at dusk from the fields, totally exhausted, they would have to line up for roll-call, and bow pleasantly, as if returning from an active pleasure trip. There was also complete disregard for any complaints of illnesses or shortage of provisions. Desperate cries for mercy also brought no relief. Their stomachs were always rumbling with hunger, even shortly after consuming the meagre portions of fish and rice rations. They were now faced with a modern form of poverty, with the sickness rising in undulating waves. Death became so common that little sentiment was wasted, and they were soon confronted with the anguish of a fresh hell. The uncertainty of survival would soon be overwhelmed with an intensity of pain that tightened every nerve. Time became timeless; every minute was life, yet life soon became a tale of misery, disease, and severe hardship. The physical struggle merely to survive was enormous, and with pause in the pain came the oppressive heat, sticky and persistent, sapping away what little strength they had.

They proceeded with the daily routine in one of the few patches of cultured jungle, maintaining an exhausting rhythm, which produced agonising tiredness, and working until the dusk fell. They were pushed beyond the limits of their strength, until their bodies ached with stiffness. Columns would return staggering with fatigue, like creatures of burden being driven to their grave. They tried living life to the full but fears and foreboding only filled them. This site had its own life, its own terrifying secrets and over each of them hung the uncertainty of the morrow. Soon the quality of life became a blur of hideous incidents. The still warm rays of sunlight fell in brilliant strokes on the quiet fields and numerous trees, whose green and yellow leaves rustled with painful memories of home. Thoughts of certain death couldn't be pushed aside, and at night they sat together in silence and discussed their fears. In the tranquillity of this peace, children dozed and listened to the grinding of the hundreds of insects that lived in the forest. They had grown closer together than ever before, in the starlit night, and sleep was the only activity that made any sense.

The morning dawned with a blustery day bringing with it dust, like a sandstorm. It started like any other day, and lives would change for many when the daylight gained entry through the upper cavity, pleasantly brightening the room despite the shuttered windows. Yet, for all of them to try to enhance the quality of life in this hostile and overcrowded camp was unthinkable. For the survivors, the future looked black, as a malaria epidemic was feared, if the quinine supplies did not arrive soon. Although they were all seized by the indefinable emotion of never being free, they would sometimes laugh and joke to avoid the sadness that choked them. They would discuss stories about home, loved ones, memories and deep thoughts. They appeared to find happiness in thinking of better times, and believed that love could be a healing influence. Whilst the earth was engaged in the process of elimination, they fell silent, dampened by the impotence which internment imposed on humble people. However, late in the evening, they soon became weak and despondent, then hope died in their hearts. Suddenly the night faded into the hollowness of the blackening sky and all the stars were hidden. The moon was now just a vague shimmer, stroking the vast horizon like an exaggerated apparition and casting shadows of deep purple over the restless campsite.

There was an early dawn and the rays of the rising sun had risen sharply, pouring onto the open grounds and flooding the roofs of the huts. In the brilliant light of the morning they moved slowly, methodically, about their arduous tasks, cultivating the unyielding land. In all the heat and nothingness, their tired minds still clung to the various threads that there once were. The air was still and thick with humidity. Suddenly there were several flashes of forked lightning, followed by the rumbling discontent of rolling thunder in the distance. The changeable weather had been exceptionally bad for the past few weeks. Sometimes the downpour came in the middle of the night with no warning, for a moment only a ghostly atmosphere. Then it fell without stopping in torrents and without any mercy, pounding down relentlessly all night.

Soaked clothing hung everywhere on grubby furniture and ledges to dry, bringing daily life and survival to a perilous halt. The grounds with poor drainage were soon saturated from the constant downpours, and water stood in shallow pools all over the camp. It was impossible for the soil to absorb any more water and the weak sunshine wasn't strong enough to evaporate it. Now reduced to sharing what little food they had, they were ridiculously thin. Many were living skeletons with wasted faces, their eyes glazed with anguish and despair, easily falling victim to a spate of illnesses. Others were brooding, frustrated, wanting to live again in human dignity, but the monsoons, misery and sickness stretched into an endless future, eventually culminating in the final and crowning disaster of death itself, reaching out from the poverty of resources.

Christmas 1943, slipped away unnoticed and, with the coming of the new year, the harsh conditions hadn't favoured many. The past months had proved very difficult for all of them, as time controls and perceptions exploded. Men, women, and some of the children had been working extended hours in adverse conditions, cultivating the barren land. Exhausted and soaked to the skin, they flung themselves onto the straw mattresses every evening, overwhelmed by a crushing sleep, and disregarding the sinister location. Except for those few moments of distraction, there was very little time to amuse themselves.

What faint light there was drifted in from a nearby village, more reflection than light and certainly not strong enough to show up any silhouettes. The pale light from the tiny oil lamps only cast strange mysterious shadows, producing an atmospheric aura that sank into them like the spiritual damp. With the distant sound of birds heralding the return of another dawn, a heavy mist rose above the mountain tops, the remoteness forming a thick white canopy. Here, the forested slopes were cut by deep ravines and waterfalls, but the small rivers and streams were often too dangerous for safe passage. Near a track, which wound up between the rocks and stands of pines, ran a small stream, which produced a constant supply of fresh water. This had to be carried to the site in buckets hung on each end of a bamboo shoulder bar. Unfortunately this strenuous task always fell to the older boys. Peter and John knew how to handle this tricky business, performing the daily task admirably. However, it became more dangerous with aching tired limbs and starved bodies. The risks of misfortune multiplied with every day that passed. They were eager to please but underestimated their failing strength.

In the compact little schoolroom, a gaggle of boisterous children wandered around the wooden benches clutching feebly at the few books. Aunty Irene waved her hand dismissively.

'Now be quiet and sit down quickly all of you and we'll start with a geography lesson. It's time you all learnt about the country that you were born in,' she said, feeling rather pleased with the exceptional attendance. A sharp chill of pain coursed through her when the commandant entered the room shortly afterwards.

'Is everything all right? Do you require more benches?' he enquired, glancing quickly around the room.

'Yes, please,' she replied, forcing an unsteady smile and trying desperately to project an image of self-esteem and control in the tense atmosphere.

The children sat in an uncomfortable silence, the sight of him and the samurai sword hanging from his waist sending a surge of terror through their bodies.

'Don't be afraid, everything will be all right, believe me,' she whispered as he left abruptly, after his short visit. It was the type of comment people always said, when they felt trapped in unreasonable circumstances, something fabricated and fearless, a shutting of eyes, an instant denial of the danger they might be in. There was something about her voice and her face was frightened, her arms folded tightly across her chest. Slowly the tears trickled down her cheeks, revealing instant apprehension, now that fear was a constant companion.

When dusk fell everything was motionless as everyone observed the curfew and dropped out of sight in the hushed darkness. This provided enormous difficulties for it was impossible for them to tread their way through the blackness of a congested room, without falling over bodies, occasionally to angry protests. Everyone detested the squalor that they were continually subjected to, but they also discovered, quite by accident, in their behaviour a pattern of companionship and loyalty in this uncivilised refuge, which they would never encounter again. The work killed time, but it did not kill the thoughts, which went ceaselessly round and round in their heads. It just dragged on endlessly and the constant alternation of anxiety and hope was nerve-racking. The last hours of labour were the most anxious; they were always the hardest. Hunger and fatigue became unbearable, as time moved with impossible slowness. They had lost all contact with the world outside their own camp. For them the modern world ceased to exist. Their hope became a faith, and the faith determined at all costs a dream and the dream a reality.

At last December 1944 had arrived and their third Christmas, with all its festivities, was the most poignant period during their captivity. However, many refugees had died through lack of medication, and their losses were deeply felt in the camp where they had lived and worked together for the past two years. The spring morning was sunny and beautiful, although they were in a remote corner of the world in a conquered country. The weather was delicious, except for the dreary morning roll-call, and despite the discomfort and inconvenience, there were constant rumours of an Allied offensive. This secretly lifted their fading spirits, so they embraced and guarded these whispers with an engraved passion.

The proportion of sick had risen alarmingly, and the hot weather didn't help the feverish or the undernourished. Those with suppurating wounds, who could not be moved, were denied the right to remain unconscious. Sick refugees never received any kind of treatment, and invariably suffered from very low morale. For the present no one seemed capable of any rational thoughts, only the continuous fear, languor and the ominous threat of a painful death. They weren't even conscious of the horizon, which appeared to pass into the infinity of the sunset, and it took only a tiny effort of the mind to think of home and loved ones. As ever the barbed wire was always there as a constant reminder, but the jungle was still considered a sufficient deterrent, with its thickets and wilderness which changed into huge trees, and the creepers, which hung soggy and sweltering in the intense heat. Everything shrunk the division of thoughts into nothing. Home and country seemed so far away. All they had to do was to wait and watch the crimson sunset and for the next day to begin. Like every other day it would be conducted in a regimental fashion. They washed, fed, worked until dusk and then retired for the night.

The combination of the heat, weariness and very poor diet was now beginning to affect almost everyone. Uncle Dick hadn't been too well for quite a long time and the shortage of medicine only added to his decline. His temperature was rising rapidly and his whole body was in the grip of a fever. He was finding it very difficult to breathe easily, and even his cheerful nature couldn't dispel the sadness and thoughtfulness from his face. His insides shivered and his arms and legs felt strange and heavy. Now he was unable to purge his bowels, definite signs of yellow fever. A few more days slipped by and with his further loss of weight, everything hung on him. His face was now a map of wrinkles, with eyes deep inside pouches, and he looked more like a very old man. Dusk fell and, with the night undisturbed by enemy projectiles, there would be some comfort and sleep, that large black pit.

They had tended him with touching devotion during his seemingly long illness, but in the early hours his condition had worsened and he was still shaking with feverish chills. His family and close friends threw numerous covers on top of him, but without the liquid liberator the situation became extremely critical. My aunt's despair was understandable, and her frantic efforts to save him were justifiable as his cries for help and screams of pain could not be obliterated. He was at his lowest ebb just before the dawn and the only comfort was that the dawn would come.

Suddenly he smiled at them in a way that suggested a sense of well-being for a few moments, but he was really unaware of the stressful condition and his ambition was more forceful than the reality. As the night fell, they settled down peacefully in the oil-lit shack. The children laughed and chatted, feeling close enough to freedom. In the early dawn, even though the birds sang in the trees, the tall bamboo grass gave needed shade, and the smell of fresh wild flowers gave a certain charm to the landscape, there was no time for dreams or meditation. By midday his eyes were dull and lifeless; now in a prolonged state of high fever he had no illusions regarding his worsening health. They stared at him with sorrow in their eyes. He tried to raise a strained smile with features distorted by anguish, and then he fell back instantly, coughing, with both hands holding his chest and with beads of sweat dripping from his forehead. It was painful to realise that finally life was passing him by, as he lay there, staring at the surrounding darkness, too weak to even draw breath.

They certainly couldn't remove the sickening vice that gripped their stomachs, and watched in silence through troubled eyes veiled in a liquid film. Praying and choking back the flow of tears, my aunt caressed his thin pale hand.

'Please save him,' she begged softly.

Then he murmured, 'Forgive me, Irene.'

God didn't answer her appeal, and they knew that the moment of deliverance was approaching as he struggled with death. 'Don't leave us,' she whispered, but he silently slipped away to a less barbaric world, with scarcely an audible sigh. He had been the guiding hand, the one who made all the decisions, now he was no more.

It was a beautiful sunny evening when they laid him to rest, with the setting sun caressing miles and miles of jungle. They buried him in a small rise of ground outside the camp, alongside many other mounds, slowly moving like automatons and staring unseeing at the grave. When the local priest prayed for the peace and safety of all, they timidly bowed their heads in sorrow. However, fear and emotion rendered them incapable of a lengthy meditation, and the energy needed in still being alive shrouded their untold misery. Now they needed the strength to bear this burden and somehow bring their lives back to normal again.

Surprisingly, the morale of this isolated party was high, and with special pride they carried out the simple ceremony. However, as they were deeply saddened by the tragic loss, nothing could forestall the other emotional crisis, the flood of tears. They remained humble and resigned under the hanging gloom of those who lived in this nightmare, feeling abandoned in time, like death itself.

Outside, far beyond the campsite, there appeared to be barely any life at all. Only a very few people hurried past with joyless faces in the murky streets. There were only squads of soldiers loafing around. During the day the road was empty of automobile and animal traffic, except for Japanese military vehicles, mostly armoured trucks and a few tanks. As expectation was in the air and the sun dropped down behind the horizon the full dark really came. Occasionally the clouds parted, and the surrounding land was exposed, with an avenue of barren trees slicing the landscape.

Suddenly, the sound of gunfire rippled through the forest, and the noise reverberated around the site and resounded across the thick undergrowth, bushes, and trees. Without any hesitation they damped down the small fires and with that the light was gone. Now it was pitch-dark under the canopy of the tall trees, and even the stars failed to shine through. The night was still warm, and all that could be heard were the scuffled footsteps of weary people walking past, although, in the cool shadows of those remote areas, it was expected that wild animals had more of a presence than the enemy.

By the end of January, the weather had become unusually hot for that time of the year for anything too strenuous. But activity was the best cure for depression, so after a few days of being in a confused state they worked with feverish energy. Their thoughts were becoming increasingly stirred out of all composure, fuelled by the constant rumours of an Allied threat rolling remorselessly towards the east. It was very difficult for them to realise that the war was coming close to them at last. They clung desperately to any news that brought comfort and relief, nursing it to gain the much-needed solace. Yet stronger than the barbed wire, the green-covered hills lay between them and freedom or human bondage.

One dramatic event was the demonstration of the Allied strike force, when one sunny day a steady roar of engines drew their attention to it. High above, the heavens were full of British *Hurricanes* and *Thunderbolts* sweeping southwards. Although the situation remained obscure for some time, it broke the fantasies that once weaved through their brains and the mode of their ultimate release in the early days of captivity. The possibility of liberation was now forever in their thoughts, although it was a subject they seldom discussed and the pain of longing for home weighed heavy on their hearts. Now for the first time they kindled an ambitious dream, and were united by a strong passion for survival.

Both the boys had been ill for quite some time and hadn't fully recovered from their illnesses when they returned to school. As twin brothers they were very close; they played together and fought with each other on many occasions. However, lessons were over for the day and today as on every other day for almost two years, they were to carry out the unenviable task of hauling heavy buckets of water on a shoulder bar. After filling them from the brook at the base of the mountain, they continued up the steep slope to the campsite. As the trees thinned out, the land dropped away before them in a shallow bowl. However, by the time they had reached the bottom of the ravine, their bodies were soaked in sweat from the sun, which beat down in a merciless glare. The stream flowed rapidly through the steep rocky gorges from its source high up in the mountains. This place had been a regular haunt of theirs, despite where they were living at the present time. It had always been their secret playground, and its location tendered a magical view of the countryside.

With the containers full of water and weighing heavily on their small shoulders, they ascended slowly along the stretches of bare ground, trying to avoid the huge holes in the rough terrain and the dense thorny undergrowth that hacked at their flesh. Here the track twisted and turned unexpectedly from left to right, then rose sharply. Their mood was playful as they entered a shadow in the ravine, but their faces were creased with exhaustion. Their aching frames swayed from side to side with each ponderous step. It was now a painful struggle up the slopes of the wooded land, and the heat from the broken blacktop pierced through their worn shoes. The straps of clothing, tied around their feet for comfort, loosened as they trudged along the patchy road. Now the overwhelming weariness was beginning to affect their tired limbs, overcome with fatigue. The strain of the past had reduced them to a state of physical exhaustion.

Suddenly, with a shriek of despair, John stopped rigid in his stride, then stumbled across the ground and fell face downwards clutching his chest. His legs were kicking out furiously into space, as he tried to lift his head. In a moment of sheer panic, Peter turned his body over and removed the shoulder bar from his chest with a swift wrench. John was now gasping for breath, and his face wore an expression of helplessness, his eyes were dull and lifeless, his body taut. Fuelled by the sudden look of fear in his eyes and the faint belief that he might die, Peter realised that he had to do something, but he didn't know what. So he immediately ran off in a frenzy for his mother, shouting and screaming as he ran through the trees. When he arrived at the site breathless, his mother was standing near the schoolroom doorway talking to some of the younger children. She stared at him with an anxious intensity seeing him on his own. Her eyes glowed with anguish as she shouted, 'Peter, what is the matter with you and where is John? Why are you so upset?' The questions spilled out until she saw the fear and desperation in his face.

For a moment Peter looked frozen, speechless. 'It's John, Mum, he's fallen down and he can't breathe,' he replied with choking words, stumbling forward onto the baked earth.

'What is up with him?' she cried, shaking him furiously by the shoulders, but the words wouldn't come, only the sobs.

Now her heart froze in terror and there was an instant tremor of panic, as she made her way hurriedly towards the brook, half-running, half-walking, and praying with all her heart that everything would be all right. The fear of discovery of death weighed on her mind so much it left no room for hope and reason. Suddenly she stiffened with terror at the horrible sight of poor John's frail little body lying there in anguished silence. The blue pigmentation of his skin suggested to her that he had suffered a strained heart, but the manner of his untimely death fully justified her uncontrollable rage. When her efforts to revive him by mouth-to-mouth resuscitation failed miserably, she held his limp body tenderly to her bosom, then rested her head on his face and burst into a fit of hysterical weeping, inwardly cursing the years spent in this forested green hell. She sat for a while in her own private grief, then she carried his limp body with tenderness back to the camp in a drunken dream, her face contorted with grief and steeped in pain.

Sobs of sick and tired captives shocked her, as she entered the campsite. Many wept as others helped in earnest. Her thoughts were filled with hatred and were now swimming in emotion. She tried desperately to persuade herself that none of this was really happening, or probably the war had turned her into a person without any feelings, but her heart was telling her to cry again. Now she was faced with the anguish of further fresh suffering, plus the uncertainty of even surviving. In a matter of a few moments she had aged a number of years, for when death continues it becomes unbearable, then even the outburst of tears is no release.

It was a miserable afternoon, grey and overcast. Peter and Maureen stood by their mother's side, occasionally breaking into a gentle sob. The make-do wooden box was lowered down on top of their father's resting place. Feelings of grief, contempt and turmoil were etched on their faces. They stood perfectly still, staring intently at the open grave and grieving inwardly at their tragic loss. The sharing of grief was unburdening, as they wept together, surrounded by many friends, slowly allowing the silence to develop around them and shrouded the intense pain which gripped like a vice. For darling little John it was a sad farewell to a world in which he had lived and played.

From the tops of the mountains down to the stream, the sky was hanging low, pressing downwards like a burden. The view was desolate, empty, yet in the distance the entire landscape was covered in trees. The few bunches of wild flowers with their vivid colours, aglow in the dim light, were symbols of their grief. Even as the dusk fell in the mid-afternoon, they stood patiently in relative silence under the spreading bow of a gigantic tamarind tree. Now completely exhausted by their nervous tension, their emotions alternated between silent weeping and depression. Their minds were bent with grief and their eyes swelled with this ghostly picture that couldn't dismiss the reality. They hoped and prayed that the dark clouds overhead would hold back the rain, the simple pain and the powerless rage with which they were infused. Silently they watched with vacant stares as the grave was filled in by some close friends and a small mound raised above it. The same wooden cross was replaced to symbolise the sacred place.

'Why did John have to die?' asked Peter, his eyes wide in disbelief and sadness. He felt that he was to blame for his brother's tragic death.

A sudden flash of pain flit across his mother's face before she replied, 'I don't really know the answer to that, son,' she said in a timeless voice. 'Now listen to me very carefully. If his death is to have any kind of meaning, it's to help us appreciate what we have,' she said, choking back the tears. Then she hugged his shoulder, trying to provide some small degree of comfort to his aching heart.

The warmth faded from the air, as the evening breeze drifted in from the east.

'We must go now,' she whispered to them. 'We can't keep him and he can't take us where he is going.'

It was time for all of them to return to the sanctuary of the campsite once more.

These were anxious and demanding periods, not knowing what each new day would bring, but the camp soon returned to the monotony of its daily routine. Every day was the same; life went on and secretly they all lived in a state of suspense waiting for liberation or their doom. The weeks and months passed, and finally the spring of 1945 broke through and myriad flowering trees and plants seemed to line the surrounding area, their beauty stretching ahead on the steep uphill gradients that rolled away on each side of the mountain ranges. There was a huge chasm between the beginning and the end, when almost three years of incarceration seemed to have aged them like a defeated tribe. Now they were badly undernourished, with deep lines around their mouths. The dark heavy rings under their eyes betrayed years of misery and severe hardship in a refugee camp.

For many came that welcome oblivion, painlessness and death. The liberation of the prison camp by a British Task Force finally rescued others from an unparalleled life of misery. Perhaps one day someone will want to know but with the passage of time nothing much remains for those who somehow survived the terrifying and horrendous ordeals. There is only an awareness of unguided instability, and a sordid heartache which spreads across the years, never decreasing and never designed to reflect on the elusive. For all of those left, there will be a tomorrow for as long as the world keeps circling. There will be a blue sky, a grey one and there will be thunderstorms. The Irrawaddy River will still flow amidst the forest depths, where the wild animals enjoy their freedom. The fishermen will tend their small boats, and the tribespeople will continue to grow vegetables and fruit in the rich fertile soil of this their homeland. Where stands the camp at Samow enclosed by barbed wire fencing? Yet for the present Samow no longer existed, only on the faces of its inhabitants. How many lifetimes had passed? It is impossible to say. Thoughts of their misery, however foolish, would one day be recognised, even in death a flood of memories would pour out.

Chapter VIII

The winter of long ago had come and gone and a new summer greeted all the residents. It was Thursday 14 August 1942; my brother and I walked to school like all the other kids. I nodded at those I knew with a little more force than usual. Looking at the same set of faces didn't offer me any pleasure, so I locked myself up more than the system did in a pensive silence that enveloped me like a shroud. A little sadness overrode my anger as I tried to push away pitiful thoughts from my mind. The rugged leafy path crunched under our feet as we climbed up the slope towards the main entrance, where some of the kids were playing games before school began. It was now 10 a.m., and morning recreation at the three-classroom building we knew as school was a hub of noise. There was a small playing area, which ran the full length of the single-storey premises, built on a plateau. Towards the front, huge wooden railings were protection against the fall of the slope. Although rather small, the building was deemed sufficient enough to keep the children occupied during the long summer months in the Himalayan mountain range. Most of the girls were playing hopscotch and some of the boys were involved in a game of holly-golly. Others participated in an Indian game called gillie and dundoo, comprising of two sticks. Now bathed in the warm rays of the sun, the huge plum trees that surrounded the school were in fruit. Birds of various colours perched on the branches, chirping and revelling in the cosiness, after the summer rain had pounded the earth. I was busy chatting with some of my pals when I heard a squeaky voice.

'I know something that you don't know,' the girl said as she approached me with a smirk on her face.

She was a little older than me and someone I didn't much care for, so I continued with my conversation.

'Your baby sister is dead,' she said scornfully.

I ignored her stupid remark and turned away. She moved

closer, staring at me, while the others watched in annoyance. The glare was returned immediately.

'Did you hear what I said?' she continued scornfully. 'Your baby sister is dead.' She goaded me in mock irritation. A sternness had crept into her voice.

'You're a liar, she's in hospital,' I shouted defiantly.

A cold shiver ran between my shoulder blades, and I felt a stabbing pain in the pit of my stomach. I thought for a moment that I was suffocating, feeling stung by her tone. A thin liquid film covered my eyes, and the shock of hearing of my sister's death generated outrage. The balanced flow of blood within me turned into ripples, releasing a destructive mood of untold anger. It was her careless, contemptuous manner that taunted me into hitting her in the face, full-blooded with my clenched fist. Suddenly a thin red stream of liquid life dripped from her nose onto her dress. She ran away screaming into the classroom. This brought her big brother, Arty, waltzing onto the scene with a vicious gleam in his eyes.

'Why did you hit my sister?' he shouted, pushing me and throwing his weight around.

'Because she is a big liar,' I replied in defiance and feeling very upset by her remarks.

In a roadway situation I would have had time to run by using my speed to outdistance him, but this was a playground and I knew I would have to face him, there was no where else to go. Although he was much taller than I was, I was agile, but that wouldn't stand up in a brawl and I felt that I was in for a good hiding. I wasn't frightened, I was never afraid of anything and certainly didn't subscribe to the theory that it was better to walk away from it than deal with it. I had to somehow banish the emotional jumble in my brain and revert to something more reliable, like fury. Thoughts of fighting in the playground were new to me, but the prospect of getting walloped in front of all the girls felt awful. The sad memories only confused me and I couldn't afford that, but Audrey's voice gave me confidence.

Audrey Reynolds and I were very close, sort of childhood sweethearts. She was the same age as myself, with blue-grey eyes and a pretty smile. Her main fascination for me was her long, silky, reddish brown hair that stretched down to her waist.

'Come over here, Colin, you shouldn't be fighting in school,' she pleaded.

My concentration was broken by her voice, which allowed him to get an armlock around my neck, and with his other arm he was squeezing the breath out of my lungs. I felt that I was suffocating as my eyes bulged from their sockets and my body started quivering. I had to regain some advantage or suffer further punishment. Remembering my previous schooldays in the ring, and with an instinctive rugged manoeuvre, I belted him in rapid succession with rigid blows into the middle of his stomach. His release was like a breath of fresh air, and now with my temper surfacing I hit him flush on the snout, which seemed to be softer than I expected because it split down one side. Now a flicker of excitement surged through my body as I punched him in the face. With an energetic aggression, I launched at him, tripping him over, and as we rolled to the ground I sat on top of him and punched him repeatedly about the face with rage, deciding that exposing my vengeance was fully in line with my present mood. He started to scream, covering his face with his hands.

'You're hurting him,' yelled his sister, trying to pull me off but a deep voice inside of me told me to keep on.

The other children had formed a circle of anxious viewers, shouting, cheering, pushing and shoving for a clearer vision. My fury was designed to hurt as I persisted in belting him. The blood flowed from his nose onto his chin and throat, staining his shirt. Suddenly I felt myself being lifted by the scruff of my collar, the clothing tightening around me. Miss McCullock, the headmistress, had arrived on the scene, and with both hands dragged me off my frightened opponent with a minimum of effort. She was built like a sumo wrestler, with a face like crumpled crêpe paper and bold piercing eyes and her tremendous size was awesome. She towered over us and we parted with an expression of mutual dislike.

'What do you two think you are doing? This is a school playground, not a fairground,' she remarked angrily. 'You're a disgrace, now get into my office immediately both of you,' she shouted, her overpowering voice echoing throughout the playground like distant thunder. 'The rest of you back to your classrooms now,' she commanded in tones of authority. Then she tossed Arty a handkerchief for his nose. 'I will not have fighting in my school, do you hear me?' she bellowed again.

I stared at her defiantly with a look of fierce satisfaction. The sweat ran down my face and a cold chill settled on my neck as I inhaled deep long breaths, feeling reluctant to involve myself in any office discussion. I didn't argue with her. Several of the children looked on with curiosity and optimism as they moved towards the school. I raised my gaze from the playground to the mountains, and with a stubborn feeling in my thoughts and a sudden rush of blood, ran off. I sprinted through the forest at breakneck pace trying to disbelieve the words that were revolving round and round and tormenting my brain. It was a mocking sound that carried with it a harshness through the early morning air. I couldn't control my emotions any more; they burst open and brought silent tears trickling down my cheeks.

Frantically heading for home, I seemed to be floating along the ground between the trees, and somehow even the bushes opened up as I glided on the surface without a scratch. My shoes hardly made a sound as I sprinted across the rugged wilderness, full of determination and zest and with a minimum of style, as the troubled sadness spilled over me. The path home wasn't far, yet it seemed endless, and the birds called now and then but the stillness of the land carried something that I could almost touch. I passed stands of tall pines, through which the sun flashed prints of light and dark rays, the warmth drying my tears and leaving patches of their traces on my angry face. I'm sure the forest of many eyes and ears silently watched and listened with dignity.

I finally reached the verandah, gasping for breath in the brilliant sunshine and drowning in a sudden flow of sorrow. I was tired and listened to the rhythm of my heartbeat as it came in waves, tugging at my insides, which were shivering with thoughts and emotions. I entered the bungalow, breathless and exhausted, and the abrupt silence worried me. No one was smiling; there was the feeling of tension you get before a thunderstorm, a sense of something holding back. My stepfather was sitting in the lounge, but his face didn't betray his misery. The tears that stood like a transparent shield in his eyes told me that death had arrived into our home in this remote area of the Punjab.

All the time my sister was ill in hospital I'd prayed to God repeatedly night and day, to the One who listens, rewards and punishes. 'I'm very sorry if I haven't always believed in you, but please forgive me and help my sister to get well and come home soon. She is so little and you gave her to me to love and play with, please don't take her away now,' I said quietly with tears in my eyes. But he must have only watched, because he never answered my heartbroken plea. I stood for a moment feeling tempted to turn and leave, but for a few seconds I found a small comfort in the silence within me. Then the silence became dark and frightening, as it would to a small boy who couldn't believe it. I felt alien and in a second all sound of movement ceased, as I slipped quietly into the bedroom, lay on my bed and sobbed. Night finally came, but it was impossible to sleep. Everything seemed to be filled with so much pain that I just tossed, turned and cursed the human nervous system. It was another night of broken sleep. Although the moonlight struggled to penetrate the curtains and gently caress the floor, there was serenity in the room that we once shared.

'Where's Mum?' I asked my stepfather the following morning, noticing that she wasn't around, which I thought was strange.

'She decided to stay at the hospital until all the arrangements have been completed,' he replied sadly.

The house, usually the centre of chatter and laughter, now felt cold and empty. The day that followed was cloaked with a heavy sadness, which was only an extension of painful grief. My own mind was a jumble of uncertain feelings, when I realised that she would never grow up like me, and I would never be able to talk to her again. I couldn't believe that she had survived that horrendous journey, when she was so very young and now that we were safe, she had her young life snatched from her.

On the day of her funeral, Friday 15 August 1942, several mourners packed the little chapel on the hillside. Their eyes focused on the tiny casket embraced with colourful wild flowers. Numerous others waited outside, although many of them were strangers, having only recently arrived at the site. They paused to pay their respects to the baby girl who had touched the hearts of so many, perhaps because of her age, or perhaps because she was the first one to lose her young life since this epic journey began. They approached quietly, each one offering their condolences to my stepfather, who was standing alone. My mother had become spiritually ill within herself and had refused the prescribed medicines. She had to be heavily sedated and remained in bed. The military hospital had allowed a young nurse to care for her in the bungalow whilst we were away.

The poignant service finally came to a close amidst muffled sobs. The people with tear-reddened eyes shuffled slowly outside into the midday sun, with a deep sense of sympathy. My stepfather, preceded by the minister, carried the small wooden casket on his shoulder. The young minister, although sad himself, had an impressive voice, which echoed in the hushed atmosphere inside. My Uncle Ossie supported his brother-in-law on one side, as he moved cautiously, enduring the pain and discomfort, occasionally swaying sideways from time to time. My stepfather had some real toughness about him although still suffering from battle fatigue and having survived one horrendous campaign against the Japanese in Southern Burma. There he had sustained severe concussion and a badly shattered leg. He was trapped in the reeds near the water's edge in the Sittang River, during the retreat. A Gurkha soldier dragged him to safety, as he struggled to breathe in the turbulent current. Now, here he was, gutted by his sad loss, his face a collection of separate emotions and, if he felt as I did, I would guess that his insides shivered and his arms and his legs felt like those of an old man. He raised his face to the sun for warmth and the feeling of calm and control returned; no one noticed his brief lapse but me. It was all inside him and he knew that now he could handle the situation.

The sad gathering moved cautiously in a hushed silence, holding their own deep sense of sympathy as they proceeded down the rugged winding slope to the small cemetery. It was tucked away in the shadows of the immense forest and neatly sheltered out of the rays of the sun; it looked peaceful and secluded. It was surrounded by a low brick wall, and wrought-iron gates under a dainty stone archway allowed easy access. The trees in the copse were mostly pine, whose dried brown needles formed a cushion underfoot. Then the trail circled the newly dug grave and the mound of raw brown earth beside it. My sister's burial was a tranquil ceremony conducted in the huge expanse of the Himalayan mountain range, now cocooned in the heavy forest, vast and primeval. Only the chirping of little birds filled the stillness of the mountain air, but for her it was a final farewell to a world she had never known. We stood motionless, listening to a short sermon, disturbed by faint sobs. The sky darkened as a solitary cloud floated across the sun, allowing only tiny speckles of brightness to touch the mourners. A slight breeze blew and the cellophane around the sprays of flowers rustled on the raw earth. There were numerous wreaths of vivid colours, mauves, whites, pinks and yellows, glistening against the shades of dry grass, and a very special one from her family. As I gazed upon the little coffin in the open grave, a garland of exotic blossoms made a yellow explosion on the lid. I suddenly realised the full weight of my despair and how absolutely I had given up hope. I began to think timidly and gently, still resigned to the idea of death. I was soon motivated by hate and the fear that I would never see her again. Now this huge jungle would become an everlasting memorial to her in her final resting place.

After the gloom of the previous days there was an emptiness in me but death had not finished with us. Within two weeks the remaining five babies also passed away, leaving the entire camp numb with grief and with depressing thoughts that suddenly filled us with anxiety. Everywhere there was an uncomfortable silence, the silence of people in pain, the silence of people afraid. Saturday began with a visiting delegation from the hospital, who then requested that the parents of the little ones who had passed away attend a special meeting at the small surgery. The chaplain was also invited to console many who still felt bitter and no longer cared. Their faces went deathly pale when the coroner informed them that these strange deaths were due to a gastric disorder. They had firmly established the fundamental causes of these disorders. Because of the inadequate conditions during the evacuation, the babies had all been breastfed and samples of the milk that were taken had proved positive. The doctor pointed out that the contributing factors for the infection or poisoning were caused by the four months of continuous travelling, physical weariness, lack of nourishing food and the insufficient supply of fresh water being the main factors. A shadow of doubt and hatred passed across weary faces when they left the surgery. It was no wonder that their tears and sobs were soon to become curses, to those barbarians who had driven us from our homeland.

Sunday flew by like a gust of wind; it had been a hellish week for everyone. There were no good sounds or friendly noises. The following morning was my first chance to return to school, since that awful day when I'd skipped off without permission. Beyond the verandah some kids were already playing outside, enjoying the early morning rays of the sun. I was beginning to come to terms with my sister's death; at least I kidded myself that I was, although in fact I was still suffering from deep sorrow.

'I want you to stay at home today, son,' were the first words with which I was greeted by from my mother.

'What for?' I asked, feeling a little annoyed with her suggestion.

'Because! That's all you need to know. Just take Trevor to school and return home immediately. I've got a special little job for you to do, and it won't take you too long.'

The room was silent when I left, shrugging my shoulders and feeling a little ruffled at what she had said. I had always enjoyed school and had been looking forward to seeing some of my friends again, but was taught never to disobey. Within fifteen minutes I had returned to a strangely quiet house.

'Where is everyone?' I asked my mother.

'Your uncles have gone to Murree on business, that's all you need to know. This is what I want you to do and quickly,' she said nervously, then turned and went into the bedroom.

Within a few minutes she returned, cradling a small bundle all neatly wrapped and tied with some ribbon. I looked at her a little scared, but said nothing, for in her eyes lurked deep sadness. She was always a very energetic woman, and most of what she did was motivated by a genuine desire to help.

'You once mentioned that there were many caves sheltered high up in the mountains, and that you had also been inside some of them.'

I nodded warily at her remark.

Her hands trembled slightly as she handed me the package, then speaking almost in a whisper and struggling with her words she said, 'These are the rest of Baby's clothes, some of them are brand new and many are what I made myself. I want you to take them into one of those caves and bury them, so that no one can ever find them. Just seeing them around only increases the pain. No one must ever know where they are.'

Her words came out slowly as she spoke. For a few moments thousands of questions flooded my mind, and strange images floated through my head like hazy pictures. Her instructions baffled me, for nothing seemed to make sense at that time. She gently wiped away the tears that slipped down her cheeks, and the urgency behind her request showed plainly in her eyes. My sister's sudden death seemed to have affected her badly, which was quite natural, and I wasn't in a position or perhaps was too young to help her overcome her intense grief.

'But, Mum—' I started to protest, but it was useless.

She stopped me immediately. She raised her eyebrows. 'Just do as I ask and not a word to anyone,' came her heartfelt plea.

'All right,' I said, breathing a deep sigh and feeling a strange sensation inside of me. I had no real obligation to my mother, as I was only a child, yet somehow I wanted to please her, to do as she asked, without questioning her motive. I felt that she was hurting, with a deep penetrating hurt that would linger for ever like a dark hanging cloud, waiting to burst forth with rain. In her eyes I could see emptiness and intense pain. They appeared to be hollow spaces, looking at me, but not seeing, yet begging for help from immature innocence. Sometimes life is the process of finding out too late, instead of seeing the obvious. I placed the small bundle under my arms, and after a moment's hesitation walked out of the house towards the forest. I left a flood of tears spilling down her face as she began to sob helplessly, watching me journey up the mountain.

It was a trip that I really didn't want to make but somehow the silence had a way of clearing one's head. I clambered carefully up the steep gradient. Some of the route was in bad shape and the leaves crunched willingly under my feet. I paused halfway up and looked around at the tall unbroken pines that stretched out of sight in all directions. Their cones and brown needles were scattered all over the ground. High up in the trees, birds called to each other, and even the squirrels looked down at my progress. They were watching me curiously and showing no signs of fear. Somehow there was always the feeling of inquisitive eyes peeping at me through the branches. My heart pounded as I continued, every little noise making me shiver and my heart flutter. After an endless search I finally reached the isolated cave for which I'd been searching, sunk deep inside the mountain. I'd been inside this one many times, but my head was full of mixed emotions as I crawled silently through the opening. It was empty, but smelt stuffy. I knew that jackals and bears were often associated with dens of this type. Judging by the droppings and scattered bones, this one belonged to a bear, but had long been discarded, I decided, with a sigh of relief, and looked for a niche.

I found a cleft inside some feet off the ground. After holding the little bundle close to my heart, I kissed it before placing it into the deep crevice. Then I carefully sealed the access with some rocks that were lying around. I sat on a huge boulder for a while, trying to assemble my thoughts, with my eyes fixed on a ray of sunlight straying through the opening. I listened to the buzz of insects and the whispering of the wind in the trees outside. I even hummed a tune that we had been taught at school recently. This only made me cry, great painful sobs, which almost tore me apart. In a faltering voice I tried to remember some of the words, 'You'll take the high road and I'll take the low road, but I'll be in Scotland before ye.' This brought a flood of tears, as happy thoughts of the past invaded my solitary being. However, the solitude did give me a certain freedom and peace of mind.

It was soon necessary for me to leave as the last vestiges of sunlight started to disappear. The clouds had broken up, but it was still mild. I sealed up the main entrance to the cave with stumps, branches and brushwood that lay around in patches. I turned and glanced back, then prayed that no human figure would ever mar this sacred place that belonged only to me. Under the dark grey sky it all looked very sad and I was contorted with pain.

I was afraid because nothing made sense, but fear never does. Anyway, I will always have the memories, and this sacred place will remain my secret.

I walked steadily through the darkening forest, where the tall trees stood erect. The sacred cave, now concealed to my left, was lost from sight, sheltered in the woods, waiting for the safety of the night. Nothing was visible but the shadowy forms and barbaric obstinate nature. It had been a long tiring day and dusk was descending as I made my way home. Everything was silent, except for a few birds whose shrill sounds echoed in the air, and bats flittered around me like shadows in the semi-darkness. I hurried along, slipping and sliding down the steep descent, as the jungle chill weighed heavily on me with a sulky oppressive spirit. Then as the trees thinned out I reached the base of the mountain. Now the lamps were being lit in the looming bungalows, testimony to the falling darkness and that my journey had taken much longer than expected.

When I reached home I tiptoed across the verandah and slipped quietly into the dining room. I was surprised to find my mother waiting patiently for my return.

'Where have you been until now?' she asked. 'I've been worried sick. Do you know what time it is?' Her voice was almost inaudible and hesitant with fear. I stared at her with a piteous expression and shrugged my shoulders, but didn't answer her question, still feeling very upset within myself.

'I was making sure that Marjorie's clothes were safely tucked away and well hidden, so that no one could ever find them, even if they found the cave,' I replied. Yet for me the rush of remembrance was really hurting inside. We spoke about happier times while I ate the meal that she had kept for me. They say that the sharing of grief eases the burden, so we wept together, giving me time to dwell on my sad journey. The afternoon sun had left me weary and the dark had almost arrived as I settled down for the night and sank into the depths of sleep.

The weeks passed slowly and painfully. By the end of August my stepfather had left to rejoin his regiment. My uncle was preparing for the post that he had been offered as an electrical engineer on the Indian railways. The families were still caught up in a crisis of tearful despair, and small groups of evacuees drifted into the camp at various intervals, each one proclaiming the human instinct for survival at any cost.

The season so far had been a warm one and all the signs pointed to a summer of unusual severity. It was a hot, windless day, and beyond the shadowy hills strange clouds appeared on the horizon. Even the sky seemed to hang low above the ground. I stepped from the verandah and walked to the entrance of the campsite; suddenly my eyes became riveted upon a batch of evacuees struggling mournfully along the rough, dusty track. Their arrival heralded opened doors and stampeding residents to the top compound in a flurry. With these new images impossible dreams were stirred in many heads, and they stimulated courage in the fearful. I could feel compassion and admiration for the hardships that they must have endured. For they had all survived the best and the worst that the jungle could offer them. This whole scene of determination and courage seemed touched with the stillness and silence of a recurring dream.

We all had something in common with the weary figures crowding past, whose normalities had been subjected to horrendous ordeals. We had once been doomed, yet were hopeful now. Mother joined me as we watched in silence, full of optimism and expectancy. A feeling of solidarity lay not so much in how they were dressed, but in how they moved with that same apparent look of fear. The pitiful procession halted near what appeared to them as a colonising zone, but it was only the grassy knoll next to the canteen. Their isolation was immediately invaded by an avalanche of residents, eagerly seeking any kind of information or seeking lost relatives. There were sad faces saying things to no one in particular and endless conversations in different voices – everyone seemed to be mixed up in a crazy rhythm.

Through this packed crowd, a tall, strange-looking man dismounted off a chestnut horse with a lot of difficulty. Helped by his companion he breathed laboriously in short gasps. They made their way slowly through the aisles of boisterous people, peering anxiously for some family recognition. He stopped at intervals to control his balance with a set of crutches. Above a huge beard his bespectacled face looked extremely pale. His gaunt hollow features betrayed his agony but his sunken glazed eyes revealed more than a touch of friendliness. A momentary chill ran through me when I realised that it was my Uncle Leo, and his friend, Arty Apker. They had survived the arduous trek after all, although they looked as if they had suffered agonising hardships on their journey.

My mother froze on the spot, as the tall dark figure approached her like a moving shadow. She saw a lean, rather shabby face staring down at her, eyes wide above the fringe of beard. Instantly she knew who it was.

'Leo,' she said, almost breathless with relief. 'At last. I'd given up hope.' The urgency in her voice was contagious. Her eyes gave several exaggerated blinks as if to clear them of tears, as he put his arms around her. Her affection for him returned with a rush.

'Gwen,' he murmured feebly, almost scared, his face now expressionless, yet serene, but his eyes filled with tears.

Mother then put her arms around Arty. 'Thank God that both of you finally made it,' she said excitedly. Arty had been a family friend since childhood.

'We almost didn't make it, Gwen, but I'm very pleased to see all of you,' he replied. There was tiredness in his tone.

I stared at my uncle and wondered if what I was seeing could possibly be true, as a cold shiver travelled through my entire system. His face was tight, and his eyes were hard-packed with emotion. He had always been so athletic and muscular, and suddenly I was realising full well what this powerful man had secretly endured. Inside the bungalow the two brothers and a sister were happily reunited, in close company with a special friend, although it sounded like a squabbling family party. Outside the lethargic group had begun to disperse to the various dwellings organised by the authorities. Some had been fortunate to meet up with relatives and close friends.

Arty and my uncle had been inseparable since their boyhood days and in maturity often hunted together during the holidays. Occasionally I had had the privilege of accompanying them. This bond that they shared came from deep within themselves, so it was of no real surprise that they had made the journey together.

Now that they had arrived, Arty would soon be leaving to rejoin some of his relatives who had arrived safely in India. However, shortly before he left, we sat and listened to a detailed account of how their incredible good fortune had brought them this far. Inevitably this would lead us to the cruel realisation of my uncle's deplorable condition, yet there was no mistaking the note of menace in his voice.

They decided to attempt the journey by crossing the Hukawng Valley, then heading south-west for the Naga Hills in Nagaland and the Indian border. For a while they found themselves trapped in a flow of congestion, with hundreds of anonymous anxious faces. They left the main batch of refugees, believing that small groups were less conspicuous to enemy reconnaissance aircraft and also that a steady stream of civilians would unwittingly blaze a trail for the Japanese to follow. They moved cautiously during the day and concealed themselves at night in the thick undergrowth, where they welcomed some sleep. However, unknown to them, the enemy's advance had been swift and relentless, with patrols constantly skirting the area. As they travelled parallel to the main road they could often hear the noise of vehicles, most of which was enemy traffic, a ritual that was as persistent as the savage sun.

After the first few days their progress finally became very slow and exhausting, as thirst clawed at their throats. They painfully climbed small hills and pushed through the long spear grass that colonised the land. Down in the valley they fell upon a small village occupied by tribes from that area. They moved cautiously and silently towards the huts, assuming that it was safe, having decided to ask for help. The villagers spoke little or no English but gave them some food and drink. There the air was clear and pleasantly warm, and it was the very sort of evening that allowed them to settle down. In the stillness of the night, thoughts and dreams clouded their senses. Within a few minutes of lying down fully clothed by the roasting fire, they had fallen into a dreamless sleep.

Early the next morning they continued with their journey, walking along the jungle edge. At midday they approached another village which was bordered by woodland and appeared to be uninhabited. It was so quiet that their suspicions were soon aroused. They crept silently into the first hut, which was vacant, so they decided to stay for a rest. Caution could mean their survival. Suddenly their peace was shattered by a group of yelling Japanese soldiers running from one of the other huts. They ranged down on them and fired their weapons rapidly. They were so outnumbered and afraid they jumped up and dashed off into the jungle, pursued by a hail of bullets. However, they managed to escape from the enemy without being hit, but in their mad rush they were badly cut by the thorny undergrowth. They lay motionless in the tall grass, straining to catch any sound of the enemy as the firing stopped as quickly as it had begun. They tried to spy any movements but there weren't any, so they backtracked into the undergrowth. Eventually they were met by some Burmese guerrillas who had a camp set well back in the jungle, where it would be very difficult for the Japanese to find them. It was an impressive stronghold, with an abundance of fresh food and water. After settling down, they were given rice, fish, boiled eggs and plenty of weak tea; they stayed for a few days then left with fresh supplies.

They continued throughout the day along rugged paths and paddy fields, sleeping during the night. However, despite their improved diet, they were always soaked with sweat or by the incessant rain. This didn't help to dispel the natural fear that the jungle had induced, filling them with an oppressive claustrophobia. During the next few days they travelled through mangrove swamps, impenetrable jungle and rainforest during the day and on into the night. Here they passed groups of refugees who had fallen by the wayside and died, not having been prepared for anything like this, yet they hadn't encountered any of the real dangers of war. With fear of capture always on their minds they watched and waited in the darkness, a stark reminder that danger was never far away.

Continuous travelling through tough bamboo forests, thorny thickets, and small villages finally brought them to the mighty Chindwin River. They crossed the turbulent water in a *periagua* (a small canoe dug out of a tree trunk) which they found abandoned on the riverbank. The little boat leaked excessively, but they were not to be defeated and kept baling out the water. They eventually reached the opposite bank, exhausted and crippled with fatigue, along with the uncomfortable fear of being intercepted by patrols on the shore.

They struggled through swamps and finding a vestige of a path was impossible as the bogs seemed to go on for ever. When the twilight settled in, the rain came down in sheets, the water running in torrents across the track. Camping for the night was of no help, as the matches in their pockets were so wet they couldn't even light a small fire to keep warm, and they lay down on the wet ground. This terrain was only for the hardiest and was usually covered by mists or rain, but was the perfect haven for a long rest. When they awoke, it was another very hot day and even the long grass looked parched. Suddenly the clouds were streaming across the face of the sun, and they hit long stretches of sunny windy weather. In these swampy and humid lowlands, the climate was unsuitable and impossible for them to survive. They continued through the fens throughout the rest of the day, as the surrounding area appeared to be nothing but marshland, trudging into dense thickets with enormous trunks that soared up until they were lost in a thick canopy, which shut out all the sunlight and dripped water continuously. Some were festooned with a tangled mass of creepers, which climbed the adjacent trees, and the sunless air hummed with insects.

Gradually the terrain improved and there were signs of vegetation and wild banana plantations. Although they craved some rest, they kept on moving without any sleep, through dense undergrowth, stumbling over huge roots. The sun lashed their sweating bodies with a scorching merciless fury, and the fear of interception was never far from their thoughts. They crossed open country and paddled through paddy fields until late in the afternoon. So far it had been an agonising and perilous journey. They stumbled along with their heads lolling from side to side like rag dolls, relying on self-sufficiency and luck. Their sight blurred and bodies debilitated, oblivious to the location and conscious only of their failing strength. As the rain continuously poured down, their progress became sluggish and excruciating. Only then did they realise their big mistake in trying to cross this immense forest range and mountains without the help of guides.

They finally accepted that in a head-to-head confrontation with the jungle, the jungle would always win. They walked briskly, constantly looking back, staring at shadows and listening for strange sounds. Here there was no human settlement in the rain-soaked wilderness, so now completely exhausted and badly in need of some sleep, they collapsed in a thicket. They were so weary and far too tired to even build a shelter. After eating what little food they had left, they slipped into a dead sleep, feeling safe for the moment. It wasn't the escapism they thought it was, just a different set of prison bars beneath the cold unfriendly stars.

The morning dawned grey and gloomy, giant clouds rising on all sides like the smoke from remote chimneys. Uncle Leo stirred from under the dark canopy and woke with a hideous scream, which sounded like a rumble from hell. He leapt to his feet and tore frantically at his shabby torn clothes. His heart jumped into his throat at the sight of his body crawling with swollen black leeches. They were forming crazy patterns in their obscenity with scarcely an inch of skin showing through the blackness. Arty stared at him and was startled by the terror in Uncle Leo's eyes The slimy creatures were embedded deep in his flesh, satiated and bloated with his blood.

'Get them off me quickly,' he screamed, trying to tear them off with his bare hands. Arty immediately lit a small fire, regardless of the imminent danger. Then minutes of agonising frenzy followed as they removed the filthy creatures with burning wood and naked flames, amidst his own screams and smouldering flesh. His entire body convulsed with exhaustion and revulsion, and the smell was inescapable and evoked nightmarish thoughts.

The full significance of these slimy creatures didn't dawn on them, until their frantic movements ruffled the surrounding bushes. To their horror they stumbled across the sordid remains of a solitary traveller, unseen the previous night because of the fading light and adverse conditions. They also discovered that the bloated creatures had covered what was left of him. The extent of the mutilation was indicated by the amount of blood that had been absorbed from his body remains. Huge maggots crawled from open sores and sunken eyes, thick slimy pus flowed from large ulcers. Countless mammoth flies swarmed and buzzed fiercely around the decomposed carcass. Buried just below the surface was also a pair of rotten wooden crutches, which suggested that the unfortunate traveller had been suffering from some form of paralysis or deformity. They now feared that the leeches might have transferred some of the infected blood into my uncle's system. The little medication they had was used to relieve the pain and sterilise some of the infected areas of his body. They remained for another day and night, before resuming their journey.

However, they allowed the storm to pass over their heads with apparent indifference although some words of indecent vocabulary struck their ears in this land where both man and beast might struggle, sometimes even be entombed. They finally reached the outskirts of a village on the Indian border, and as they approached liberation, the misery of the earlier darkness had almost faded from my Uncle's memory. The workers on the collective farms went out to welcome them, many of them on shaggy mules, thus restoring their faith in the human desire to survive. It was the end of an incredible journey and the greetings exchanged between them were pulsating. Uncle Leo spent a number of weeks recovering in the military hospital in Kohima, near the Indian border. There the serenity of a convalescent ward helped him to recover sufficiently to travel. He was discharged along with his friend, and made numerous enquiries through the army and the Red Cross to locate the whereabouts of any relations who had arrived in India. They finally made their way to the Murree Hills in search of solace, family and freedom.

The house was silent when he finished his story, and I tried to remember what he had looked like not so long ago. Now his face was ashen and withdrawn, and he didn't seem to blink, just continued to stare. Mother was a mixture of sadness and comfort, shaking her head in disbelief. I moved away from the table and went to my bedroom, as it was getting late. Then tried to think of the times I had spent with him hunting in the jungle. It was getting late, but there was a comfort in keeping the dark at bay. Yet I dreaded the moments before sleep, when one allowed the imagination to rush in and change clear images to terrifying ones.

Chapter IX

Trying to come to terms with his furnace of affliction, my Uncle Leo settled down to this new environment with some resolution. I could see his aggravation and fear in the deep sadness that lingered in his eyes. He couldn't function normally; there was no pain, just numbness moving slowly past his knees towards his stomach. There was also no magical solution to cure his condition. Each day he dragged his feet along the floor with the help of crutches, trying to keep the muscles exercised. During his leisure moments when he was alone, the room exuded an atmosphere of suppressed tension. His emotions were a mixture of anger and grief, coupled with an undercurrent of misery. He opened up a vein of instability within himself, into which he quickly retreated. I continued with my own personal role of massaging his legs each morning and night with olive oil, rubbing the fluid well into the infected area. Admittedly it was a frail effort with not much chance of success, but I was pleased to perform this task, which was more than just an academic exercise for me. It gave me a sense of satisfaction. Besides Uncle Leo's age-old way of life had to change quickly, and rapid exceptions had to be made. His older brother, Ossie, left to uphold his newly appointed position on the Indian railways, although his main priority was to secure a bed in one of the major hospitals for his younger brother, now that his health appeared to be deteriorating with each new day. However, I admired him for his sheer drive and determination.

Before long the confusion of summer began to wane for all of us living in this unbalanced society. These were the down-to-earth realities. So far we had met the challenges and survived this journey of startling contrasts. With the advent of twilight, the setting sun bathed the campsite and surrounding forest in a flood of deep crimson light. A steady escalation of sleep filled a painful vacuum, but the mournful cry of jackals howling in the jungle penetrated our wooden bungalows.

I had a good reason for waking up the following day, Sunday 30 August – my twelfth birthday had arrived. I woke suddenly, slipped into the bathroom, washed and changed, and followed this by a quick breakfast. There was a normal morning's worship in the small schoolhouse, specially converted each weekend for the holy services. The gathering of families now scattered into little groups, hedging their way home and discussing current rumours that the war was going badly in the Far East for the Allies. Despite the morning heat, a cool breeze wafted across our faces bringing with it the scent of fresh mountain pine, and it was as if we had lost sense of time as our heads went round in the heat. Life in the camp had now settled down to a monotonous routine. We'd completely forgotten our circumstances when the atmosphere suddenly changed. Our ears were alerted by the faraway babble of an approaching band of impatient fellow evacuees, their movements trampling the rough surface and instantly disturbing the serenity to which we had become accustomed.

The camp immediately came alive and buzzed with excitement. It was opening time for the forest; there were more noises and louder rustling of the dry leaves and the sun was dazzling high in the sky. I blinked a few times before shielding my eyes to watch in excitement. Now the grassy stretch of land was carpeted once again by a growing cluster of anxious people. The familiarity, the feeling of routine was already there, a pressure slowly building, an island of sensitivity. I stood on my toes, craning my neck, and my eyes opened with none of their usual reluctance. My mother had joined me and our steps were unsteady; there was an element of caution about us. It was then that we noticed a solitary figure slowly edging his way through the excitable concourse directly to where we were standing. His head turned as he searched for someone in the crowd. I squinted to sharpen my perception. His progress was snail-like; he appeared to be struggling around in a maze, where all the exits were closed, heedless of some mournful cries, moving like a sleepwalker, silent as a shadow. He looked grief-stricken, as if he were holding up one of the great pillars of this vast universe, an assumption we all at sometime or other conformed to.

He smiled wistfully as he approached in our direction, lacking a normal rhythm. His sad eyes blinked in a face mapped with anguish as the sunlight caught shades of grey and white hair hanging in loose strands.

'Gwen,' he said in a thin quavering voice, holding out a frail trembling hand, looking much older than his thirty-one years. He cleared his throat and flushed uncomfortably, his breath coming in short gasps. He opened his mouth to speak, but no words came, only a steady flow of tears from sunken eyes.

My mother stared at him astounded, unable to believe what she saw. Her own expression remained blank and her eyes were swamped with emotion as she continued staring at him. She couldn't speak for a moment, then, whispering slowly, she asked, 'Stan, is it really you?' Her words were choked. He had aged a lifetime since we had last seen him almost five months earlier. He was a hollow shell of a human being, with mournful, fear-struck eyes, which mirrored the terrors within him, like a faded photograph.

'Yes,' he answered, his voice trembling as he lowered his eyes to the ground.

'But where are Eileen and the children?' she asked impatiently.

His face filled with anguish. The grief-stricken silence showed the aching emptiness, and his troubled appearance was hiding a terrible secret. 'I've lost them all, Gwen,' he said in a faltering voice, a hiss with an edge to it. Then he broke down and wept uncontrollably as she put her arms around him. They were tears of admission of a helplessness, which she could feel. His whole body shook, caught unawares by a sudden tiredness, and he tried desperately to assemble his thoughts. For an instant they stared at one another, than held each other again, and for a moment all sound, all movement ceased. Above them the vast empty sky lurked over the Himalayan mountain range, and the forest shimmered in the sultry air. Even the sun was saying a silent goodbye, almost lost behind the trees.

'We'll talk about it later,' Mother said. 'Let's get you inside the house, time to relax and rest, get you well again.'

She held his arms and tried to calm him as they walked. All he could do was shake his head, a few incoherent words emerging from between deep sobs, with a subtle breath disturbing the eerie silence.

Monday morning arrived with a dawn light filtering through the curtains, a bright pleasant last day of August. I gazed out over the grassy stretches and woodland near the main entrance, wondering if that road would ever be busy again. But all was ominously silent inside the bungalow. I had always enjoyed school, but Mother's suggestion that I stayed away for the day brought a pleasant respite. The previous night had been a restless one because sleep wouldn't come easily. I seemed to have lain awake for long periods behind closed lids, questioning my own emotional thoughts. After my breakfast I continued with my usual role as masseur of Uncle Leo's legs, still not understanding its true purpose. Then they all sat in a fearful silence on the verandah away from the glimmering sunlight. I sat on the step and turned away from the small gathering; discipline had cautioned me to sit and listen in frozen reticence. There had to be a perfectly rational explanation for my Uncle Stan to turn up on his own. The latter was silent for quite some time before speaking, his eyes conveying a deep frustration. They filled with a sudden crazy swelling of tears, as though engulfed in a deluge of sad remembrance.

'The world is full of injustice,' he said softly. 'You know there is a line you cross, from which you're never coming back.'

We listened nervously as his voice drifted away and into his eyes crept that distant look which frightened us. For the next few hours he unravelled his pitiful story as we listened. He spoke clearly to begin with, but with a heavy sadness, which only he generated with an occasional stutter. There was something brave about the way he searched his cargo of memory, so we sat silently envisioning in our minds the tragic events.

Several days had elapsed before they considered the options that they had, and like everyone else the fear of being interned by the Japanese became the deciding factor. Rumours of the atrocities were rife and he couldn't subject his family to those elements. He really didn't know where to turn, as at the present time the town was in absolute chaos with huge crowds surging everywhere. Somehow he then persuaded himself that if there was half a chance of getting away then he had to try, so common sense had prevailed after all. Then he said something that I didn't quite understand. 'Although the fundamental source of human weakness is to possess a conscience, and believe me, Gwen, I do have one now. I am the man who always acts according to my sense of duty, now I am the witness to that sad allegiance.' He then went into an angry silence, and I knew that he was thinking seriously about all his family.

They had planned everything meticulously down to the very last detail. With sufficient petrol for the long journey to Myitkyina plus some spare in a container, their determination grew. Uncle Stan was also very informative about the area, and had already been notified by the higher channels that there were numerous flights from that particular airfield. The authorities were catering for families with young children, so, with the bare necessities neatly packed, sufficient food, water and some medical supplies, they decided to leave the following morning. Apparently, as the night rolled on, Aunty Eileen found it extremely difficult to focus on what had been prepared. Deep inside she was beginning to regret the decision. The idea of leaving was as frightening as it was exhilarating.

The next day, after a restless night, they awoke to gleaming sunshine pouring through the bedroom window. They were tired, edgy, and found it difficult to concentrate, but were still full of confidence, although there was a strong pull of despair, knowing that it would be the last day in their own home. Finally they channelled through the atmosphere which was heavy with discomfort, when they stepped through the front door that morning. Deep thoughts were filled with anxiety and emotion, when they realised that the journey was to be more of an event than the destination. It was also going to be very difficult, especially for the children. With her searching glances directed at her husband, seeking an explanation, an imploring look flared in my aunt's frightened eyes, and her face hardened considerably.

'I fear for our safety, Stan,' she said softly, as he gathered the remaining bundles and packed them tightly into the boot of his old Buick.

For a moment he felt sick, but the air smelt of freedom so this dangerous venture was a necessity. 'We have to leave immediately, Eileen, or risk being captured by the Japanese. Surely you must understand what that means,' he replied.

She just hugged herself, with that uncertain look on her face, and nodded. He paused for a moment to study his map once again, then bundled the three eldest children into the back seat of the car.

'There isn't much room in here,' said Peggy, who then shuffled about to get herself comfortable.

'Try and behave yourselves, we won't be too long before we can stop,' he replied persuasively.

Robert, being the youngest, would sit on Aunty Eileen's lap in the passenger seat.

A short silence ensued, only broken by the chirping of Aunty's fantail doves in the aviary, which only upset her further. Across the street, many European civilians were also packing; it was obvious that they wanted to escape as soon as possible. It was now time to move quickly, their journey to the north had begun. He had selected a route out of the town, and would only travel in daylight, although there was a possibility of running into damaged trucks, carts and hysterical civilians. Making several detours would slow down their progress. Already their departure came to a sudden halt, and the children were becoming restless. He then realised that the consequences of his sudden decision could prove fatal.

Although we all sat quietly and listened, Uncle Stan would frequently go into a trance. His voice became a whisper, his face distorted into a grimace of anger and penitence. His eyes shifted slowly from side to side, then finally recoiled into recognition before continuing.

The small car jerked and jolted with its heavy burden, because the main road north was rugged and still carried the reflection of the burning sunlight. It was badly congested, packed with a stream of weary refugees trudging along with the age-old timidity of terrified people. All were searching for any type of airfield. Most of the transport was primitive, bullock carts, cycles, and many were walking with their belongings crammed into prams. Some even had their pets with them.

There were men, women and children of all ages and races driven into a state of mass hysteria, showing a kindred spirit and dogged determination to survive at any price, although many of the elderly were already staggering with exhaustion from the oppressive heat. The problem faced by all of them needed little explaining. High above, dark clouds approached from the horizon, obscuring the last rays of the sun, and a slight breeze ruffled the bushes on the roadside. Whenever possible, Uncle Stan drove hastily, seeing only frightening thoughts parading in a chain before his eyes. In their wake clouds of road dust coiled into the dry atmosphere. With the coming of sundown it became overcast, and very soon the whole sky was clouded to a dark-grey. They stopped by the wayside away from the crowds, and slept in the car near a field that night. With it came faint pictures of not very long ago. There were also signs that the monsoon wasn't too far away, when suddenly a tropical squall fell in torrents. It was the rainy season, and the heavy clouds signalled difficult times ahead. Shifting mud slipped down the hillsides, carrying with it damaged roots, broken branches, dead leaves and bringing most of the human traffic to an instant halt.

Early the next morning after a rushed breakfast of sandwiches and hot coffee from a flask, they continued slowly. Their fears had not included the possibility of travelling cramped and almost airless because of the intense heat in a small car. The journey was made worse by the now dusty crated roads swarming with flies, and the soaring humidity, in a country with an unforgiving nature, an area of violent rivers, rugged mountains, dense jungle and numerous wild animals. It was precarious and foolish to underestimate the hidden menace. When they finally approached some marshalling yards, there were no signboards at the railway station to inform them of their whereabouts. However, the sound of planes suggested that they could be close to the airfield at Myitkyina. Believing that no evil is allowed to last for ever, they continued, and after stopping and starting several times, the exhausting journey came to an abrupt end. There was something macabre ahead of them, a feeling of unreality. Their hearts froze in horror when they approached one of the most crowded places on earth, now awash with thousands of refugees. The atmosphere was heavy with smells, and noisy with the sounds of shrieking and wailing beneath the crumbling trees and burning wrecks. Their plight was so forcibly expressed that their agonised shouts couldn't possibly remain unheard.

The airstrip had been strafed by a squadron of enemy fighters, to ensure the safety of the advancing task force. This brutal act also served to emphasise the awesome realities that lay ahead for the local population. The air reeked with the sickening smell of charred flesh from badly injured animals, which were crawling through the dust and writhing in agony. Here the odour of decomposition was entrenched in the atmosphere, a graphic depiction of mass murder. Much of the transport was either badly damaged or in flames. The situation was intensified by the fact that the aerodrome was being evacuated. Groups of people were shouting and screaming incoherently. The smoke-filled air hung low, making their eyes burn and choking them as they tried to breathe. Many of the refugees had already scattered deep into the jungle and the mountains. The field was alive with an urgent buzz of mixed languages, arguing, abusing, ordering, like a vast flood of human misery prepared to endure the most severe handicaps.

My Aunty and Uncle looked at each other for some time without speaking, and only blank despair flooded their hearts when they were informed that the advancing enemy was approaching the outskirts with devastating swiftness. Some of the weak and injured stayed behind to listen to prayers and encouragement presented by a Catholic priest. If our Creator had listened to their prayers then heaven would have opened up her portals to succour their agonising grief.

There were numerous groups of soldiers, some of whom were badly wounded. All were willing to take their chances against the elements as they also joined the mass exodus. A small group of soldiers led by an officer approached my uncle.

'Where have you come from?' he asked.

'Maymyo,' Uncle Stan replied anxiously as he stepped from the car, suddenly feeling the heavy jungle air cloak around his body. 'I'm hoping to catch a flight to India with my family,' he said, angling for a favourable answer in this remoteness.

'Sorry, but there are definitely no more planes. You would be better off returning home, the enemy are only a few miles away,' the officer replied impatiently, and deep in his eyes lurked sheer desperation.

Uncle Stan shook his head in disbelief, but decided it would be safer to turn back quickly, fearing that a careless catalogue of events would continue way beyond his personal control.

They passed through many small villages, where the dusty roads were littered with dead and practically every dwelling was deserted, before they finally arrived at a town called Bhamo. Here the main road was also blocked with refugees, peasants, and farm workers carrying some of their tools. All of them were heading away from the enemy advancing from the north, and from those forces that had landed in the southern regions and were now on the outskirts of Mandalay. With their petrol running low, the journey ended and the intensity of hopelessness spread across their weary faces, Uncle Stan immediately hired an elderly Kachin guide, and headed west for the Indian border in company with hundreds of others. After a few miles their eagerness soon faded, as they consciously reduced the distance between home and the formidable terrain ahead. They were already exhausted from the lack of sufficient sleep and the endless tiring journey. After an hour on the trail they decided to stop near a huge expanse of open fertile farmland. The night was surprisingly cold after the heat of the day, so they doubly welcomed the warmth of a blazing fire. Here myriad mosquitoes buzzed near the smouldering flames and the fire crackled, shattering the stillness of the friendly night. After an enjoyable meal the light faded appreciably by the minute, and everyone settled down for a peaceful night around the burning embers. As the twilight fell, the refuge appeared more frightening.

The sun topped the faraway jungle and the portrait of an ancestral dawn stared down on them, although it was still quite early. After another hurried breakfast, the guide then led them into the dense forest along wild boar tracks, then up and down hills, which were bold and impressive, and where most of the area was thickly covered with thorny undergrowth. By now some of the groups were already getting separated and the families with small children were soon falling behind through exhaustion. The intense heat was beginning to sap what little energy they had. After an incredible week, the family appeared to have lost all sense of reality, and soon became detached from the main party. Now Uncle Stan found himself practising lines for future conversations with the family, and reciting rhetorical chants, for his figuring had to be precise and his timing faultless if his family were to survive. He could feel the fear, anger and despair pounding through his body like an erupting volcano. Soon the excruciating heat was intolerable, it felt as if the branches of the trees only served as conductors of the heat. Now the dark forests impeded their sluggish progress as they moved cautiously through the trees, on a path, which twisted and turned its way over a series of wooded ridges, then began to descend towards flatter country. They had to cross numerous paddy fields and barricades of vegetation, then continued down the sides of grassy hills. Here, they were eyed by some scattered cattle busy chewing the cud, considering whether to slink over for a closer look, but deciding to bend down and eat more fresh grass. Because of this unexpected encounter, the guide suggested that there had to be a village or settlement close by. Far ahead was a patchwork of shade and light, as they finally arrived on the banks of the frightening Irrawaddy River sparkling in the sunshine. There was no mistaking it as they approached. Uncle Stan could see the curve of the fierce current, glistening between the banks of tropical forest.

Here the sunshine dappled the reeds near a tiny fishing village on the valley floor. There were a few huts perched on the river's edge surrounded by dense undergrowth, but the air was hot, humid and moisture-laden. Suddenly a strong feeling of doubt crossed Uncle Stan's face. He suspected that he'd been wrong to bring the family there that day. However, this doubt had long been repressed, and now he felt for the most part a fusion of irritation and anxiety. Unfortunately, it was now the monsoon season and with it came the rain, one single drop then a torrential downpour, when everyone scattered back and forth like insects in search of shelter, but the huge banana leaves made useful umbrellas. With the incessant rain, the wind rose and died, then rose again, blowing stronger, tossing the tops of the giant trees. In this area the temperate climate was perfect for growing vegetables and fruit. They walked languorously towards the village; they were badly in need of some rest, and also hoped to purchase some dry fish, rice, fruit and fresh greens. Although they were all overcome with fatigue, the very thought of sleeping under cover for that night was an added pleasure. It also provided them with a certain degree of comfort despite the danger in their wake. Here they met up with two other families who were travelling together and were encouraged by their enthusiasm. They were very friendly and helpful, and suggested that they pool some of their resources to secure the use of the *sampan,* which was available, for the river crossing. It was an enormous relief to be moving away from the conflict, and they remained totally absorbed in this belief.

It had already been dark for some time when they sat down near the small fire they had kindled. It was burning brightly and produced a wonderful source of heat and comfort while they enjoyed a full meal. The night was clear and cold and the sky covered with flashing stars, and for the present, time appeared to be standing still. Now they were exhausted and their heads were spinning with the vastness of the jungle, as the night closed in completely. They finally collapsed onto the thick matted floor inside the thatched hut, too stimulated to fall asleep. In these moments of loneliness Uncle Stan could feel the tension increasing, his heart pounding and the pressure building up inside him. They lay awake, replaying the past few days over and over in their thoughts, finally dropping off, waking occasionally from a series of short patches of slumber, only to find that it was still dark.

With the breaking of dawn, the sun glinted on the valley and an early meal was greatly appreciated by everyone. The journey across the river was almost one thousand yards of raging muddy water and they were waiting for the slight drizzle to ease. By noon the rain had ceased, so after a hot meal, which produced a sense of well-being, they decided to continue with their journey, even though crossing successfully wouldn't bring an end to all their problems. When they were all aboard they were barely a couple of inches clear of the water's surface. The guide rowed them slowly across, and the men changed places and took turns in this arduous task. Occasionally the bottom was awash with dirty water, which had to be baled out, making the journey seem endless. A flicker of interest came into Uncle Stan's eyes, when he crawled to the bow of the unsteady craft. He could feel it plunge up and down in the curl of grey water as he tried to gather his senses, staring at the long dirty swell chucking up spray into his face. He did not think consciously of anything; his brain was so confused and felt stretched like the river itself. He kept questioning himself, wondering if his judgement had been correct and fearing that judgements made in the heat of emotional reactions were rarely sound.

He crouched in this relative shelter, observing the forest itself through the branches of the leafless trees, while most of the children lay motionless in the bottom of the boat. For them nothing appeared really serious, as the sun went on shining. At this moment there was no national emergency, and if there were any danger, it would come from enemy gunboats patrolling the river. The idea of death troubled him and suddenly he felt a little afraid. In search of freedom they were being forced into this nomadic lifestyle. Finally they collided with the opposite bank and the tiny craft scraped the sandy bottom, clinging tenaciously to the contours of the vast river. High above the forest, a veil of mist hovered like a false ceiling. The one thing on his mind was to keep going, so they left the boat and the awesome river behind them and trudged relentlessly on as their shrunken stomachs began to protest angrily. It was well past noon and the temperature was rising. The only vegetation was thorny shrub and tall cogon grass, and small lizards and insects scurried from the sunshine into the shadier areas. As the late evening approached, with it came the incessant rain once more, erupting in a white savagery and running in torrents across the rugged tracks. Very soon sleep, that gifted alleviator of aches, pains, and fears, beckoned like whispers from the grave. They took refuge in a banana plantation, where the huge leaves offered some shelter and protection from the howling wind that blew with ferocity in this unfriendly environment.

They stirred to a clear crisp morning and perfect weather conditions; even the low clouds had vanished, leaving a blue ethereal sky. They travelled along dry dusty roads covered with brush and deeply rutted cart tracks. All day they journeyed tirelessly through swamps and thick secondary jungle, occasionally stopping for something to eat. Frequently they strayed into the side pastures for a well-earned rest, but there was no sign of human life. Here the horrors that had been predicted were soon borne out. There were numerous dead bodies lying in ditches. Some had obviously been searching for shelter in the aching emptiness, others for a quiet rest in the uneven tracks. Unfortunately, hunger and exhaustion had finally extinguished their sorrowful lives. They eventually came to the top of a small hill, devoid of any kind of refuge and without fences to mark the roadway. However, there was one, on which an endless stream of humanity was slipping, falling, dragging one another to their feet again. Their leg muscles were taut with the strain and tension. It was a chaos of spirit and physical torture, on ground that was rough and irregular as the road wound round eroded with deep clefts.

The sun climbed high in the sky and finally the heat began to tell on their aching bodies. They halted at dusk, feeling that they had pushed themselves beyond the limits of their failing strength. After a light meal of fish and boiled rice, they settled down for another night as the warm sun set behind the mountain range. They wrapped their aching bodies up in blankets and kept warm beside a small fire. Now the war was momentarily forgotten and thoughts of trails ahead shut out of their tired minds. It was a beautiful spot for quiet meditation as the moonlit night shoved storm clouds scudding away to the east. They fell silent as the dusk circled above and watched as it engulfed them with the respect that it enforced on simple people. Dawn was breaking and the eastern sky was bright, yet suddenly the temperature rose steadily, but this respite could not last for long. They struggled on with the sheer agonising torture of no breaks, through patches of marshland and stands of trees. There was no sign of the human life they thought they had seen from yesterday's hilltop, only the pleasant sound of birds chirruping amongst the branches of the dark green mango trees rising here and there.

For almost three weeks they had struggled with anxiety,

apprehension and despair, but continued with this fetish journey through tangled foliage and swamp-infested marshland. Here the danger of giant tiger leeches clinging to their aching bodies was a constant threat. Even the trees had grown to an enormous height, looking magnificent as they towered above them, melting into the inky gloom. It was then that, although he could hardly bear to recognise it, he noticed that Peggy appeared to be in some kind of discomfort. She had been complaining of agonising pains in her stomach and was continually vomiting. Now he immediately recognised the warning signs, and from the glazed look in her eyes waves of conflicting emotions swept through him. Guilt and horror, but fear was the most powerful. Suddenly a sense of despair and misery filtered through his anxious mind and his heart ached as the heavy burden of sorrow anchored his thoughts. She had lost the compulsion to eat properly, her body had taken on that wasted look. There was a fragility and constriction about her that stretched his anxiety to the threshold of despondency.

It would soon be dark again when the jungle would come alive, with countless mosquitoes droning in their ears, biting at their hands and faces. He quickly bedded Peggy down for an early night, and cosily wrapped her in a blanket close to the fire that he had lit. The heat of the burning bamboo was intense and would soon banish away the cold and remove the darkness, damp and degradation, ingredients that would destroy. Not much could be seen in the gloom, but faint shadows thrashed about against the backdrop. Some were huge and jagged, but he was indulging in feverish imagination. This period had marked their third week of travelling and the strain was beginning to tell. Although feeling completely exhausted, the children settled down to enjoy a light meal. He knelt down close to Peggy and gently wiped her forehead with some cool water, caressing her hair and spoke softly to her.

'How are you feeling, Peg?' he asked quietly.

'My head and stomach hurt terribly, Dad,' she replied nervously. It was a frail effort, her voice was weak and the expressions on her fragile face was swift testimony of tremendous pain.

'I know, love, just drink this. It will help to settle you down.'

Gently he held her head while feeding her some Milk of Magnesia from a spoon.

She sipped it slowly and gravely. Her eyes drifted towards her mum, whose face betrayed a poignant look, and her eyes carried that same blank intensity behind a thin film of tears.

'Go to sleep, my baby, you'll feel a lot better in the morning,' she whispered, then gently kissed her on her forehead, praying silently to herself through a swollen throat and burning eyes. Deep inside she was still fearing the worst as Peggy seemed to drift into a torpor. Then she slowly opened her eyes and saw her father again, but couldn't speak. The intensity of her expression crippled him, for in his heart he knew that he needed help and medicine urgently. Failing this, he would soon lose his eldest daughter, and the sinister blanket of failure swept through his tortured mind.

Very soon the horizon faded into the infinite desolation of a darkening sky, and the evening fell rapidly across the hills. Now the moon was a ball of orange light, ducking behind the ridges as quickly as it had risen and they were enveloped in total darkness. They all knelt and said prayers amid heavy sobs, believing that one can find God anywhere if you need him. For Uncle Stan and Aunty Eileen sleep would never come, as an early-rising sun climbed high in the sky. Now the thick swirling mists that surrounded the impenetrable jungle blended with the blue smoke that eddied around the fire. They also knew that because of Peg's premature birth, she had always been susceptible to any illness. He was now faced with a serious problem as her condition worsened. Her pulse had grown weaker and the soft eyes sunk back in her pallid face were now streaming with tears. The ever-present fever had started to destroy her body's thermostat and was causing rapid dehydration. Her bowels were seriously infected and she was losing a fair amount of blood with the constant diarrhoea. For the moment any further progress was certainly out of the question. He immediately sent the guide on in front in search of the nearest village, using an old disused tiger track. Although it was rugged, narrow and thickly overgrown, it would definitely reduce any available route by a few miles.

'If only I could get hold of some sour milk,' he whispered.

Aunty Eileen didn't reply, feeling stifled by her own incompetence.

'It would help to tighten her watery bowels, then she may have a chance,' he continued. But they both knew how slender those hopes were in this wilderness. She just sat there, stroking Peggy's cheeks tenderly, without saying a word. 'I know what you are thinking, love,' he said, placing a gentle arm around her shoulder.

'What?' she replied, choking back the tears in a voice that was almost a whisper.

'That we should never have attempted this senseless journey,' he replied, secretly having second thoughts about it himself.

'You're perfectly correct,' she said angrily, but with compassion. 'We should have stayed behind in Maymyo with Irene and her family. Now it's too late.' Her comment, however truthful, was received in silence, and behind the mask of assurance he believed that she was probably right. They waited patiently with quiet thoughts, tears and silent anger for the guide's long overdue return in the jungle gloom. There were no clouds and the moon was just rising, sitting perched against the edge of the horizon. A brilliant infinity of stars hung in the blackness of the sky. Even the trees seemed close together as myriad fireflies twinkled around the fire's glow. They prayed and kept a constant vigil but no deliverance from above came to their aid. Finally, Peggy drifted into a coma, the passing hours seemed an eternity as the tears flowed unrestrained down anguished faces. Suddenly a weird and unwelcome silence descended upon all of them. She never regained consciousness and silently the tool of suffering vanished. Painfully, the only sound left was a cry of protest and the weeping of her distraught loved ones.

Soon the atmosphere of panic thickened, for there were always the children, their small features staring and hating without comprehension, looking for comfort and explanations with a sense of horror. The night felt strange as they silently mourned their terrible loss with an impenetrable sorrow, and still haunted by their own thoughts and fears. They stayed awake for a while and, with reddened eyes and drawn faces, talked mildly about life, moments they had shared at picnics, the long walks picking wild flowers around the lake and paddling in hidden streams near Arnisakan Falls, trying desperately to seek any conceivable source of comfort to ease their dreadful pain. The children cried incessantly, huge gulping sobs of grief; none of them were impervious to suffering. They stared sadly at their sister who was about to leave them and finding it very difficult to imagine life without her anymore.

The cool shadows of the night passed and the hazards of daylight greeted them with a blaze.

'I wish we'd never come, Stan, honest,' Aunty Eileen said, her voice was deep and sad.

He returned her gaze before answering darkly, 'So do I.' His tone was more venomous than usual. Now he was perfectly aware of the thankless task ahead; any thoughts of the future filled him with dread for a moment. He was so reduced by his ordeal that he felt weak as he started furrowing a grave in the rough earth. He began by angrily pulling out all the grass and lumps of soil with his bare hands. Although the soil was soft and damp it was difficult, and it also needed enormous concentration just to perform this painful task. Finally, with the help of a broken tree branch, he ploughed a deep enough crevice. Time passed slowly as they watched; the tears and sweat blended with sorrow slipped down his cheeks in an endless flow into the empty orifice. Her small frame looked deathly ashen in the pale light, as he cosily wrapped her up. They watched nervously at what looked like an enormous parcel held closely in his arms, a blanket holding together something that resembled a small human form. Numb with grief he buried her with some fortitude, and left her sleeping peacefully in her final resting place. Now a small mound, a little bamboo cross and unforgettable memories would be the only memorial under this vast, faceless curtain.

He sat, deep in concentration, tense, nervous and feeling as if a heavy burden had been placed upon him. Now the pain was unbearable; he closed his eyes, fighting off the horror that gripped him. His mind was caught up in his own nightmare in a series of deranged tangled images, and the loud roaring in his brain drowned his inner thoughts. His wife and the children seemed to cry out for spiritual solace, when they continued with this perilous journey. Descending north-west through a maze of butes and gullies, maintaining their stubborn silence with an expression of deep sorrow and puzzlement.

At this moment Mother was far too distressed to listen any more, feeling under siege herself, and moved briskly to her bedroom. The rest of us remained silent. I glanced across to where he was sitting, speechless for a moment, his eyes glistening with unshed tears as a terrible sadness played across his face. I watched as he visibly shook himself free from the tension that was choking him. 'I need to go and lay down for a while,' he said with a sad smile. 'I never really thought that I would get through all this alive,' he murmured very softly as he left the room, now surrounded by an unnatural stillness.

The following day after a quiet breakfast, we sat subdued and listened once again to Uncle Stan's tragic story. I think we were all expecting worse to follow. He paused for a moment and cleared his throat before speaking, as if the ebb of life was pouring all over him. Panic and despair surfaced on his features when he continued.

The sun rose quickly that morning and the dry jungle was breathless. After a hasty meal they carried on through this difficult country along a dusty track. They halted frequently, there seemed so much to think about and events far too grim to contemplate. However, he refused to grapple with them and returned to immediate decisions. They trudged through tall grass and sudden streams; occasionally there were moans of protest from the children but they had to press on. As the day advanced, the land yielded no moisture at all, even the sun mounted and shed no merciful light but a relentless glare on their aching bodies. Finally, a period of relaxation was certainly well overdue; it was time to rest and consume some food and drink, a necessity particularly for the children. They were already feeling aggravated and extremely tired; the cuts and bruises on their arms and legs were causing considerable discomfort and agonising pain.

The sunshine of a few moments before soon grew pale and a cool breeze blew like a present from heaven as they emerged from the jungle. The countryside suddenly took shape on the outskirts of another village in the distance. Immense trees stretched high in the sky, forming a canopy that excluded the sun, except in the clearings where its rays pierced like sunbeams through a sheet of mist. The children had been bitten by various insects and now were so tired; this was the perfect spot to settle down.

Uncle Stan went about the usual business of lighting a small fire, and watched the thin streams of blue smoke rising through the air. Now thoughts of their recent loss nagged in his brain, creating an encirclement of uncertainty. Anxious moments passed as they swallowed portions of boiled rice, meat and some fruit, then snuggled together in the depths of their lairs, in the flickering light of an open fire, which burned furiously for added warmth. The moon was hidden by the clouds, but some light glared through the bare branches and the fields glistened in the darkness as an eerie stillness settled on the night. The two little boys were soon curled up asleep, leaving no fraction of themselves uncovered. Poor Peta was still mourning the loss of her sister. She needed consoling and sat between them for some much-needed affection, occasionally shivering from anxiety and shedding the odd tear. For a change, the night was mild and undisturbed, as wisps of cloud floated across and drifted down the valley, leaving the moon hanging majestically in the sky. Uncle Stan glanced across at Aunty Eileen, who was still in a state of despair.

'Stan, let's go back home right now,' she said in a voice full of supplication.

He couldn't believe what he was hearing and stared into the fire, adjusting some of the ashes that had fallen down. The sparks jumped and spluttered in the darkness before he answered her.

'If we go back, Eileen, then our Peg died for nothing. Is that what you want on your conscience?'

She covered her face with her hands and sobbed, fully understanding what he meant. 'I just feel awful leaving her here all alone in this wilderness,' she said feebly, holding her hands as if in prayer.

'She isn't alone, the angels are protecting her,' he replied with an air of assurance.

'Then let's leave as soon as possible, Stan, while it's safe and the children still have the energy,' she suggested quickly and in a quiet voice, so as not to disturb them.

He listened carefully without saying a word, feeling relaxed at her anxious proposal. Then he agreed to an early start in the morning, knowing that they had no alternative if they wanted to remain alive, although deep in his heart he knew that they all might perish. He hugged that secret to himself.

The temperature had risen a little, so he decided to stoke up the fire with numerous damp logs in order to maintain an all night warmth, and to distract any intending predator. This was an habitual ploy used by everyone for added safety. He gazed wide-eyed into the fire glow, feeling engulfed with sad memories and a mixed cargo of emotions. It had turned into a cold uncompromising night when all the stars gleamed down relentlessly and bathed them in a cold white vapour. He gradually sank into a welcome sleep. It was still dark when they awoke the following morning, shivering because of the heavy overnight dew that had fallen, but he decided to make an early start.

The next few days were a nightmare as they wandered through the jungle completely lost, and soaked by the frequent showers. The journey had become hazardous to the soul, the human spirit against the elements. There was a feeling of increasing unease as their food stocks ran low. Now they were surviving on a regular diet of dug-up roots, washing them in rainwater that had collected in some of the plants. This was a harsh provision for survival in the menacing forest. There was also very little fresh water, except in the irrigation troughs and some scattered water beds. The wooded area very soon became thicker with the tall trees arching overhead, the forest canopy concealing the sunlight. Soon the humidity added to their discomfort and the sweat burst through their pores with a positive violence.

The bamboo forests appeared to cling in dense folds along the ranges, like quills on a porcupine's back. Although the air up there was much cooler, allowing them to breathe more freely, the signs of weariness were soon recognised as the children stumbled to the ground.

Very soon the hours seemed much longer, and even the days appeared to lengthen. They had walked for the full day and saw nothing, no tigers, no monkeys and no snakes. Their mouths were dry, with the occasional dust cloud blowing in their faces. The children were not in a talkative mood, strutting with annoyance and tiredness. They progressed slowly, then stopped when the sun was high. There certainly was no beauty or simplicity about this journey. Then they reached the bottom of a valley where a stream ran swiftly between rugged rocks and large boulders, flanked by huge trees on each side and row upon row of purple hills stretching as far as the eye could see. There was nothing to see but the horizon for miles, leaving the view desolate and empty. The view disappeared, and the heat of the sun was replaced by the cool shade of the giant trees.

Venturing deep into the undergrowth in search of a clearing and a much-needed rest, they descended steadily as seemingly mile after mile slipped past. Then, in a moment of hasty judgement and with no apparent thought of any immediate danger, Uncle Stan casually stepped on something that moved vigorously amongst the bushes and completely lost his balance. His boot seemed to get caught in a jungle root that surfaced underfoot and then dipped back into the dank earth. Within seconds he was firmly embracing wet vegetation and peering into hidden darkness. Young Robert, who had been thoroughly enjoying the comfort of a shoulder ride, suddenly found himself being hurtled through the air like a rag doll, pawing frantically at vacant spaces. He hit the floor hard, bounced a couple of times, before coming to a stop on the green rough between shrubs and low bushes. He lay for a few seconds before pulling himself up onto his knees, then ran to his mother with anguish spread all over his face. Fortunately he wasn't hurt.

When Uncle Stan finally recovered his stance, the silence was oppressive and the air smelt of rotten leaves and damp vegetation. He was horrified at being swiftly eyeballed by a banded krait, which rose threateningly in front of his gaze. He watched it closely, knowing that he had no effective defence against this formidable reptile. Past experience had taught him to respect, and keep some considerable distance from such creatures. They were venomous and their bite was lethal. He tried desperately not to break the silence, not moving or speaking during this gruesome encounter. His eyes were glazed with intensity, and his features hardened with an expression of simulated anger. Life and death were now locked in a hideous embrace. He had to keep calm, taking in long slow gasps of air, and control his panic. The future looked black and the miracle, which a few weeks ago might have saved them, seemed much less possible now with this threat.

A lump formed like a gloved fist in his throat, and his heart began to palpitate. The blood gushed around inside him incessantly, and fear drained his mind. His insides froze and his quivering frame was soaked with terror as he crouched low in the semi-darkness, breathing heavily and feeling all alone in this alien situation. He wanted to scream for help, and had to fight hard to exercise self-discipline so as not to provoke providence. The dance of death continued in grotesque silence, in this frantic hellhole. He watched with terrified fascination as hideous death scrutinised him with its flashing forked tongue. 'Stay calm,' a voice whispered urgently in his head. Now his body began to pulsate rapidly, and his insides cried with unbearable agony. He faced the final eruption of an approaching macabre and agonising death. Suddenly, in one deft movement, the glistening reptile just slithered away into the deep undergrowth. Uncle Stan emerged, stumbling and breathless from physical discomfort and masked all over in dry brush. Then he swallowed hard, never having envisaged being so close to a certain death by a concealed menace.

Aunty Eileen, after going through the emotions of fear, unravelled her own thoughts and rushed forward to help.

'You look terrible,' she remarked, as she offered him her outstretched hand for support. The silky skin on her forehead wrinkled in a deep frown, when he reached out and grasped the hand tightly.

'There was a bloody krait in those bushes; he was so close I could almost stroke his head,' he bawled, feeling very upset and terribly shaken. 'I was absolutely terrified and really thought that my days were numbered. Can you imagine the situation that you would have been in, and the problems you would have had to face, without me?' he said anxiously, then placed a reassuring arm around her shoulder to confirm his deep concern.

'It sounds so ridiculous, you are joking, aren't you, Stan?' she said with a look of uncertainty.

'I'm telling you the truth, dear. It was a banded krait. I've seen them before. Anyway, I certainly wouldn't joke about anything like that,' he replied, trying to regain his breath, as his heart pounded and the blood throbbed in his temples.

'Are you sure that you're all right and you haven't been bitten?' she asked, still feeling a little shocked.

'I'm fine now it's all over. I was lucky, thank God.'

Despite the absurdity of it all a smile surfaced on her tired features, and she felt refreshed under the balanced warmth of the sun. With all the trials and tribulations, they nestled beneath an umbrella of branches for a rest and some food. Then they continued walking over the primitive track that lay ahead. Since their guide hadn't returned, all they had was an old map which Uncle Stan consulted from time to time with enormous difficulty, searching for villages which were few and far between. The air was still fairly warm and the ground dry, so they walked all day, struggling to keep awake despite the twists and turns. Trying to conserve what little energy they had, they manoeuvred according to circumstances with their limited resources. In the soaked stillness of the air came the occasional plangent and fluty bird notes. These were pleasant sounds to their aching ears.

Now approaching their sixth week, they miserably battled on over the hills, through the swamps, and across open stretches of land. Conscious only of their aching limbs and rapidly failing strength, now exhaustion was threatening to overwhelm them again. They entered a shallow ravine and were taken by surprise, when they suddenly stumbled into a tiny village. There was nothing to indicate its whereabouts on the badly crumpled map. It was a warm, hazy, quiet afternoon and no breeze stirred the thatched roofs of the huts. Their location offered a beautiful view of the countryside, which plunged down to a distant river. The villagers were enjoying their afternoon siesta in the shade away from the midday sun. Suddenly a solitary figure emerged from the shadows and made them welcome to shelter inside the compound. The fragrance from the garland of sweet corn reminded them of their rumbling bellies. Almost immediately they were provided with food, a variety of sweetmeats, plump crab apples and some peaches. The fresh bread was dry and crumbly which immediately provoked a longing for a drink.

Here there was a chance to lie on the grass and grab a quick nap. The children had behaved impeccably and were now resting. Although the day was at its hottest, the heat unbearable and the numerous flies persistent, it was impossible to try to keep awake. Uncle Stan asked the headman if it were possible to stay the night in this well-sheltered glade. With the vision of sound sleep, the world would seem less like a minefield under the vast empty sky above. The hills lurked in the distance, but he could actually hear the gentle breeze rustling in the branches of the nearby trees. Besides, it was a pleasure to be in the company of some friendly villagers, and they found it peaceful and serene. But in the misty void Uncle Stan tossed and turned, his mind still in turmoil. Behind closed lids, images of Peggy danced in front of him and happier times flashed through his thoughts as he smiled to himself in memory. Then the pretty pictures faded, for there were single moments in life which were final. It was late in the afternoon and the evening shadows lengthened with the sinking of the sun. Shortly afterwards total darkness engulfed them as the temperature fell sharply. The conversation was about whether they could survive in an area they didn't know at all, especially now that weariness had taken a stranglehold on their limbs. Suddenly the night was filled with the sound of crickets, a vast mindless machine grinding without end, but sleep wasn't long in coming near the cosiness of the open fire. Very soon the safety of the darkness gave way to the hazards of the dawn, and a hard cloudless sky.

First they made a cautious assessment, then after the refreshments and feeling boosted from their well-deserved rest, they rolled up the blankets and clothes in a groundsheet ready for the next stage. They left the village and trod through heavily wooded country until late in the afternoon. They emerged onto open scrubland, then snaked across till they arrived into the country late in the afternoon, although their progress had been snail-like amid such serenity. It would have been foolish to have taken it all for granted. In due course, the evening shadows soon crept over them once more and it was time for an early rest. The night was far from clear, only the ghostly starlight illuminated the silhouettes of the hills and valleys along their route. Then the family repeated the same procedure for protection from the cold with a cosy fire to bed down next to. The meal was the same rice and beans, although the little white bread did relieve the repetitive diet. They spent the night under a giant tamarind tree, where the dark canopy overhead afforded no glimpse of the heavens. The deep jungle filled them with dread, but the glow from the fire and a thick carpet of dead leaves covering the ground did offer some comfort. Uncle Stan also knew that many animals welcomed the coming of night; when the last gleam had faded they were the scavengers.

With the early morning sunrise, their hunger satisfied, they moved on once again, through clumps of bamboo and other bushes, interspersed with open glades. They still openly questioned the futility of this absurd and dangerous journey. Uncle Stan found it almost impossible to keep his mind on the erratic rhythms of his heartbeat, but forced himself to concentrate on those nearest to him. The children were now wearing an array of torn and tattered clothing, which only added to their strange appearance, and they continued to question his decision. As they climbed higher and higher, the air grew crisp and tangy with mountain freshness, so they followed the road that curved and twisted around hairpin bends. On one side the ground fell away straight down into the valley below, and on the other it rose cliff-like until it was lost in the jungle-covered peaks high above. The wind gusted up clouds of dust, which obliterated the path. They were thicker than fog, and irritated their eyes and made their throats sore. At least they had a reprieve from the increasing humidity, as they descended sharply from the mountain peaks into this tropical jungle.

The heat was relentless from morning until dusk, and the narrow track looked like a white ribbon, spiralling through parched fields, which were divided by cactus hedges several feet high and almost impenetrable in depth. They trudged on for hours and even the hills on the horizon appeared to remain the same distance away from them. They crossed small streams, rocky terrain and paddy fields, occasionally listening to the rumbles of emptiness from their stomachs. The sweat coursed down their tired faces, carving furrows in the dirt. The aim to reach a village was stubbornly pursued, even at a cost of maximum endurance and suffering, so they hastened along, for deep in Uncle Stan's thoughts were images of wild animals.

Even though the sun was high, and although they were shaded in the jungle, the searing heat was unbearable. The steaming enervating warmth only increased their thirst and fatigue, and now food seemed less important than the need for fresh water. Here the rugged paths were littered with wrecks and numerous unmarked shrines to those who had perished, a final tribute to their courageous effort. Thousands choked the main cart tracks to India, toiling in an endless stream, but many would die from one cause or another. Somehow they pressed on hopefully with their sparse belongings, for the spirit of the refugees could not be broken. Their faces showed the signs of strain on haggard features. Adding to this physical exertion was the persistent thoughts that the enemy themselves were closing in behind them. There was also the danger of bands of marauders, still roaming and looting where they could, lying in wait to rob and murder helpless civilians.

With the assistance of another agreeable guide, Uncle Stan decided to leave the main group, believing that a small party would appear less conspicuous and progress more rapidly, although the presence of the forest and dense undergrowth could often be misleading. When the darkness came, they would use the secondary roads, keeping well away from the sight of towns, trudging through the cane and paddy fields, and some small vegetable farms, which would not attract attention. Further on, a stream flowed fast and deep between the high banks of spongy mud. They continued across the thickly forested valley, along a rough disused footpath, which led them to some bushes. They looked carefully around to see if anyone was following, then sat on the warm earth. The only noise was the ripple of the river close to them. After resting for awhile they continued, then suddenly Uncle Stan felt a surge of jubilation when he caught sight of a fishing village, rising like a mirage above the water. He was half convinced that he actually heard voices more ancient than his own, whispering in a language, which he seemed dimly to remember. However, the journey was taking its toll, especially on the children.

Eventually they arrived at the picturesque little site, surrounded by lush vegetable fields and thankfully with no evidence of previous Japanese occupation. They camped on the banks in an oasis of palm trees, and by the time darkness fell, pangs of hunger had manifested themselves. For a short while they huddled together against the stifling breeze, as the blue smoke puffed from the fire. Their hunger disappearing with a bowl of curried fish and rice. This was followed by the comfort of a good night's rest and some moments of supreme ecstasy. Suddenly the moon was swallowed up and low clouds were blown over the mountain tops. These were moments of peace following their recent loss, in which they tried desperately to regain some of their sanity, but it was not possible. There was always the awareness of danger and their own limitations.

It had been a chilly night, and there was a heavy dew on the blankets. It was cold and damp, with the smell of stale air. With the assault of the friendly dawn and a hurried breakfast, they wrapped up their few articles and resumed their journey westwards towards freedom and safety. The chosen route lay across a country of deep-ploughed earth, near swamps laden with water buffalo, and consisted of uneven ground, which carved its way through forbidding ranges, usually patched with villainous-looking cacti, clumps of tall reeds and dense bamboo grass, which spread across like the bars of a cage.

The rest of the day was pleasant as they approached a lush green valley, and a gentle breeze stirred in the trees, which reached down to the edge of the mighty Chindwin River as it meanders on, the banks sloping fairly evenly towards the river on each side of the low green hills. Summer was well under way in this pretty, hilly countryside, as the river swung round in an exhilarating steady swoop, akin to a yellow surge storming the willow-like rushes along the banks. Now there was excitement, tension, elation and triumph but always tempered with caution at the danger all around. As they entered what they imagined was a village, the headman came forward to greet them, his hands folded together as if in prayer, and his head bowed gently. He smiled and welcomed their intrusion with open arms, then advertised his presence with an ecstatic wave of friendship. Soon everyone gathered in a procession, with a thunder of applause. Numerous figures of Burmese monks, draped in their saffron-coloured robes, paraded majestically in the vicinity of a beautiful pagoda, the top capped by a crown of tinkling bells, which sounded delicate in the passing breeze. They were in the grounds of a huge monastery that nestled against the banks of the river, bursting with cosmopolitan charm and historic vibrancy. The leaf tapestry gave an electrifying effect, as the reflections oscillated on the water's surface against the rays of the sun.

After the long tiring journey they settled down for the night in one of the huts, and enjoyed the pleasures of cooking a hot meal. The thought of lying under cover on a dry floor raised their spirits remarkably. With their tummies full, the children were soon asleep, so the adults enjoyed playing a game of cards under the light of an oil lamp, trying desperately to get used to this strange mode of existence. Both of them believed that under the tattered clothing human shells were managing to survive and maintain their sanity and reminded themselves that a journey like this never lost its age they were all travellers.

'What's going to happen to us, Stan?' she whispered quietly, so as not to disturb the children.

'We'll be all right tomorrow, once we have crossed the Chindwin River, especially now that we've had plenty of fresh food and drink,' he replied calmly. 'Let's get a good night's rest and pray for guidance.' Then he kissed her gently on the cheek.

Suddenly there was silence in the little hut as their eyes sought the rafted floor. Night fell rapidly and the moonlight faded into darkness, the flames from the fire being the only light that shone as they sank into an inert state of relaxation. Within minutes their much-needed sleep was invaded by the sound of relentless screaming outside. The peace and quiet had been shattered by someone who had burst breathlessly into one of the other huts. Then the screaming stopped and there was silence again. Then came a chorus of male voices. They were frightened, shouting at each other with homicidal emotion, a great human buzzing. Now Uncle Stan feared that something was terribly wrong. Daylight beckoned the coming of dawn, so he rushed outside to find out the reason for all the confusion and disturbance. He then discovered that the commotion was related to the appearance of a native. He had arrived from another village a few miles away, having run for most of the journey. His face was deathly white, partly due to exhaustion, and his expression was of fear and grief.

The native had been approaching from a southerly direction, having left his village the previous day. It was late in the evening when he heard strange voices ahead of him. He crept forward quietly and slithered cautiously under the reflecting light, breathing as little as possible, searching for refuge in this flimsy shelter. He could see figures emerging from the stunted woods into a clearing, and crept forward to pay more attention. He saw a small Japanese raiding party, who were shabbily dressed and carrying rifles and bandoleers of ammunition on their shoulders. They were led by an officer, whose face was mean and angular, with raised cheekbones and a vicious grin.

A sense of horror gripped him and he had butterflies in his stomach. He watched a British soldier, who was partially wounded, his wife and two little girls being tormented by the patrol. For him it was the realistic image of war, a sudden glimpse of hell. He couldn't help feeling a surge of pity, listening to their pent-up breath coming out in gasps at the threat of this intrusion. Although he couldn't understand what the patrol were saying, the orders and words sounded belligerent and severely threatening. He lay in utter silence, and witnessed an act of Japanese atrocity, which convinced him that the stories he had heard about their cruelty were not mere inventions. They bound the soldier's arms and legs, then raped his wife simultaneously amidst the shrieks and screams of his young family, which echoed in high-pitched tones through the wilderness. Then, not satisfied with their merciless abuse, they blindfolded the man and callously decapitated him with satanic barbarism. Watching the slaughter brought horrified screams of terror from his loved ones. His feet were still kicking, when they forced his wife to her knees facing his twitching body. Not satisfied with this savagery, they finally completed the ritual butchery by ruthlessly bayoneting the remainder of his family. The blood ran river-like from the gaping wounds.

The act of violence imposed on this young family was the most horrifying scene he had ever witnessed. Their execution seemed to have been a foregone conclusion at the hands of these sadistic captors. Although driven to a frenzy, he had to exercise extreme discipline by grinding his teeth in suppressed rage and restraining his anger. Remaining motionless, his helplessness in face of such adversity had affected him deeply. Everything had happened so quickly that he hadn't been able to grasp the significance of this ruthless brutality. He waited for them to leave, and for the sunset to turn into darkness, before emerging from his hiding place. Then he dragged the bodies into the jungle and covered them with some branches; there was nothing else he could do for them. Now the jungle would serve as a fitting memorial and an open casket, carpeted by the mists that cloaked the mountain ranges.

The family's obvious fatigue seemed to have dissolved in this pleasant settlement. Here the gentle breeze ruffled the surface of the river and tempted the budding wild flowers to unfold and blossom on the banks. However, following this terrible chain of events, everything appeared to be in a state of confusion, and now panic reigned. The expressions on the faces of the villagers betrayed a sense of general uneasiness. They were afraid and conscious of the knowledge that any suspicion of assisting or collaborating with escaping refugees would have disturbing consequences. It now became a necessity for them to move on quickly, for it would have been foolish to expose the family any more than was really necessary. They decided to leave the area at once, despite the comfort of such a resting place. Although the climate was temperate the area certainly wasn't designed to become a plantation. The human body could become accustomed to anything, but this feeling was a bad omen for them so early in the morning. It was a bad omen for the day, especially with the fear of the fast-flowing Chindwin River barging around at the back of his head. The turmoil remained for a short period, while the first glimmers of the morning light fell on faces creased with fear. As they surveyed the immense countryside, there was plenty of light, fresh air and sun. However, what it lacked was peace and quiet, but they would soon have that when they left.

Near the river's border, numerous water buffalo were being bathed ready to resume their daily work, and women washed articles of clothing on rocks near the water's verge. Outside the little hut, an infuriating melancholy squawking of winged creatures certainly wasn't an idyllic calming influence. Suddenly the halcyon dawn and the cloudless sky gave way to a deluge, and the heavy rain fell in sheets. Everyone literally hurled themselves for cover under the oasis of palm trees scattered along the banks. Within a few hours the torrential downpour had ceased, so Uncle Stan decided to cross the river immediately in a *periagua*. He had purchased the craft from the villagers at a modest price just for the crossing. The broad choppy surface was approximately four hundred yards wide and looked savage and menacing, but he wasn't really troubled about the situation that lay behind them. He wasn't even upset by the wild rumours of the advancing enemy, he was more afraid of the dangers ahead.

Uncle Stan allowed himself some comfort by being alone at the bow of the craft, while the family huddled together in the middle. Slowly the boat moved cautiously towards the west bank, being vigorously sculled by one of the natives who had agreed to assist them. He soon reverted to a silent prayer when the water lapped the sides perilously, and occasionally dribbled into the boat, the balance being so precarious one dared not move. Everyone else on the bank was listening and looking intently towards the rumbling heavens, which they mistrusted now that the clouds had rolled back. The crackle of distant thunder echoed, threatening another deluge of immense proportion. Now Uncle felt as if a river of new life were flowing through him, as the water slid past with an easy slowness in the windless air.

Many of the other crafts were crossing their path on their way back to the east bank, their primitive nets laden with an abundance of small fish. Despite their enormous feeling of delight, with the sight of the bank hidden under a veil of mist, and safety only a few yards away, they suppressed their feelings, which normally they would have expressed in other circumstances by waving and shouting. They kept perfectly still with the fear of capsizing the boat never far away from their thoughts. The discomfort of cramp prompted some sympathy. Finally, with a sense of enormous relief, they came to a halt on the opposite bank and joyfully stepped off onto the solid earth. The thought of walking on the firm shore, in a more tranquil setting, seemed like the end of their adversity. Their exhausted brains clung to this illusion with a vengeance. They gathered their few belongings and headed through a plantation of wild bananas, immediately disturbing a belt of green parakeets, which descended swiftly from the branches, as the day shimmered and the temperature climbed relentlessly. All afternoon the sun burned down with savagery, through the shadeless expanse and the plains that rolled away inland. Splashed here and there were huge patches of cactus hedges, capable of tearing one's flesh to shreds. Suddenly the need for drinking water became an urgent problem and the only certain memory was the long, continuous, penetrating heat.

Their anxiety continued as the symptoms of tiredness betrayed their aching bodies. The ground around their feet erupted into clouds of dirt and dust, and the ever present sweat traced channels down their sorrowful faces. Unexpectedly they then came upon a trail of burst suitcases, along the primitive track, which gently undulated, and fronds of bamboo, which the wind had blown, scattered across the uneven broken route. There were the now familiar handcarts, prams, and bicycles stumbling along like a fallen army, the human traffic solid on the slopes. Coolies, villagers, groups of Indians and Burmese tribespeople squatted on the roadside, one hundred passing faces or one thousand peering glances. Then, of course, there were numerous dead lying uncovered in the ditches. It was a continuous trail of unheroic agony, people of all colours and creeds, men, women, children and babies having succumbed to the many uncontrollable diseases, typhus, typhoid, malaria, dysentery and the exhausting starvation.

A cocoon of dust descended slowly, revealing a ridge of mountains in the distance, and deep down in the valley miles of darkened jungle only seemed to exemplify all the weariness, the horror, the heat and the ghastliness of this long retreat. Beyond the curtain of dust a few people were sitting sluggishly on the hard trodden earth, eating scraps of food feebly, some with knotted faces staring at the barren soil. They waited for the cool of the evening to retreat to the safety of the jungle. Here a tiny stream flowed down from the hills between small rocks, and it was the perfect spot to rest for the night as the dusk began to creep in. The main thing was to get something to eat and supply their hungry bodies with some energy. It was a warm and quiet evening, although there was a velvety blackness about the sky. For a while all thoughts of the war were forgotten and the trails ahead were duly shut out of their tired minds. After a light meal of soup and corned beef with bread, they all bedded down in the comfort of a blazing bamboo fire, and the huge banana leaves acted as insulating mattress material.

In the serenity of this upturned soil and obsessed by doubt, Uncle Stan gently stirred the fire, feeding its rage with branches and dead wood. There were certainly no praises for the desolate light, when he once again carefully studied the crumpled map, eagerly searching for a future route. The past few weeks had proved to be desperately hard on the family, and the strain was now beginning to tell. They were exhausted and finding it very difficult to cope with this stressful situation. Occasionally he gave the two boys shoulder rides alternately, but even this was beginning to wear him down. Peta struggled on, holding hands with her mother and listening to the fairy tales that she could remember.

At dawn, which was shrouded in a damp mist, they washed in the nearby stream and filled their water bottles. After a little breakfast they resumed their formidable journey on stretches of bare ground, badly rutted with cart tracks and the occasional clump of stunted brush. The air was filled with fresh woodland smells and birds of every kind were fluttering through the branches of the trees. Savagely the sun poked its nose out again, peeking from behind the clouds and stabbing at their aching bodies. Very soon the forest folded over the rising escarpments of rock, and myriad mosquitoes buzzed around in an endless motion.

Eventually dusk began to fall and the light faded appreciably by the minute. The night came suddenly in a swift black haze, which swept across the horizon between the hills. Soon the wind crept down the valley, carrying the warm darkness with it, and the ingrained crusts of forest looked shadowless in a cloud of vapour. There was the constant echo of insects on the move again due to the artificial light and human activity. The whole jungle began to crawl, as the day sank fast in deep ridges of purple and red. Even the silence was limitless, deep across the forested hills, and interrupted only by the eerie sound of jackals crying with their human wail throughout the night, their breath floating in puffs of billowing vapour from eager jaws. They bedded down once again around a cosy fire, after a quick meal and many prayers, trying to dream their way back to their own way of life, which grew larger by imagination. Towards the dawn, when the creatures of the night vanished into the jungle, they awoke with stiffened limbs. In search of freedom, they continued with the same procedure, familiar regions to explore, and rivers to cross, in the shadows of the great forested mountains. Each day was a struggle to survive, and the next day the struggle continued in this unforgiving land of extremes.

My uncle was on the verge of giving up when he saw the outskirts of a small village, yet there appeared to be no signs of life within. Then slowly the inhabitants stirred like the living dead and emerged from vacant spaces like some miraculously preserved hidden dynasty, imbued with a great feeling of enthusiasm as they gathered together transfixed with curiosity. Men, women and children, dressed in their native attire, were at first suspicious but soon showed their friendliness. The headman spoke nervously partly in Undue and part in Burmese, but in his eyes there was a glint of professional hardness. Most important was his amicable offer of immediate shelter for the night, plus a light meal of fish, mushrooms, and rice. The night was surprisingly cold after the heat of the day, so they were eternally grateful for the warmth of a cosy fire near the opening of the hut.

The dawn found them all sleeping and it was almost broad daylight before they struggled into wakefulness. Early sunlight splintered through the joints of the thatched roof, and outside, the paddy fields stretched far into a fairly visible clump of dark trees. There was a late breakfast for the family but Uncle Stan neither felt hungry nor tired. Only a single urge filled his mind almost to the point of obsession. They had to get to the Indian border soon and in safety. He had to remove the constant fear, which affected him more than the physical discomfort. Quietly and with anxiety, they gathered their possessions and moved on. Their native friends watched with interest and cheerfully waved their goodbyes. Tomorrow they would continue to work in the fields as though nothing had happened.

They steadfastly moved through the trees and dense undergrowth as far as possible and parallel to the main road, which proved unexpectedly difficult. The strange sound of reconnaissance aircraft flying well below the clouds had them scattering behind the bushes for cover, listening and eyeing the sky carefully. There was an unnatural stillness as they left but the silence was full of menace. Continuing for a while, they finally stopped under some huge banyan trees for shelter from the blazing sun. Nearby, a gathering of huts lifted their gloomy spirits. Inside one of them a family was enjoying an afternoon meal. They were given a pleasant welcome by the inhabitants, whose faces bore surprise and curiosity. The invitation to eat and to stay the night elevated their fading morale. The interior was clean, as indeed all the huts were during their short stays, when they occasionally made a brief contact with small bands of refugees.

As the darkness fell it began to rain heavily thundering down through the thickly congested trees. They sat and ate in relative shelter and were allowed to purchase fruit and vegetables for future use. The children chatted excitedly and the night passed without any incident, just the usual conversation from the villagers. Dawn crept up with a grey light that seeped through the trees, and they were soon ready to move again to the patter of rain on the already wet grass. The air was damp and a cool breeze had sprung up from nowhere as the sun glowed dimly behind a veil of cloud. A drizzly day, even thunder, Uncle Stan thought, as they waited patiently for the persistent rain to ease. Just beyond the tall brush towards the west, a small stream barred their intended route. Its current was now swollen by the recent deluge of the last few days and any instant progress was halted. It was also a lot wider than Uncle Stan had first thought, and was protected by a dense mat of bushes spreading towards the swirling water. For a moment he was afraid, and couldn't understand the reason for the sudden anxiety within himself. He finally convinced himself that his fears were only in his imagination. The natives had told him that it wasn't too deep and wading across the shallow area was possible with caution, although headway would be extremely slow. It was crossed quite often even by the children, who often played and swam in the water, which was usually warm. The women always washed clothing in the stream, beating them on the boulders near to the surface. Although the bottom of the stream was rocky, it was sturdy, creating an enduring image. Further downstream it reminded him of the rippling Chindwin, as it dropped away appreciably, masking the darker side, which threatened to suck you down, if you ventured out into the bottomless quicksand.

Muddled and incoherent thoughts were barging around in Uncle Stan's head, mocking and taunting him as imaginary figures of all the fears and his many doubts rose up before his eyes. His brain was working frantically to find solace and remove the confusion. Once again it was stretched to its full capacity, both physically and mentally. Suddenly an incredible feeling of loneliness overpowered him, when he gazed at the stream with considerably less enthusiasm. For a while he even felt suspended in time, between the past and the present, which stripped away his confidence. The sky cleared for a moment and all the clouds had rolled when Aunty Eileen spoke softly, 'You aren't seriously thinking of wading across that awful stream, are you, Stan?' she asked, looking frightened as she watched the menacing current and the danger that lurked. She could feel her throat closing in, tears of fear and panic flooding her eyes. He tried to smile but not very successfully. They hated disputes and arguments and had very seldom quarrelled. She wanted to hear the truth.

'Not for quite a while, we'll wait until the water level drops and the current slows down. Don't worry, dear, I won't take any chances. I wish I knew when the men would be returning from their visit to the other villages downstream. One of the boats would be handy, anyway it is the safest place to cross,' he replied, showing no visible signs of fear.

'I hope you know what you are doing, Stan,' she protested

again, with a feeble grin and a look of accusation in her eyes.

They had previously waded through swamps before, which had proved very rewarding. However, this was a little higher than the stagnant marshes, and the water was flowing very slowly. He placed an arm around her shoulders to comfort her with a friendly smile and remove the look of horror from her face, although he himself was tense and strained inwardly, sure symptoms of his own apprehension, and feeling convinced that this earth was the insane asylum of the universe. Shielding his eyes against the sun, he glanced across at the opposite bank where everything appeared deathly silent. High above in the cloudy sky, a flight of crows glided above the ridges of the bleached bamboo forest. The stream looked black, and uninviting wisps of greenish scum floated in patches. Even the surface appeared to boil, in between the masses of dense jungle on either side. It suddenly seemed to be wider than he had at first thought, which left him in a cold sweat of remorse and indecision, and created an agonising cramp in the pit of his stomach.

They were now all steeped in anxiety and a lot of fear, so he decided that a short prayer wouldn't be out of place. With a huge sigh of relief they knelt down together and prayed for safety and guidance.

'Father make me a vessel of the cleansing light and deliver me from evil, and if thou pointest the way, I shall follow.'

Then Uncle Stan rose steadily to his feet, feeling that he was now fully prepared, although for sometime they looked at each other without speaking. Then a slow ripple of conversation resumed between them, anything to create some air of normality, some sense that they had to go on. The stream at this point was approximately fifteen yards wide; however, the rainy season was adding some unexpected difficulties. The sky was deepening now and a few lowering clouds began to darken the surrounding area, threatening heavy rain. He had hoped that this would cut short the term of misery. They had travelled far and nothing exercised more influence on their minds than the thoughts that they had got over the worst.

'Eileen, you remain here with the children, and I'll cross the stream first with all the bundles, then return for Peta.'

He knew exactly what he was going to do, and without a moment's hesitation he waded through the swollen stream carrying the packages. Much to his surprise the water appeared warmer than usual, although he found it more tiring than expected, as he struggled a little against this viscous element. Then he returned immediately to prevent their unnecessary waiting. Close to the bank stood many of the huts, although they were deserted. For the present they seemed to take on a tone of the surrounding landscape, as the horizon blanched into the endless menacing sky. Aunty Eileen and the children waited and watched anxiously, hushed by the immensity that faced them. What Uncle Stan really believed was what his deepest intuition whispered, that this decision was the correct one. The family sat near the edge of the stream in the shade under the trees, as he approached them. Aunty Eileen stared at him for a few seconds, unable to disguise her fear of water. Then she gave a huge sigh, shrugged and agreed with his supposition, gradually feeling a little more self-confident and relaxed.

'Do you really believe that we shall be all right?' she asked hopefully. Her voice was hesitant with suspicion.

'Everything will be fine, Eileen, so please don't worry,' he replied, speaking softly to her and trying desperately to hide the constant turmoil embedded in his own mind.

She smiled, hoping to retain her composure. Her face was narrow, slightly tanned and smooth like the rest of her body, yet it still had the look of troubled patience about it. She was strangely oppressed once again by that feeling of doubt, which had been with her ever since she had woken up.

Uncle Stan then knelt down next to Peta. 'Come on, little one, jump on my back, and I'll piggyback you across,' he whispered softly.

She looked at him with her cautious eyes, a little scared, but said nothing, just placed her arms around his neck and he stood up to leave.

'Daddy, do we have to travel like this?' she asked, on the verge of tears.

'I'm afraid so, darling. We can't very well stay here, it's far too dangerous.' His voice dropped to a murmur.

Tears began to flow and trickle down her cheeks as she spoke between heavy sobs. 'It's not fair, it's just not fair.' She could hardly speak for crying.

'I know,' he replied sadly as they crossed very slowly. 'We have got to keep going. I've tried to explain all this to you before, now just hold on tightly.'

The water slipped by with a regular motion and its warmth made him feel a lot happier, although time seemed interminable. Increasing speed would have been silly and could have proven dangerous for the both of them.

When they reached the opposite bank, he placed her down gently next to the bundles under the shelter of some trees.

'Now you sit and wait quietly until I return with your mum.'

Although she was only seven years old, she was an obedient and intelligent little girl, and nodded to him bravely. For a moment she closed her eyes and a faint flush diffused her pretty face, as she felt isolated amongst the barrage of trees that surrounded her. However, they did offer some protection against the steady trickle of rain that had begun to fall. Their obvious anxieties showed on the faces of the others on the far side, as he splashed through the murky water. This had a visibly depressing effect on Aunty Eileen, who didn't appreciate the unforgiving weather. High above, the storm clouds gathered menacingly, and the rain had now become heavier, as Uncle Stan glanced up at the turbulent sky, feeling agitated and disgusted. The roll of distant thunder gave further warnings with a sweeping curtain of torrential rain. He now wondered if it was all too late. His mind was a reservoir of remoteness, even the stream looked daunting and bursting with the muddy water bubbling furiously. There was urgency now; he couldn't leave little Peta on her own for too long under these appalling conditions. Now his stomach muscles tightened, as he watched the cold grey mists floating across the surface of the stream. This would soon become a raging torrent, now that the monsoons were in full blast.

He hugged Aunty Eileen tightly and spoke with some urgency. 'We've got to move now because the weather is deteriorating fast. I'll strap Robert onto your back, with this broad scarf wrapped tightly round your shoulders, so it won't come off. He isn't very heavy; anyway this will leave your hands free. Leon can sit on my shoulders, which I'm sure he will enjoy. With your hands, you can hold on to this piece of timber, which will be behind me. Just follow close behind by clutching the other end firmly. The water is just below your waist, so we'll wade across very slowly. We don't have to hurry, dear.' His voice lapsed, discouraged by the constant rumbling of the water around him.

For a moment my aunt stared in disbelief. 'The idea is nonsense, Stan,' she said very quietly, gazing at the stream as the rain slackened appreciably. Her mind raced as she spoke and she pushed her fingers through her long hair now tied in a knot, in an irritated gesture of impatience.

'We won't be rushing, so don't worry,' he replied, trying to sound convincing.

She grimaced, feeling certain that everything ultimately might prove disastrous.

'We'll move very slowly, Eileen, I promise,' Uncle Stan said, then bent down and asked Leon to jump up onto his back.

There was a moment of silence and numbness that appeared to last for ever before they entered the stream. She still felt that within the next few minutes something terrible could happen.

'Now hold on to this piece of wood and follow me carefully, Eileen. Please try not to panic,' he begged, with a touch of urgency in his voice.

Her heart was pounding as she reached with moist hands to grasp the timber. Without pausing they all slipped into the stream slowly, scattering the insects and dragonflies which perched on the reeds. The water rose slowly as they approached the middle and around them the waves swirled and rippled menacingly just below their waists. Fear dwelt in her eyes, as she stared directly ahead of her, with an empty gaze, which never wavered for a moment. The worried lines were etched deep on her forehead, when she gripped the piece of wood tightly between her hands, as if her life depended on it. Her earlier courage was beginning to desert her, as they approached the marshy area of the stream. Walking was now becoming very difficult, their footwear made sucking sounds with every weary step. The danger of remaining too long in one spot gave them the feeling of sinking deep into the soft earth and being dragged under by the current. Aunty Eileen continued by instinct alone, studying every passing ripple nervously. The current appeared to grow stronger with the trickle of rain. Unaccustomed as she was to water it made her wince; her inexperience was now all too evident and it showed. Her face became distorted with the adamant dislike of this liquid element, and although the waves sprayed onto their weary features, there wasn't the slightest murmur of complaint from her about these unreasonable demands.

Uncle Stan turned to offer her an admiring glance for her undoubted courage, only to find tears falling unheeded from pitiful dark eyes. She cast an imploring glance at him with a smile, but her pale lips remained silent. He saw fear and desperation in her eyes. Her hands trembled around the staff, as she tried to overcome her natural aversion to water. She was hoping not to disturb the boys, who appeared to be enjoying the ride, drying her eyes roughly with the back of one hand. Now a tremulous smile crossed her face, as the damp weather brushed their faces with its moist fragrance. She was trying to control her breathing, but panic came in spasms and showed no signs of diminishing as she faltered, trying to wade through the sludgy water. Occasionally she swayed, with uncertainty at every step. Her clothing hung heavily on her shaking body, and she feared any distraction might cause to her slip and fall. She was also terrified of feeling the dark water covering her face. The sky was growing paler above the forests, but there wasn't much further to go as they crossed the mid-section. Despite their general unease and disillusion they derived a certain pleasure and satisfaction from the attempt.

On the opposite bank, Peta, who had been waiting patiently for them, seemed more excited than frightened as she stood up and waved. Uncle Stan shouted to her to sit down but, feeling a surge of jubilation, she ran to the edge of the water. She expressed her impatience and obvious delight, with a childish display of innocent gymnastics and shouts of enthusiasm. Almost immediately, being distracted by Peta's appearance so close to the stream, Aunty Eileen swayed badly on her unsteady legs, with the excess weight of Robert on her back. She wobbled to and fro, trying to maintain her balance against the swirling undertow. But with every physical law made impossible, the inevitable unfolded dramatically as Uncle Stan turned to support her. The fierce undercurrent wrenched at her weak and tired legs and threatened to suck her under. He shouted at her to hold on, but her frightening screams became tangled up in her vocal chords as she fell backwards. Her vacant eyes stared in maniacal fury, then her long hair broke from its knot and coiled about her face. Gradually releasing her grip on her only lifeline, she was dragged under by the vacuum of the churning twisting water. Little Robert's choking cries only added further misery to their problems. Together they were gradually sucked through the blackness of the muddy rapids into the black pit of despair. A ferocious inhuman shriek of terror filled the air and stretched across the running stream.

'Eileen, where are you?' he shouted with horrified disbelief, his mind totally confused.

An arm reached out from the depths, like an ancestral ritual. He grabbed frantically at her struggling body, his fingers trying desperately to hold on to the dead weight. Tragically, in this moment of hideous frenzy, he accidentally dislodged Leon from his shoulders, throwing him headlong into the volatile maelstrom. He stretched out his other arm to hold onto him, but was unable to prevent Leon's small frame spiralling into a bleak chasm whose depth he could not define.

A feeling of panic and devastation, which was so complete, now engulfed him. He was literally unable to function with any self-control, and terror swept through him like an icy cold gust of wind. An attack of anguish and intense pain so powerful invaded his entire body. Suddenly the impending horror became all too clear when Leon surfaced and started screaming for his mother. The water bubbled in and out of his mouth, as he sank and disappeared out of sight in the gurgling darkness. Everything happened so fast that Uncle Stan could only watch the small shrieking bundle of humanity vanish. Stark terror haunted his eyes, as Aunty Eileen again slipped from his grasp and drifted away like flotsam being relentlessly pulled below the surface by the swift undercurrent. She emerged from the depths, fighting tenaciously to retain her composure and sanity, in this hideous encounter with the stormy elements. Gasping for air, she sucked in a deep breath, but took in slimy water deep into her lungs. She tried desperately to dislodge herself from her son, still strapped to her back, but couldn't. He was now choking and suffocating with the sludgy water.

'Eileen,' Uncle Stan shouted once more, but she never heard him, just screamed and splashed about frantically in a whirlpool of distress. Her cries were now weak and blurred. He watched in disbelief and revulsion as she sank below the surface, her muffled tones vanishing with every breath and sending shock waves through him. She tried to breathe again, but with the vast amounts of water, she was choking, writhing and struggling to survive. It was a nightmare beyond description, now his scrambled brain plummeted into a bottomless chasm.

Suddenly her hands reached out of the water, clawlike at his face, wriggling and twisting with demented fury. He pulled away and grabbed frantically at her wrists, but he found it impossible to maintain his grip. She broke away and fought him with hysterical strength, but he pulled with all the energy in his arms as she gradually slipped away again in the inky blackness. The sound of the rippling water drowned out all her screams. Now Uncle Stan's legs and arms started throbbing as cramp reared its ugly face. My aunt's movements were being restricted with the weight of Robert's lifeless body still strapped to her. Tension and exertion were taking their toll. She drifted away into the deep, half-drowning, swimming, floating, sinking, and then surfacing again. The simple soft sound of her voice in the distance dragged him towards her again. He trembled with the fear and dread of the unimaginable perils, as he snatched at her once again. She fell silent and his fingers, half-dead with the cold, gripped like talons at her long hair, hovering just below the stormy surface. It was a moment of absolute chaos and confusion. He clung on tenaciously, despite the gaping chasm, tightening his vice-like grip, when he saw the fear in her eyes. A gurgle escaped her mouth and, in spite of all his efforts, the turbulence was far too formidable. It wrenched her weakened body swiftly away, leaving her long tresses firmly in his grasp. She sank almost immediately, with Robert strapped to her back, and disappeared out of sight, submerged immediately under the raging waters of an unknown river, which had grown like a huge swamp with no beginning and no end.

The aftermath had slipped into its last stage with tropical swiftness. Even the isolated signs of humanity had disappeared into the sombre landscape. The air had now turned a darkening purple, as the black cloud of sorrow momentarily imprisoned his brain, sending it into a dispersing rotation. Suddenly he burst loose, screaming and weeping uncontrollably in the water. Never in his wildest dreams, could he have predicted such a grotesque sight. A few weeks ago life had had a certain regularity and sweetness about it; they had loved and lived life to the full. Now he had witnessed an apocalypse, struggled with death, and God, who watched everything from the thunderous sky, did nothing.

He was finally dragged onto the riverbank by some of the natives, who were returning from the other villages because of the worsening conditions. He couldn't stand upright he felt so weak, so he crawled on his hands and knees. Every muscle in his body began to scream out in spasms of pain, and every joint ached. His head throbbed from the effects of sludgy water, and the sudden brightness stung his eyes. Now there was a mixture of guilt, despair and bitterness as his throat tightened and ached with the sense of loss. Many of the younger villagers, who had seen everything, scanned the river's edge for any signs of Aunty Eileen and the boys with no success. Stunned into silence at the full horror, women watched, weeping, some with babies clutched in their arms, younger children standing by their sides. Confused and nervous faces stared at him with heartfelt pity.

The air was now mild, and sweeping behind him was the dark murderous stream that had claimed his young family, slipping past in an endless sweep eastwards. He felt too exhausted and far too weak, fumbling around like a blind man. Suddenly, in a vision, he once again witnessed thrashing young bodies buried beneath the turbulent surface, and rage swept over him like a gigantic wave. He turned silently away, oblivious to everything, and began the long walk to his daughter. It was very quiet, with not even the sound of any birds. Some of the women crossed themselves as he passed, praying for him. 'I have seen the hell on earth today,' a voice whispered in his head.

Peta was standing by herself, paralysed, shrouded within the black embrace of loneliness. Lines of fatigue were etched under her eyes and the weariness was like a veil over her face. She had watched the cataclysm alone and terrified with endless tears streaming down her cheeks. For her there was no glancing over the rainbow, only a cold return to reality, then a retreat into herself, for the misery would be embedded in her mind for ever. Mirrored in her eyes the filthy stream slithered by like liquid mercury, the water dark, forbidding and icy cold, akin to the glaciers, which fashioned the chasms thousands of years before.

For Uncle Stan, horrendous thoughts flickered and danced through his skull like birdlike images. An onslaught of conflicting emotions swept through his shivering body, dripping with dirty pungent water. His mind was saturated with grief over such a futile fatality, which had taken the lives of his wife and sons. Everything was suddenly terribly real, the startling awareness of what had really happened and why he was there. He appeared to be silent for a long time, and his normal mechanism for dealing with stress rose to the surface. He collapsed to his knees. His body reclaimed the tightness of sheer exhaustion and unbelievable discomfort. His eyes watered and the pupils sank beneath a flat glassy sheen. The speckles of darkness in his head sank deeper and seemed to last for ever.

From the gloomy spell came a faraway voice. He struggled to stand upright and force open his eyes. It was his daughter standing in the shadow of the trees. She ran to him sobbing, huge gulping sobs of frustration and distress. Despite the anguish and the darkness that engulfed him, he continued climbing up the banks to her, keeping the river within sight. He gently knelt down on one knee to embrace her tightly, his clothing heavy and wet with filthy green slime.

'Peta,' he whispered with choking emotion, wiping the warm tears from her face. Then he tried to regain some composure, by kissing her tenderly on each cheek. His touch was so delicate she couldn't stop weeping within the comfort and safety of his arms.

'Daddy,' she sobbed, not looking but placing her arms around his neck, the tears streaming incessantly down her face. 'I'm frightened,' she said in a whisper, and swayed with a touch of recurring dizziness, as her grasp tightened with unguided childish innocence.

Her father felt so cold that he had to make a conscious effort to prevent himself from falling over. His throat swelled and suddenly went dry as he tried to swallow and couldn't. 'You don't have to be afraid anymore, my darling. I promise that I won't ever leave you again,' he replied, choking back the tears, and placed a consoling arm around her shoulders. She stopped crying, rubbing her reddened eyes, as her head throbbed and weariness made her feel on the edge of sleep.

The area near the river was soon crowded, pulsating with anxious low whispers and exchanging glances. His eyes just stared sightlessly at the passing images. He carried Peta to a little hut, which had been offered to them as shelter for the night, her eyes fluttering in a blank expressionless face.

'Daddy,' she said softly, her voice frail and blurred, 'Have Mummy and Peggy, and Leon, and Robert all gone to heaven?'

Those few words brought a huge lump to his throat, as fragments of past and present flew through his tortured mind. 'Yes, they have, my baby,' he replied. 'Now just you go to sleep.' He then laid her down on the mat gently and covered her up with some dry garments, which had been left for them. 'I'll be outside if you want me for anything,' he said, then disappeared behind the leafed screen to change into some dry clothing.

He walked outside into the dusk, closing the thin matted door behind him. There were matters that needed to be resolved, and he wanted no distractions, as his eyes searched the heavens for vindication. His thoughts drifted and his throat was knotted with anguish, even breathing became impossible, as he reached the edge of the bank. Then he glared at the intimidating stream, looking strange, forbidding, and merciless all by itself, churning menacingly in a relentless squall. Now his body had its own rhythms, its own uncomplicated and imperative claims of pure loss and death. The steady drizzle had finally stopped, and a slight breeze had sprung up from the north, gusting now and then into cold little pockets of air, which had grown colder by the minute, and suddenly bringing with it a tatter of bluish sky, which moved swiftly between low clouds. He needed to be alone in some secluded corner, a place where animals sought solitude, a hiding place, and a place of death. Something terrible had happened, and he wandered through its reverberating aftermath. Now the riverbank looked like a burning hell, but it wasn't. The real hell was revolving inside himself, like a cyclone. He felt that his life had disintegrated into a fine dust, which would be scattered everywhere by the slightest breeze, with the prophet of doom observing his movements from above.

He glared up towards the heavens and raised his clenched fists with rage in the harsh light, screaming his wrath, with a parched throat and burning eyes. 'Where were you, God, when I needed you? I pledge you my solemn oath that from this day onwards I will never enter your house again.' Now feeling devastated within himself, he was completely lost in the sadness of his own thoughts. Whatever one thought or did, one preserved what they valued the most, and that was his family. He heard himself screaming as terror engulfed him. He tried to clear his throat but couldn't, his heart was in his mouth. Now his mind floated into a chasm deep inside his gut, his thoughts were his own memory returning to his abortive entombment. He struggled to sleep but found sleep elusive, and felt warm and cold at the same time. As he drew in a deep breath, visions of the dark abyss came flooding back and the nightmare was to him a reality.

Bright morning sunlight burst through the cracked thatched roof from the sky. It was a deep purple and slightly hidden in a white mist, which drifted across the trees like a torn curtain. Peta awoke, innocent to the horrors of the world, from one of nature's essential cycles, shaking her head and looking vaguely troubled at the human occupant, who was a motionless heap under the blanket. Raised in the habit of cleanliness and obedience, she gave herself a quick sponge out of the bucket, brushed her teeth, and then readily woke him up. He frowned and gazed broodily through the rays of light, at the small figure standing in front of him. The long night had given him so little sleep, and he had lain awake listening to the sound of gentle thoughts, which were filled with poignant reminders A feeling of coldness reasserted itself on his restless skin again. There was something terrible about that sound, which vibrated between the leafed walls and the eroded bowl of hills, which slanted across the horizon. It seemed to leave him with a sentence of eternal torment. His bleached face had that tired expressionless look that came from prolonged weeping, but the silence and solitude was soon broken with the faint warmth of the early sun.

Rushing down a quick morning meal, Uncle Stan once again found himself becoming unsettled, partly because of his instant refusal to put this personal tragedy behind him. Trying to ignore the elements and feeling totally insulated by Peta's presence, he decided to move on. It was a snap decision, one of those hunches, yet he really didn't feel too well within himself at that moment.

'We'll collect our things and leave straight away,' he said loudly to Peta.

'Stop yelling at me,' she shouted.

'I'm not yelling, I'm speaking distinctly,' he replied.

She looked at him with those sad eyes, a little scared as expected, but said no more, just mumbled a few words under her breath. They moved hastily, throwing their few possessions into a bundle. This would also contain some food, fresh water and their clothing, which had been dried around the fire.

'Aren't you feeling too well, Dad?' Peta asked calmly. Her face was pale and impassive but she came forward for a warm embrace. It certainly made him feel a lot better. He immediately dropped the baggage, lifting her up in his arms and hugging her tenderly.

'Now are you ready for a long walk?' he then asked, setting her down.

She nodded, almost in tears again, and his poor stomach felt severed from his body. Thoughts of leaving without Aunty Eileen and the boys flooded his aching heart. Maybe getting back to the immediate priorities would lift his spirits, and remove the harsh realities of life. His only fear was for his own preservation.

A vague sense of emptiness descended upon them, as they pushed on through this wild stretch of country along a dusty road. Then they crossed a series of rigid features jutting out from the slopes of the hills. Now they were approaching a new area of existence, rarely entered by human endeavour. Behind them the wind sang in the scrub trees. The sky was perfectly clear, as they strolled in single file along a disused track. They concentrated on nothing almost with the dispirited muteness of battle-weary soldiers, in a jungle that was so dense the sun couldn't shine through it. A light gust of wind puffed through the trees and bushes, so they stopped. It was time for a short meal, near a pool of sparkling water from a spring that came cascading down from the mountain. It was a beautiful spot for quiet meditation, as the sunlight danced on the surface making the ripples sparkle. But when the temperature rose it felt as if the whole world would melt in a sudden rush. Time soon passed, the journey was on again and they ploughed through swamps and marshland, until they approached a main road dotted with unmarked graves and its pathetic cargo of human flotsam. Here children bawled their indignation at their discomfort, being jammed tightly on creaking bullock carts travelling along the badly crated path, now packed with refugees of all nationalities with one single aim. Most of the elderly were barely able to place one foot in front of the other, emaciated pitiful creatures with blank expressions, stumbling towards certain death.

They passed the pathetic train swiftly, touched with sadness and an immediate apprehension. They moved cautiously through the day and concealed themselves in the thick undergrowth during the long night for some desperately needed rest. The night noises of the jungle were loud when every kind of animal and bird seemed to be squawking or rushing about in the deep upper darkness. Soon the moon showed, looking like a piece of chipped glass, with an almost blue quality about it, as the light faded and dusk fell. By now even the crickets in the brush had stopped their whirring in this barren wilderness. The cry of wild fowl and the shrill chirps of small birds heralded an early dawn, after which they were soon back on the road again in a workmanlike way. Life seemed less important now but they had to survive, and it wasn't altruism, just self-preservation. Now tension, suffering and the sustained efforts from aching bodies contributed to an anxiety they couldn't control. With all the constant pressure hovering around, Peta was becoming strained and less responsive, and he simply couldn't ignore her physical decline, which had increased steadily.

It was becoming impossible to preserve health throughout such a prolonged struggle. They sat down for a cool drink and something to eat under a huge papaya tree in silence, until a large crow perched secluded in the trees broke the solitude. Uncle Stan already had fleeting thoughts that they probably wouldn't survive this horrendous journey, but they had to try, if only for her sake. His family were always in his thoughts, although laughter no longer had any more value than tears. He certainly would never forget the war which had destroyed everything that was part of his life. In this serenity the trees were mostly teak, rising gently towards the horizon and seeming to crowd against the sky. The delicate wild flowers were knee-deep and swayed effortlessly in rhythm with the cool breeze, like a moving carpet.

As the evening fell they were looking at a valley with an unbroken floor of green, and blue-cloud shades drifting over it. The road weaved through a magnificent flame of trees in full bloom, a huge orchard of wild bananas, dorians, and lime. They stayed and rested for the night, building a shack with banana leaves and spreading a thick layer to insulate and cushion the hard ground for some sleep. Soon the shadows of the trees grew longer as the sun seemed to die a little, and it was time to bed down by the warmth of the fire. Here the fireflies produced double-barred flashing lights illuminating the black night.

They awoke to the sound of birds singing unseen behind the leaves of the branches. The sun itself was hidden behind low cloud cover and the ground still damp from the night's slight shower. They had their usual early breakfast and, after packing their scanty belongings, they continued with the aid of a soft breeze, tropical in its warmth, which had suddenly sprung up. They trudged through dry dusty grass breast-high and the occasional clump of low trees. By mid-morning the heat was growing in violence and any pleasure from the savage sun had long been killed off. Even the earth was blistered by its constant glare, and the thick fog of dust perpetually rose and fell along the route of this endless heatwave, as the sun blazed down like a naked flame. The day showed no signs of coming to a close, and by noon they were famished and tired, due to the morning's exertions. The sunlight continued to stream down, even the shade blazed incandescent in the haze, helping the glow make a prison of the atmosphere. By dusk the skies were low and black; now the thunder rolled and the wind blew with an all-out fury, very quickly bringing heavy rain which finally turned to hail.

They had to scamper for protection under a huge banyan tree, whose low branches provided shelter like an enormous umbrella. It would also hide the much required fire. It was a pleasant respite from the heat of the day, the shimmering hazy brilliance of the full afternoon, and the dry wind that rustled across the plains. Having caught up with a couple of families resting there for the night, they wouldn't be alone for a change. The darkness was absolute as they all settled down, and the only sound was the crackling of some dry branches on the fire, as the orange and red sparks spat skywards. They awoke to a radiance of dawn, which seeped through an eastern sky. It was warm and sunny, with a pleasant southerly breeze bearing the fragrance of dry earth and summer leaves. This masked the stale odour of the damp undergrowth. The other families gave no importance to staying too long, and soon bid their farewells, moving along the paths to the west through densely wooded thicket, where the ground appeared to be rocky.

It felt like a time of lost hope, when Uncle Stan took Peta's hand and began walking westwards, the bundles strapped high on his back.

'Wait,' Peta said suddenly, afraid to go any further. 'Where are we going, Dad?'

He turned and smiled at her, tightening his grip on her hand. 'Don't worry, Peta, we are going down there and we won't be rushing, I promise,' he said and pointed to a narrow ravine, which followed a cart track along a hillside with tall trees on each side. Now there was no hesitancy, not even a hint of an argument, as they proceeded down a long wooded slope towards a thickly forested area. Here the branches seemed to overlap, looking as wild and untamed as the jungle itself. They trudged alongside some paddy fields where the women and young girls worked ankle-deep in mud and water, which had been stirred up by the oxen-drawn ploughs. They were fortunate to purchase some food and fresh water, before continuing on throughout most of the morning.

The eastern sky was bright, and the temperature rose steadily behind them. They walked slowly, weighed down by a black mood of depression, and crucified by the unrelenting heat, reminiscent of days gone by. Ahead, the low hills were completely covered by rolling mists, hanging over the slopes and, down below, the valley was obscured by a mass of jungle-green fern. Here they rested in eerie silence; neither spoke, neither made a sound, both still feeling deeply moved by what had happened. Peta appeared to be crying most of the time; she could only remember the love and tenderness that they had shared. Now they had all gone, and these thoughts slipped repeatedly round and round in her head.

They welcomed the sight of the thick bamboo forest with bushy undergrowth. It was perfect for a night's stay under a flashing sea of white stars hung in the sky, winking down through the darkness at the earth. Now even the trees whispered urgently, coinciding with their rapid breathing, but in the silence they finally drifted off into a deep sleep in this shallow dormitory. Once again sleep eluded him, the mounting uncertainty and turmoil were ripping his insides apart. He felt his conviction was dissolving and eating away at his conscience.

Morning found the atmosphere still shadowed by a purple dawn, sunlight and the creaking of grasshoppers. For them unfortunately the meal was sparse using the last of their food. They had to find a village; it was now an emergency as they headed towards a narrow valley sheltering between two peaks. Peta was looking very tired, unhappy and forlorn. Her eyelids were heavy through weariness and her mind seemed to shrivel up gradually, with no thoughts or emotions passing through it. Her movements were those of a sleepwalker suffering from stomach cramps. There was a throbbing weakness in her legs as she tried to breathe until the cramps ceased. The fragility showed as she swayed backwards on her feet and stumbled to the ground. Falling awkwardly, she impaled the palm of her left hand on a broken bamboo shoot that protruded from a damaged tree. Overcome by a wave of darkness, she gave a high-pitched shriek. Her face was distorted with anguish, as the shocking pain shot through her arm like a bolt of lightning. Suddenly a fresh flow of blood brought a scarlet flush to her twisted features. The screams set the birds cowering in the nearby trees in a perennial rhythm.

'Dad,' she shouted in a wailing tone. He turned and ran to her in a frenzy. The howl funnelled away deep into the forest and disappeared into the unchanging landscape. Now she began to shake and shiver all over, and her mind and body went into shock. The pain was violent but she tried desperately to get up; it felt as if her hand were nailed to a stump.

'Don't move, just stay where you are,' her father shouted in an urgent attempt to keep her calm. He began to cry himself, watching the torture pencilled deep in her angelic face.

'It's hurting, Dad,' she cried in a weak voice.

'I know it is but please keep very still,' he told her once more. Then he gently and very carefully removed her hand from the jagged stake, as she struggled with the throbbing.

The wound streaked her fleshy hand with crimson threads, and for her the immense pain was relentless and excruciating. It was far beyond anything she had ever experienced before. The arm appeared to be dripping, as the blood ran, jelly-like, from the gaping wound to the ground. He was certain that he looked as scared as she must have felt, as he almost turned his face away from the sight of it. Fright drifted through all the hollow places in his system like an early morning fog in swampland. Now it was very difficult to find any words of comfort, as she relaxed still panting and sobbing for a while in his arms. She needed all the sympathy and tenderness that he could provide, but his protection gave her very short release from this ceaseless and terrible suffering. He cradled her head against his shoulder, feeling distressed by the lifeless feel of her small frame. She was so weak and fragile that he picked her up in his arms for added comfort.

The jagged angular gash carved in her hand was gaping and pulling damp strands of flesh and tendon across the wound like red trellising. Uncle Stan then sat Peta down and bathed the wound delicately with a little fresh water mixed with some disinfectant. This only made her scream louder when it stung. She twisted and turned, trying to remove the hand from his grasp, but somehow he managed to remove odd bits of grass and dirt before adding a little Germaline. Then he bound it tightly to reduce the flow of blood. They rested for quite some time, so she could enjoy a little sleep after her horrendous ordeal. Aspirin to relieve the pain a little was all that he had to give her.

'It's sore, Daddy.' She began to cry. 'It's hurting me all over,' she said, weeping hysterically, then went back to sleep again.

Suddenly a blind crippling panic began to suffocate him.

The cramp passed slowly but the intense pain didn't. With the frequent throbbing, the feeling that her arm wanted to separate from the rest of her body gradually increased. She continued sobbing for a while, then slept peacefully with the utmost reluctance. However, in spite of their tiredness and discomfort, Uncle Stan had to summon the courage to resume their journey before he became upstaged by fear. Proper medication was the priority.

Soon the warming sun made its usual appearance, breaking through a flurry of clouds. Peta tottered on gamely once the pain had dwindled a little, with her arm strapped firmly to her chest. They entered a ravine, their feet squelching in the mire left by the recent rain. The track started to twist and turn before plunging into the basin of the valley. Then the view disappeared, and they were surrounded by mountains. Soon the growing warmth of the sun was replaced by the refreshing air of a variegated glade. The weather was ideal, bright clouds casting slight shadows, with a little breeze. So they paused and settled down for a rest and a meal.

Ahead of them stood the boundless expanse, a natural infinity, which nature had built in harshness, tucked into the elbow of this country. This had Uncle Stan wondering if being invaded by an avalanche of trees had any significance beyond the obvious and filled him with constraint. They walked together in a slow-motion dream, through these immense silent woods. Now his inner feelings of disquiet only intensified with each passing moment. It seemed impossible for this existence to continue for much longer. The stillness of the forest was oppressive, but with the coming of dusk everything appeared calm with the mute hush of peaceful darkness. It was to be an early night, and even though a slight breeze blew through the pines, the sky remained mercifully placid.

They awoke suddenly with stiffened limbs and chattering teeth, but were still immersed in a fantasy of mounting excitement. After a skimpy meal they moved on through the jungle, overgrown with vegetation and thick creepers, then followed the contours of the eroded hills and headed east. Here brightly coloured birds and butterflies fluttered among the trees, yet there was still an air of solitude and abandonment. As the day passed Uncle Stan thought more and more about his family, and couldn't banish the pictures of them from his mind. As he took a deep breath of the forest pine, the smell he drew in with the air was one he could easily distinguish. It was thick, unpleasant, and growing stronger.

Suddenly Peta cried out, 'My shoulder hurts, Dad.' Then she started to tremble and sob. He sat her down gently, and undressed the wound very tenderly.

'I'll put some fresh ointment on, it will help to ease some of the pain and probably take away the swelling,' he replied.

Deep inside Uncle Stan knew very well that there was nothing else that he could do to help her. Gangrene had infected her arm and ravaged her small frame. She was also feverish, a heavy cold was stopping her breathing, and she was worn out by the increasing burden of pain. All this sure scared the hell out of him, and he knew very well that he had a good reason to be moving on quickly. The jagged gash was black and festering, Peta was shivering violently and her teeth were chattering. Now he was feeling very uneasy, and his hands trembled with anxiety as he re-dressed the gaping wound. He felt he was living in a godless world, and travelling on a road to nowhere after all the upheaval and innocent deaths.

'I want to go home, Dad,' Peta said between spasms of huge gulping sobs. Her face was squashed with anguish. Fear leapt through his body, on hearing her begging words.

'We'll rest here for a while, then we will go home, if that is what you want, baby,' he replied with a feeling of misery, which engulfed his entire system.

She smiled at him as though reassured by what he had said, and there was a brief sparkle in her eyes as she relaxed a little.

'I wish that your mum, Peggy, Leon and Richard were still with us,' Uncle Stan whispered.

It was as if a curtain on a window had been pulled open, giving a sudden glimpse into the depths of loneliness. The empty silence in Peta's expression was depressing. There was some likeness to her mother, maybe the look of resignation and hopelessness that was in her eyes.

Uncle Stan's problems were mushrooming, and the tension was increasing. Peta was delirious now that the wound was suppurating, and was also suffering from a very high temperature. Her body began dehydrating swiftly, as the fever started to destroy her thermostat. In his aching brain, life had lost all its importance and meaning. He looked at Peta for a moment, nothing more, for his mind was somewhere else, caught in a crossfire of deep emotion. It had been a long hot day, and the shadows were lengthening across their path, as the sun burned the ground with its heat, forming sandy wastes. He had also been making heavy demands on the resources that were available. He was having to carry her now, which had slowed down their progress considerably. The strain soon put a damper on what little energy he had, as they went through numerous damp patches of thicket and the almost sepulchral silence of the dark jungle.

Occasionally speckles of bright blue shone through the tops of the tall trees, as he searched for an outpost in this huge wilderness. Everywhere seemed strangely quiet, and the silence created a depressing mood of uncertainty in the suffocating atmosphere. Staring with impassive arrogance at the dazzling plain, with the distant mountains, was awesome; it diminished him. With the unkind breath of progress creating so many problems, and after what seemed an eternity of laborious trudging across ploughed fields, paddy fields and cultivated crops, they finally approached a tiny village. It was elegantly trapped in the broken uninterrupted lines of the natural jungle, and was blanched with an endless supply of radiant sunshine.

An instant look of relief flashed across Uncle Stan's weary face, as he had been gripped by the continual anxiety of having walked in the wrong direction. Almost immediately there was the never-ending cacophony of noise from the inhabitants. They swarmed out of their huts to greet them with huge smiles of friendliness and overwhelming passion in their desire to extend their hospitality. As the light faded, dusk hovered like a pessimistic inhalation, and an extreme thirst for much wanted sleep weighed heavily on his listless aching body. Now flooded with exhaustion, and his mind blanketed with only one thought, a pall of gloom hung suspended over him. Peta began to slip beyond the edges of physical tiredness, as he held her limp body and comforted her. She wept inconsolably against him with choked sobs. He watched her face and the painful struggle on it. There was also the sadness of memories of those who had recently departed, which filled him with untold agony. Throughout the long night he cradled her, holding her little hand tightly, talking to her and begging her to live, in a soft, low voice.

Uncle Stan wasn't seeing all this, and couldn't believe what was happening. A handful of natives came forward to help with food, fresh water and numerous herbs. The personal presence of the womenfolk was a gift he couldn't refuse, although the conversation was strained. With these simple people in close attendance a fear came over him, a fear of negligence, of things gone terribly wrong. He constantly washed the wound with a mixture of warm water and herbs that were given to him. Outside the indistinctive hum of chatter from the villagers appeared to rise and fall in tone, disturbing the peacefulness of the hut. There was a trembling in Peta's features, which he hadn't seen before. If he was harbouring any thoughts of her surviving, they soon vanished. He now knew that he was going to sacrifice his last child and that she would never grow up, as he had always believed.

His throat burst open with screams of despair as he watched in stunned belief as his daughter drifted into unconsciousness. It lay on his thoughts like mould, stultifying and sour. Now he reproached himself for allowing all this to happen. The rest of the night was consumed by silent sobs and floods of tears, which no one could console. He kept a constant and heartbreaking vigil, always trembling with fear and despair through painful eyes and hideous loneliness. Peta finally passed away slowly during the early hours of the dawn, stripped of human condition. He had witnessed terrifying and harrowing experiences he'd never before known in his life. The sight of all his loved ones screaming and writhing through their final moments of agony had become no more bearable with familiarity and disillusion, with so much accumulated misery and suffering.

Even now the last vestiges of the nightmare were deeply imprisoned in his mind. As the sombre daylight approached he was still absorbed in his own personal grief, and his piteous life was now concealed in a whirlwind of destruction. He passively wrapped Peta tenderly in her earth-stained clothes, which would now be her shroud, together with her few belongings in a blanket. There was a pounding of immense grief in his chest. He looked down at his hands and they were trembling as he carried her small frame with the stealth of a cougar. By the time he had knelt down to lay her to rest peacefully, the humid air was suffocating him, and tension was gripping his insides like a steel vice. He covered the small grave with damp raw earth near a hedge of saplings, in an ancient village clinging to the hillside, cementing the final episode in her young life. This pleasant sanctuary gave her final resting place some privacy, under the geographical features of this Eastern splendour. An impressive gathering of villagers, steeped in their own tradition, knelt together, laying garlands of colourful wild flowers on the small mound of rough earth.

Now Uncle Stan stood alone, sobbing persistently, motionless and cloaked in a silence as great as the universe. He remained obstinately quiet for some time, locked in his own thoughts. Then very softly mumbled a short prayer, which he could hardly remember. It came to his lips, like a menacing growl from the back of his throat, but had no real meaning to him. He felt detached and separate from reality, which seemed to pass over him like a silent dream, and his limitations were now stretched beyond human endurance. Suddenly the hideous aching ebbed away to a stunning and positive silence, which began to stifle him. It had been an exhausting few days, and for the first time he fell into a dreamless sleep. He awoke after a long and deserved rest, still consumed by a strange compulsion to resume this perilous journey. Now the jungle would become an everlasting memorial to all his family. He then travelled northwards into another chapter of history with a hunger for freedom. If he failed this he would be on his way to join the dinosaurs. Continuing through a tangle of abandoned greens shrouded in an oppressive silence, he trudged aimlessly and hopelessly in a pedestrian manner. He knew within himself that everything was lost, yet he tried desperately to save the moment. His family filled his thoughts, and his inner feelings kept him weeping. He had acquired all the horrible memories of war and would never forget the terrible experiences he had encountered in this hostile world.

Now he had to stay alive; he had to have hope however faint, even though death would be a blessing. He was still saddened that he would never see his family again, and was also disheartened that a life that had possessed so much was now in shreds. It was the loneliness and helplessness that hurt the most. When everything you have loved is stolen from you, it's very difficult to find a good enough reason to live. His aspiration to a purposeful and happy future was finally shattered in a tide of dirty water and the menacing jungle. All his plans were cemented in a roller-coaster path of terror and annihilation. With a sense of guilt he would leave them all behind, cocooned in a secret and peaceful domain of their own. The demonic howling in his brain trapped him in a hideous solitude, governing his imbecilic behaviour.

He trudged wearily on, trying not to get caught in the deepening darkness. His pulse rate abated and his brain slowly cleared, yet fear and pain still vibrated deep in his chest. Finally the sun dropped behind the range to the east, but the sky held enough light for him. He continued upwards, and waded across a mountain stream as the plain darkened behind him. Growing short of breath, he ran headlong to the summit like someone possessed. The constant thought of death stalked his every move and, lurking in the distance, was danger of the more sinister kind. He'd all the time in the world, yet he glanced back on several occasions until he was certain he wasn't being followed. The pursuit of his premonition plunged him into another nightmare. In his thoughts he could see the broad sweep of the Irrawaddy fast flowing through the jungle, and on its banks a collection of tattered bamboo huts. These were the humble dwellings of the tribespeople, a secretive little place in the dark recesses of his dreams, a variation of his conscience.

Exhaustion threatened to overwhelm him as he hobbled on aching legs. He struggled through rugged ranges, which resembled uncharted volcanic peaks, into a windswept and treeless plain, which seemed to stretch for ever. Now he felt that this area was the only place on earth where the climate was unsuitable for human survival, and there was no clear memory of what had happened. The anger inside him was a good friend, it gave him a purpose to live. He couldn't remember how long he'd been walking or even where; he could have been moving in circles. All the jungle now looked the same. The weather was kind for a change, and the long hours slipped into one another, dissolving away time itself. He kept feeling unsettled. It wasn't that he wanted to put off the moment, but something was frightening him. There was a nagging sense of unease, a niggling buried deep in his subconscious. His movements were now clumsy, slow, and rigid, his arms hanging down his sides loosely, like unwanted garbage.

Suddenly his eyes started watering with exhaustion and the strain of trying to see where he was travelling in the murky conditions of this unfamiliar territory. The blackness had grown colder as the night suddenly became an early dawn, when he woke up in some hospital near Sibsagar, having crossed the Hukawng Valley – known to everyone as the Valley of Death – by mistake. Here new hope was restored with loved ones at last, after the nightmare of an incredible and terrifying journey of madness. There was an end to loneliness, isolation and most of all fear, a word of four letters that encompassed so much terror in the human mind. Far too much of himself was imprisoned in the past, his deepest emotions buried. The past could be understood and forgiven, but never truly forgotten. For him to try and pull himself free from it would surely be an impossibility. All that remained were the memories.

After hearing my uncle's tragic and harrowing story, I crept into the bedroom and tried to shut myself down emotionally. I felt wrapped in a silence that was masking what I was really feeling. I could see his face buried in devastation, his vacant eyes staring into space and nursing a bottomless sorrow. They had travelled a long way together as a family; now he must travel alone but he would surely store their faces in his memory. The grief that he carried would never heal. I was just drifting into a fitful sleep as twilight fell, when the bedroom door hissed open very slowly. Mother tiptoed into the room and the light from the oil lamp she was carrying dotted the dusk with a flicker. I sat up in bed to speak, but the ripple in my breathing started choking the words.

'You should be fast asleep, son,' she said quietly in the calm surroundings.

'I don't believe that Aunty Eileen and all of them are dead. It isn't true, Mum, is it?' I questioned, searching her face for the words that I wanted to hear.

'You are still very young, so please put it out of your head. Uncle Stan wouldn't fabricate a story like that. As you get older, son, the path gets narrower and merciless, then the truth is a lot more difficult to accept,' she murmured in a soft detached tone.

I shook my head, unconvinced, thinking there must be a purpose for all this to happen. I'm sure that Mother was trying to shield me from the dark side of the sad thoughts that were scrambling around in my head. She looked at me with sympathy, then turned and left the room quietly. The fading light heralded the urgent need for sleep, but I couldn't. Occasionally my eyes would fly open in the darkness, and I thought my heart was being crushed in the palms of icy hands. My mind, punctured with visions of shuddering bodies in their gruesome circumstances, wouldn't collapse. A young family with so much to live for, destroyed because of a cruel war. So I tossed and turned between mixed realities and horrific dreams, which only filled a painful vacuum.

Chapter X

It was now early September, and all the residents occupying bungalows on the top plateau of the campsite, which included us, were busy moving to the lower region now that winter was imminent. We were also informed that the heavy falls of snow, barricaded high against the doors and windows, would make it virtually impossible to venture outside. This top section of the site was devoted entirely to tenancy during the summer months. Here the compact wooden buildings, with their low slender roofs, had no form of insulation against the freezing winter, which permitted the icy winds to whip inside, as though invited. The uneven road down the slope was steep and twisted sharply, so the local tribesman moved our belongings with extreme caution. A few moments of distraction could prove extremely dangerous in this alien frontier.

My mother was very pleased when Uncle Oss arrived to stay for a few days. Although his assistance was greatly appreciated, there were more important arrangements to be made. The strain of his brother's enforced illness over the past few weeks had priority. He had managed to secure a private bed for him in the civil hospital in Lahore, under the supervision of a German doctor. They left immediately after our transfer to the new premises was completed. High in the forest there was stillness, no sounds of birds and only the breeze stirring the tops of the pines. The sun, cloaked by a vanguard of low clouds, had departed and there were reports that heavy snow was on its way.

The houses that were allocated to us on the lower section were semi-detached and built to accommodate four families when in full use. During the winter months, the ground floors were shut off and only the top section was used, these being occupied by two families in preparation for the harsh winter ahead. The houses were extremely spacious, consisting of two large bedrooms, a combined lounge and dining area, bathroom and a separate kitchen. Entry to these quarters was accessible via an external, open wooden staircase leading onto the verandah, which ran the entire length of the front from the main bedroom to the lounge. The buildings stood far apart from each other, with an abundance of spare land between them. Some of them faced the steep mountain slope towards the little village of Bunsra Gali, perched on the main road leading to the summit of Murree. Although much of the paintwork had been weathered away through windstorms and heavy snowfalls, inside, pinecone and charcoal fires generated tremendous heat throughout the icy-cold winter months. Even though the sun shone regularly, grey clouds, filled with snow and squalls of wind, occupied most of the day. The southern quadrant was open land cultivated with crops and irrigated from the fast-flowing Jelum River, with farms occupying some of the outlying areas. The south-east was the prettiest; here the land rose and pine trees arched impressively to the northern limits of the site like a gigantic green mantle.

Suddenly winter showed its sinister face with predicted fury, and the heavy flakes fell incessantly, blanketing the entire landscape with a thick white carpet and assembling long spectacular vistas of unbroken snow. Even the buildings cast flashes of yellow light illuminating at different levels the whirling masses of falling flakes. The first sprinkling lay like a white coverlet upon the forest, and the freezing winds swept icy blasts across the range. It seemed to snow every day without a break with giant damp flakes floating down from the sky, twisting and swirling, sticking to everything they touched, and the cold fell on us like an icy shower.

We had never experienced shivering mornings, or even the sight of this white shroud, as the large feathery flakes fell, turning the whole landscape into a white screen. Within minutes there was no sky, no trees, no buildings or roads, only snow. The whole camp had dissolved into a pure white lamina where nothing moved but lay buried in the wilderness and paralysed with the cold, which had turned dry. Then came the violent wind piling the snow up against all the barriers, filling in crevices and leaving large bare patches looking like pieces of lace embroidery. It fell relentlessly as if heaved from the sky with unabated fury, draping a ghostly silence across the campsite with the rapidity in which it fell, and eventually bending the pines and softening the contours of all the buildings. Then it constricted the colours and made everything white and featureless, as it drifted down flake by flake through the trees. It whipped the ground smooth until it lay piled high on the frozen surface, and helped by the wailing wind the flakes eddied and swirled with an angry motion. We found this cold unbearable, piercing, and demoralising. Our hands and feet were tortured with pain, our fingers swollen with chilblains and toes inflamed with frostbite. The sun shone most of the days with utmost efficiency and regularity but with the heat of a pocket flashlight. Here the savage cold remained, depositing a film of white frost over the earth and surrounding us with a continuous element we certainly would never forget.

The passing of Christmas 1942 was welcomed with open hearts, and behind our silent faces moved shadows of past memories. Some of our prayers were finally answered when winter retreated to the highest peaks and allowed the spring to come forward, bringing with it a new promise of hope. The sun had barely touched the tops of the trees, when the grasses and the wild flowers of the giant Himalayan range grew with vigorous abundance, producing a thick green carpet, scattered with a variety of fragrant coloured plants, which appeared to take on a tone of the current landscape. Nothing of any great importance occurred during the following months, even though the residents waited patiently each day with hope and belief, always searching the trails for caravans of refugees, which were never to approach the site again. Those who hadn't fallen attempting the Trek were now interned in refugee camps and the present was a product of the past in a country under Japanese occupation, so we analysed no further than that.

There was a glow on the faces of everyone when midsummer arrived, and the last of the snows departed, leaving an immense green belt towering towards the sky. Now the temperature rose steadily and the heavy mist lifted from the earth, hiding the early dawn on this particular morning of 6 June 1944. For me it was a rather special and eventful day in my life. My mother had given birth to a baby girl, in the military hospital in Murree, and her husband had also been granted maternity leave from his regiment. The baby's chosen name was Carole Mary, and within a few weeks of them arriving home I'd discovered a new-found talent in bottle-feeding, bathing, and caring for my little sister. Most of my spare time was consumed in taking her for long enjoyable walks, through the barricades of woodland, which held many fascinations. Here I shared with her the protected velvet covering of the sky in this cosy little hamlet, a privilege I savoured with immense pride. Mother had developed sufficient confidence in me to allow me to handle her by myself; as usual she proved to be correct.

My head was packed with pleasant thoughts when I answered the knock at the front door.

'Good morning, young man,' said the smartly dressed police officer. 'Is your mother at home?' His wide smile gleamed with perspiration.

'Yes,' I replied, beckoning him inside, but his sudden appearance had me secretly wondering if I had committed an offence of some kind.

'Mrs Townend,' he said quietly to Mother, who was seated at the table.

'Yes,' she replied, looking very surprised as she rose from the chair and walked slowly over to him.

He immediately handed her the small brown envelope. 'I've been specially authorised to deliver this telegram to you personally, ma'am,' he remarked. Then he bid his farewell and left, as there would be no reply.

My mother stood holding it with resignation and a fatalistic acceptance before tearing the envelope open frantically. It didn't take a great deal of imagination to guess its contents. Her sobs broke the silence and her grief-stricken cries brought my stepfather rushing into the room. The opened cable told us once again that death had invaded our family, once again bringing with it a wave of wrath with the terrible news that my Uncle Leo had passed away in hospital in Lahore. The fatal illness had finally taken this powerful man from his family and friends. Within a few minutes, Mother had packed a suitcase and was taken to Murree by her husband, where a long journey by coach and train would take her to her other brother, Oss. He had booked her into a hotel for a number of days. She felt it was her duty to be present at her younger brother's burial.

Now, with my stepfather for parental support, I would care for my sister in her absence, waking up each night at regular intervals, to make her bottle and feed her. I tenderly bathed her every morning, patting her dry, heaping powder and not forgetting her milk at the correct time. I really did love her, so everything I did filled me with a special reverence. At first I found it very intimidating, but Mother had been an excellent teacher. Sometimes her criticism had been harsh, but always constructive. She was determined to teach me everything that I should know, and I was a very good pupil.

The days soon passed and Mother arrived home from her sombre ordeal, her face immersed in deep sorrow and searching for some much-needed sympathy, after her sad trip where all the preparations had been effectively completed. Death affects the lives of others in one way or another.

For the present, in the town of Murree, a few miles away, cinema mania was suddenly galvanised in the crowded streets. It was the first showing of the film classic, *The Jungle Book*, starring a boy star, Sabu. I had heard exciting reports and details of this colour spectacular and had already convinced myself of an early visit. Sitting eagerly at the dining table, I deliberately blurted out my burning question, 'Can I go to the flicks today, Mum, please, it's *The Jungle Book*,' I had been careful to use the magic word, please.

'Can I go too?' shouted my brother, wild with excitement.

'I'm not taking you with me, you're too young,' I replied, glaring at him, annoyed.

'I'll decide on who goes and who doesn't,' interrupted Mother, glancing at each of us. 'Just what time does this film start? I've heard it's very good,' she asked.

Bubbling with excitement, I gurgled in between mouthfuls of food, 'About three o'clock.'

'As soon as you have finished your meal you get yourself off, Colin, and don't be late home. I want you here before it gets dark, do you hear me?' Mother said swiftly.

'Great,' I replied, allowing my throat to rest in between gulps of orange juice, and my heart pumped with adrenaline. I had already lost my appetite. I left the table on a sudden impulse, after excusing myself.

I hurried along the winding road, on both sides of the rocky track. Here forests of pines and firs spread across the mountain range, their sharp pine needles rustling mysteriously in the wind, occasionally backed by the heavy ruffle of wings as birds took off. I frequently passed some women on their way home after a shopping spree in the town itself.

When I arrived in the town centre, narrow streets led off on both sides with traffic everywhere, parked nose-to-tail near the pavements. Further off, in the bustling background, side streets were packed with stalls selling fruit and Indian sweetmeats at bargain prices. My gaze swivelled to an abrupt halt at the cinema entrance, which stood well back off the main road. The facade displayed a variety of huge colourful posters relating to the main feature, which made my eyes open wide in disbelief. There were throngs of people eagerly queuing for seats with their children, many of the younger ones showing discerning impatience.

For several moments they were all moving with precision into the building, while others waited patiently in the doorway, discussing the film. Suddenly a female's voice rang out from the foyer. 'Standing room only at the rear.' On hearing this most of the crowd dispersed immediately. Some faces bore disapproval, others had mixed reactions, a few quietly groaned among themselves for arriving late. I waited patiently, full of enthusiasm, staring through misty eyes full of youthful passion and quite prepared to adapt to the uncomfortable position of standing through the entire performance. Excitedly I pocketed my change after picking up the ticket. I stood and watched the film, leaning on a low wooden parapet in company with some adults, and filled with satisfaction. It had already started later than scheduled and this was going to make my departure for home much later than I expected.

After standing to attention with patriotic ardour to the tune of the national anthem, which marked the end of an afternoon's pleasure, I stepped outside, but it was late and shadows appeared to be lengthening in the street. A haze passed before the sun bathed the town in an amber light but the night appeared to be very docile and caring. I was eager to get home as the sun sank behind the pines and the wind blew steadily, bringing with it a hint of chill. I felt no strangeness in taking the shorter route, in crossing the menacing green world over the mountain top, then following a narrow winding path on leaves flattened against the earth, innocent that I was embarking on a risky journey and with certainly no guarantee of relative safety. Here the trees were thick, with branches overlapping each other, and the air buzzed with unseen insects. I had travelled along this path many times in broad daylight; it went deep into the forest with dense undergrowth, which stretched away on both sides.

The evening had passed into its last stages and the sky was filled with heavy clouds, lit up on their outer edges. There were a few stars peeking through the light haze, but the track was now dark and shadowy. It was then that I heard a voice in my mind, clearly analysing the situation. It continued and I listened to it carefully, agreeing to everything it had to say. There was a sudden lightening of confusion, and as I ran, the branches seemed to jump out, appearing from nowhere, making me duck and weave as I moved forward. The cold air clipped at my lungs with every breath. I had to be careful running between matted tangles of undergrowth, which scraped my legs as if they were trying to stop me in the painful-looking darkness. I stopped for a moment to regain my breath; the tiredness, discomfort and fatigue of my legs were being transferred to my stomach in aching breathlessness. This only helped to increase the awareness of the dangers that could be there deep in the undergrowth. Here the jungle slipped away, and through the trees, the path then disappeared into the distance amid the slopes of the mountain. Suddenly there was silence, interrupted by the snapping of twigs and the rustle of bushes. Now there was always the danger and my own limitations, as I reached the brow of the mountain. My body was saturated with fear, and I could feel my back sweating, with beads of perspiration forming between my shoulder blades and trickling down my spine. There was something in the dark of the great forest, I couldn't see it but I knew that it was there.

I was struck by an urgency in my mannerism, the desire to get home quickly and close my eyes to this corridor of giant vegetation. High above, the stars were bright in the deep velvet sky and were glistening like specks of silver cresting the hilltops of this unchanging landscape. Here were the consistent hazards of unmapped rugged mountain paths and unpredictable cloud movements. I ran as fast as my legs could carry me, brushing aside with my arms the low branches, which kept striking my face, stopping to regain my breath, as my throat swelled up and I couldn't swallow. Then I ran on again until I had reached the area of the mountain adjacent to the vacant bungalows. I stopped to gather my thoughts and was feeling the effect on my lungs, which appeared to be bursting, when I heard a rustling noise in the woods to my left. There was a pressing urge to go over and look into the shadowy sanctuary, as I was unable to see very clearly because the fading light was diffused by numerous tree trunks. I turned and paused for a moment. Perhaps it was nothing more than an absence of light or perhaps it was something I thought I detected in the semi-darkness.

Suddenly I was afraid, an electrical coldness of which I was barely conscious spreading over and through my shivering body. Now warm strokes traced their way up the nape of my neck, and extreme tension constricted my breathing as I tried to subdue my panic. Throwing a quick glance over my shoulder, I was more aware of, rather than certain of what looked to me like a black panther. At first, I thought that it must be a trick of my imagination, caused by the movements of shadows. The moon disappeared behind a thick cloud, and now there were no stars. It was a darkness you could feel, even touch. From a distance the illusion might have been effective, but from where I stood any such thoughts would have been ridiculous. Watching it closely, I was paralysed with fear, all the nerves in my body seemed frozen, including my thoughts, as it arched up, standing there motionless, unconcerned, in all its gleaming splendour. My first impulse was to scatter immediately, but for a few agonising seconds I was incapable of moving, petrified. Any further progress was stifled as fear burned like acid in my stomach, and horror was suffocating me. I was aware of nothing at first, then my heart started a faint beating and there was a swishing of blood in my eardrums.

The silence was menacing, and the only sound was the

pounding of my own heartbeat. It was then that I felt the chilling tap of death on my shoulder. I tried desperately to banish the feeling of recycling that late afternoon meal, then gently reminded myself that, when you get through the day, you don't stay around to get your neck broken. These warning signs were not to be ignored. The ground suddenly began to shift when I turned and scampered down the mountain. The forest seemed to burst open and the branches cracked and broke. Beneath my weary legs the earth appeared to tremble like the roll of drums, and now even the wind screamed and hissed through the treetops. I stumbled and fell sprawling headlong into the bushes. Quickly gathering myself up, I continued as my stride lengthened, even though I was suffering from an awful stitch deep inside my ribs. Now the hot tears spurting from my eyes froze with the chill. Occasionally there was a flurry of shadowy wings, as the night came down. The wind moved the trees and bushes, and the undergrowth grew thicker and more tangled as the light faded. I thought that I was lost, running deeper into the forest. I continued exhausted and out of breath until the woods opened up onto the grassy patch bordering the bungalows, which clustered together at the edge of the dark wilderness.

I felt safe for a moment, but there was a strangeness with it, yet without the sense of dread that the jungle on a vaster scale inspired. I raced downhill more on impulse than from memory, following the curved road that branched off in front of these houses. They were set back on a plateau overgrown with wild flowers. I paused for a moment, when I reached the lower level, almost on the brink of collapsing. I looked from side to side and was silent as the sweat trickled down my face, but the feverish curiosity that had gripped me would not let go. Nothing was following me, it was my imagination, I told myself. Yet relief flooded me when I reached the house – home and safety. I scampered up the wooden steps, hurling myself at the bedroom patio doors with frenzied shouts. Then, in between shallow breaths, I screamed for my parents to open the door, as my heart started beating faster. Finally, a huge surge of elation when the door opened.

'Colin,' my mother whispered, almost breathless with relief as she opened the door quickly. 'Where have you been until this time?'

My footsteps clattered on the bedroom floor as I stumbled inside, frightened and unable to keep upright.

'You are filthy. What have you been doing?' she shouted, sounding very annoyed.

There was an agonised pause before I answered. 'Shut the door quickly,' I yelled. 'There is a panther outside.' The words just tumbled out, and brought my stepfather onto the scene.

'Are you serious or is this one of your jokes?' he ranted, obviously disbelieving what he had heard.

'It's the truth, honest. I did see a panther,' I said gravely.

There was a silence as they tried to digest what I had said.

'If you don't believe me, then take a look for yourself.

They looked at me with scepticism, then the volume of conversation rose with bursts of irrational laughter.

Suddenly my stepfather's expression hardened and he hesitated for a moment. There were tiny quivers of nerves of concern at the corners of his mouth. He moved slowly towards the door still questioning my bizarre story.

'I'm not making this up, honest, I did see a panther,' I repeated, sounding more convincing than before.

'Rubbish, it's just your imagination,' interrupted my mother once again, now showing complete disinterest in any further comments on the subject.

Now for a while she had me on the defensive. My stepfather on the other hand felt a little uneasy, and switched off the bedroom lights. He glanced through the bank of glass windows of the door, with me by his side. The moon had slid under the clouds, slowly disappearing from view.

The night was black but for the light that was shining from the lounge window, sending shafts of light into the darkness. Cautiously we both peered through a gap in the heavy curtains, and for a moment the ground below was clear, as we looked through the panes of glass. His gaze searched the shadowy areas. Suddenly a huge dark shape appeared and a strange silence fell between us. The panther stood, shielded by the darkness near the bottom of the steps, his eyes blazing like coals in the night. My stomach turned over as it rose, black and obscene, silhouetted against the faint light from above, its great humped back furred with clumps of brush, snarling and growling like cats do. Then it broke off into a canter that was perfectly controlled, like a slow-motion ballet, and disappeared between the trees. The whole room lapsed into silence and surprise. We stared at each other expressionless.

'It looks like you were telling the truth, son.'

I felt a surge of relief wash over me; it was good to know that someone believed me.

'I will have to report this incident to the police in Murree tomorrow morning, Gwen,' my stepfather remarked, feeling deeply concerned.

'As for you, lad, a hot bath then straight to bed, you've had enough excitement for one night,' suggested Mother, sensing my discomfort.

Her words were certainly not to be argued with, so I slipped out of the bedroom and dragged myself wearily into the bathroom. I was feeling refreshed from the hot water, but still numb and afraid after the night's experiences as I shuffled into the double bed, which I shared with my brother. He was sound asleep and hadn't moved an eyelid during all the commotion. I soon drifted off into slumberland, but awoke in the early hours of the morning with a faint headache, muzziness and an emergency call to the bathroom. Through a slight gap in the curtains, I could see that the dark outside had turned to grey. The moon had drifted behind some clouds and only a streak of light marked its presence.

The house was silent, except for the ticking of the bedroom clock and the unclothed movement of the covers. I attempted to rise tiredly from the edge of the bed, to visit the bathroom. Then I had to blink my eyelids several times, not absolutely certain of what I was seeing through the split vision. Carefully I cast an inquisitive glance at a shape, which was indistinct at first, then very slowly the mirage began to come clearly into focus. To my horror, I could see an old woman, with hawk-like features and long grey hair streaming down her shoulders, sitting cross-legged on the wooden floor. Her cheeks were indented and her sightless eyes were peering at me. She was wearing a rough crystalline gown and clutched tightly in her hands was a bowl of rice. There was something feline about her appearance. I recoiled sharply against the headboard, petrified, my concentration wavering. I desperately tried to swallow. I was trembling now and drenched in perspiration, as an ice-cold fear pulsed through me. The very presence of this sinister figure brought me close to tears, and her menacing proximity only added to all the tension. There was nothing I could do to mask my fear, so I kept perfectly still, making myself as unnoticeable as possible.

My mind was spinning, jumbled with eerie feelings about her. I lay awake in silence for a short while as her overpowering presence echoed in my brain. Then, peeking nervously through squinting eyes, I frantically shook my brother.

'Our kid, our kid,' I whispered, trying to waken him. 'There's a strange-looking woman sat on the floor near the bed.'

Surprisingly he slowly emerged from under the covers, rubbing his eyes. Then he complained bitterly at being disturbed from his comfortable sleep.

'I'm tired. What do you want?' he moaned, half-asleep. Then he glanced at the ghostly figure eating from the bowl. His immediate reaction needed no translation; he quickly dismissed my company then returned to his former position under the covers, and soon fell into dormancy. I lay there motionless, with my stomach tangled up in my throat. For once there was none of the usual bravado as fright surged through me. I was lulled by the stillness and soon aware of the sudden cold. My breathing was now laboured, rasping deep in the back of my throat. I tried to close my eyes, then opened them again, afraid to go back to sleep, collecting my thoughts and ignoring the icy draught that eddied around my whole body. Now I was feeling more tired than I had before. It was cold, cold as a freezer, and my fear had worsened, as I lay rigid, half-in and half-out of the bed, terrified at moving a muscle and immobile in the silence. Was this my imagination or was it the baptism of fear that clouded my ability to make a rational judgement? I held my breath and watched, frozen. The aged figure now stared directly ahead of her with an empty gaze, which never departed from her almost ascetic face.

Beads of sweat stood on my forehead, as I lay awake until the skies began to get lighter, and the night blurred past. No sooner had I drifted off than I was awakened, shivering in a cold moisture, and with clenched fists, to a roaring in my ears. It was the alarm waking me up with the clarity of someone jolted from a deep sleep without the cover of darkness. At the breakfast table no one spoke a word. Nothing appeared to be moving and the silence would have been total, had it not been for my brother's presence. I wondered if it was just his innocence or false bravado when he offered his frank admission.

'There was a woman in our bedroom last night,' he said and chuckled with a buzz of excitement.

I could have belted him because I had fully intended to control my emotional dilemma and say nothing. Deep inside me the bizarre experience was rolling over and over in my thoughts. The adults stared at him across the table, aghast and open-mouthed at his statement.

'Tell them about that woman, Colin. We both saw her,' he repeated. A hefty nudge from me trying to encourage silence was not enough.

'What woman are you two talking about?' interrupted Mother, showing her annoyance.

It was no longer possible for me to keep quiet and not enlarge on the subject. 'There was an old woman sat on the bedroom floor; she was eating some rice out of a bowl,' I said, feeling sheepish and fully expecting a roasting for my imagination.

For a few moments the atmosphere was hushed, even the digestion of food had been diverted briefly.

'What woman are you two talking about?' enquired Mother, and this time the question was directed at me.

'I'm not fibbing, Mum. She was sat near the bed, honest!' I spoke truthfully as I remembered the frightening incident. During my casual account of the facts, I saw in my mother's eyes a look that conveyed deep frustration and a flicker of disbelief. She pondered over the abject truth, which in itself did carry an element of suspense.

'Frankly, it does appear that the pair of you have been dreaming,' she replied, her gaze skimming across us. 'I have heard of an apparition appearing as some kind of guardian, but I don't want to hear another word on the subject, and that is final,' she said, emphasising the order with her index finger.

However, I was convinced that I really had seen a woman. Some dreams can be very vivid and in the morning make you think that they were so real, that it must have happened, but this was no dream. By this time the conversation had faded, and I was sitting alone at the table. I felt that I was surfacing from a nightmare of hidden conflicts. Suddenly the room turned colder and gooseflesh prickled all over my body although it was noon and the sun was shining.

'Get your coat on, Colin, you're coming with me,' said a voice from the bedroom. 'We are going for a walk to Murree.' It was my stepfather speaking. Although I didn't say anything, he must have sensed me standing there ready, half-excited, half in fear, because he paused briefly before entering the room.

It was a pleasant sunny Sunday in June; the air circling around seemed curiously alive, yet cool and soft. The light reflected brightly from the blaze of summer leaves on the trees along the highway.

Adjacent to the rocky path, pine trees rose with towering authority on the slopes towards the horizon.

'Are we going up the mountain and through the forest?' I asked, unafraid and full of determination in his company.

A smile came to my stepfather's lips. 'No,' he replied, furrowing his brow, 'it's much safer on the main road. There will be more movement.' Of course he was correct; we passed several women chatting pleasantly, returning back to the camp after a morning's shopping. We finally arrived in Murree where the main street was in total confusion. The traffic crawled snail-like in the tropical haze and uniformed police calls crackled and intermingled in the hot summery air. I felt swamped by all the excitement and activity. Outside the municipal building, tribal horse owners waited, screaming for information about the mauled remains of a native found on the outskirts that very morning. Apparently the return of a distraught horse to the stables the previous evening, had sparked off some fear. Many of the faces looked sad, as their loss dawned on them. However, most of the sorry onlookers were more concerned about the conflicting reports that a black panther had been sighted. It was supposed to be roaming the barricade of woodland in the surrounding mountains.

We didn't know exactly where the police station was, but soon found it after asking for directions. The approaches were blocked by numerous carts, and the main road was clogged with late shoppers on their way home. Our stay didn't take as long as we had expected; the station had been in an intensified state of tension all morning. It sounded as though they had drawn a blank in their search. The policeman listened to me, then referred to his file. I went through everything that I'd seen, what had happened and where – even the fear, which I could remember quite vividly – in as much detail as possible. The reality of this grotesque crime was probably more complicated than I suggested, because the last reported sighting had been a few days before. My stepfather assured them that there really was a panther, because he had seen it himself. They listened carefully and accepted everything. Finally, all the relevant details were taken down and entered in their reports for future reference.

It was still light, although the sun was dipping, and by now we needed to return home as the day suddenly slipped into the evening. We passed several people talking loudly, some sitting on the park benches muttering to themselves. Soon the first breezes stirred slowly in the trees and drifted up the avenue, almost thoughtfully bringing the twilight with them. We left the hill station and walked along the narrow path that weaved round the mountain. Here the fresh grass and the bracken glistened in the dusk. Soon the night air had cooled as we walked swiftly, and even the crickets droned in the long grass on this winding country road. The evening passed into its last stages with tropical swiftness, and the sighing of the wind drove the low clouds over the mountain pass. We finally arrived home, as the sky turned a darkening purple.

Chapter XI

Monday morning in the school playground was a hive of noise and excitement. The expected rumours had been rife during the weekend, sweeping across the campsite like flakes in a snowstorm. The older children and especially my close friends were deeply involved in an exciting discussion, chatting passionately about the hideous black beast, which had hounded me on the way home from the cinema late on the Saturday evening. Questions erupted in various tones from eager faces, sending a cool cocky feeling rippling through me. This only intensified my desire to use a little imagination, to add to the intensity of the incident. However, there was certainly no mystery about my motives.

By late afternoon, and for the second time that particular day, more serious gossip was flooding through the classrooms. Now some of the children favoured ignoring their classroom texts in preference to the new developments ahead, which finally spilled over into the recreation areas. For many of the families the euphoria they had relished these past few months was about to end. There was an element of nail biting before we arrived home from school, although there was no marked eagerness to go storming off. For the selected few this signalled the end of schooling in the Himalayas. It was time to concentrate on another journey, which clutched at my memory, chilling my insides once more, so I cradled my emotions.

The remarks were seemingly what I fully expected, as I casually strolled through the front door, trying to hide my annoyance.

'When Trevor gets in I want both of you to get rid of all your rubbish,' was my mother's immediate request.

'What for?' I asked impatiently. 'We'll be leaving here in a week's time, and there's only room in the trunks for the necessities,' she said, continuing with her lecture.

We sat and listened in thoughtful silence and partial attention to all her suggestions and instructions. Now that schooling was over, there would be no fooling around and no more fantasies. The army authorities had paid their usual visit during our absence, with all the essential instructions and details concerning our future movements. The original batch of families would be leaving this site together, with all their belongings, within the next couple of weeks. We would be travelling by a specially chartered train from the capital, Rawalpindi, down to the main seaport of Bombay on the western coast. There we would board a troopship for an unpredictable but necessary sea voyage, destination unknown. This was the moment that I was dreading, moving further away from loved ones presumably still caught up in the conflict.

Suddenly images and painful memories were rearing up in my mind. Then, for a while, all I felt was a sense of mounting excitement, at the expected adventures ahead. There would be no morbid thoughts for me or so I believed.

Much of the time was spent in solely packing valuable assets and unwanted goods safely in steel trunks. We pulled together in a mindless confusion, occasionally with an upsurge of panic, fuelled by the determination to do without certain articles. These would then be marked 'NOT WANTED ON VOYAGE'. We had already been informed that they would be stowed away in the main hold of the ship, until our final destination was reached. The smaller cases, which carried our immediate requirements, would accompany us to our cabins. We were all immersed in a fantasy and a sense of delicious excitement, despite persistent reports that submarines of the Imperial Japanese Navy had been sighted scourging the Indian Ocean. They had already been very successful in sinking numerous merchant ships and some Allied warships.

The penultimate morning before our departure was bright and clear as the dawn sun dispersed the overnight mists instantly. By midday the sun bleached its way down and the temperature was blistering hot once again, with the humidity hovering despite the temperature latitude. This had been a dreadful week, when thoughts of departure instantly blocked intelligent conversations. Nothing could transcend the barriers, frustrations and close down the pain. Suddenly I found myself wandering aimlessly towards the mountain gradients. I immediately tried to decide what mad impulse was enticing me to this particular area; at first it was strangely puzzling. The motivation seemed clear enough in my thoughts, so I continued with my journey slowly in silence and with pregnant pauses, stepping through the dense bushes and towering pine trees, past clumps of vivid green foliage and treading the pine needles that had cushioned the hard surface.

I felt isolated in space and the fearful ache in my heart only increased as I stealthily approached the sacred spot, the special one, which I had treasured secretly for almost a year. It nestled in the hillside. I stayed silent in front of the huge branches of the imposing evergreens, which bowed as if in silent prayer. Now they were concealing the shallow entrance, which appeared untouched. Tiny birds warbled, hopping between the twigs as proud guardians of this hallowed precinct. They just stimulated my approval of their presence with pride. I listlessly removed the now leafless branches, which I had laid away from the small entrance, carefully scanning the area for silent intruders, but there were no signs. Suddenly tears sprang from my eyes, as I felt myself strangely drawn forward into the cave. Although it wasn't fear, it was powerful and sombre. I shut my eyes but all the accumulated tension inside of me just spilled out and I immediately re-opened them.

The air inside was still fairly warm and the ground was dry, as I moved around in the semi-darkness. The reality seemed so close that I felt intimidated for a few moments. Then I tried to bring to mind the features of my sister as I remembered her, with cherished thoughts. Now overcome with emotion, I delicately checked that all her clothes were as I had left them in this permanent crypt. Then I sat down and thought about the happier moments, which were still carved in my memory. The touch of the terrain inside was a silent witness to my painful sentiment, reassuring me that I would never forget. The flow of tears fell unheeded as I tried to disregard the reality and the truth. Finally, I closed my eyes and secretly prayed for the impossible as the minutes passed. I seemed to have spent a long time staring into the darkness and burning with sorrow. It was now time to say goodbye, and the single sigh of relief that swept through me was like the last failing breeze, which marks the passing of a thunderstorm. For now I nursed a secret sense of satisfaction at this hurtful journey, and suddenly felt that devotion had overridden any guilt that had channelled me along this path of deep remembrance.

It was a sunny day when I trod sadly down the twisting rugged slope to a sheltered glade. I walked slowly, with tears for myself flooding my eyes. It had been a day like this particular one, when the death of my sister had destroyed our lives, an Indian summer's day, with soft scented breezes floating through the pines. Here the jungle air wrapped itself around the little cemetery, cocooned with dignity, still looking attractive as it nestled under the huge trees in tranquillity; nothing had changed. The memory of her loss seemed to grow stronger with every visit.

Now I was the only one there, so the day belonged to me. I passed many graves that needed tending; maybe they were old or their families had long parted. Here the birds chirped merrily, unaware of the sadness below in my aching heart. I'd visited many times with my usual handful of wild flowers, passing silently under the stone arches and through the wrought-iron gates. Today my grief was made worse, because this slender little bunch that I had gathered was to be my last. I grimaced nervously and wavered as I placed them on the tiny grave, knowing that I wouldn't ever be returning again, and even the sudden outburst of tears was no release. I sat in monumental silence with eyes blurred by almost inconceivable emotion, secretly longing for the past, for the humbleness and clarity of a few months ago. I even grasped at the more tangible memories, although, in my thoughts, it was a kind of paradise to be in her company, staring at shadows that weren't there, and at dreams that didn't exist. Yet for me I was alone and a kind of prisoner even in paradise, depending on what I was really looking for.

The overwhelming stillness was caressed by tiny mountain birds, foraging along the ground for insects and pine seeds. So I secretly veiled my grief with a wanting smile as my heart fluttered up and lodged in my throat. When I finally realised it was time to leave, the discipline I was used to made all of this possible to control. In time all my precious wild flowers would fade but never the memories and I felt convinced that there would always be this invisible affinity between us for as long as I lived.

The sun appeared to have been shining even before I woke up. It was rising with a startling rapidity revealing a wide expanse of blue for our morning departure on another fearful journey. The heavy luggage, stowed safely on the backs of mules and camels, was on the way to Murree under an army escort. Once again we found ourselves waiting for transport, clearly unamused by the constant delay. By this time the authorities had noticed confusion and commotion amongst the women, so to establish some order they lectured them on the luxurious cruise awaiting them at Bombay. I glanced back many times at this picturesque glade and the sacred spots that I would never see again. I could so easily have yielded to melancholy, had it not been for the nearness of my school pals. The square was now empty, and seemed to melt in the distant gloom; its presence only discernible by the surrounding deserted bungalows. I sat in a state of controlled emotion, knowing that there was such a long way to go. There was to be no breaking down, as I eased away this small burden.

On our arrival in Murree, the transfer was quick and well organised. We were soon on that long undulating road in the packed coach, down to the city of Rawalpindi. I was hit by a strange feeling, brief reminders of this similar journey with the baby sister whom I'd left behind. This only brought a deep pain within me, choked little sobs and swollen eyes, as the panoramic Himalayan mountain range became a distant blur and the inward tremors gently ceased. The dusty road smothered the scenic valleys below. Once again regiments of cultivated fields, farmhouses and the occasional temple slid by, nestling in the woods in this wild frontier of the Punjab. Leaving the snow-covered peaks disappearing in our wake, we found the city itself a huge metropolis. We travelled through some narrow streets, heading directly for the railway station, crammed with hundreds of curious people, many of them staring without even responding to our waves and gestures. Here inquisitive children pressed against the coaches, clamouring for any spare coins, with a show of puzzlement spread across their eager faces. For us the heat of the plains was sticky and unbearable, but our discomfort could only be blamed on the short spell we had relished up in the cooler regions of the hills.

The Red Cross and army personnel fawned around us with kindness, their understanding boundless and they turned a blind eye to many misbehaving children in this maelstrom of activity. The ceaseless noise seemed to rise up and surround us as we waited. They provided all of us with an abundance of food and cool drinks, while the coolies removed the luggage from the coaches and loaded them onto the awaiting train. They also made doubly sure that every inch of vacant space was filled with supplies required for this long train journey. It was a carefully planned manoeuvre, designed to encourage and remove all the shadows of disbelief and discomfort that followed us.

A large steam locomotive, with huge drive wheels, backed onto the carriages, which stood next to the platform. That would be our home for the next four days en route to Bombay, stopping at various stations each evening for a good night's sleep. We finally left at noon, rattling out of this bustling city, where the crowded streets melted away slowly in the midday sun, and moved through the barren spaces of northern India, passing overgrown plantations and hamlets of banana-leaf huts. In the peaceful fields spinning past the carriage windows, farmers gathered in the hay with no sense of urgency in the beautiful summery evening. They stood, smiled and waved their hands in self-conscious admiration. I smiled back, wanting to apologise for moving on. Huge buildings and thick coils of black smoke signalled our first intended stop, and a temporary release from the jarring rail track.

We'd longingly waited for the arrival of dusk and some much-needed sleep, as the train approached a network of railway crossings. Suddenly the trees were springing up everywhere, houses beginning to cluster in groups and appearing to be well constructed and comfortable, pleasantly situated among tropical trees that bordered the main highway. Even the traffic began to swell. It was Lahore, one of the nicer cities in northern India. In spite of the oppressive climate most of the women enjoyed a shopping spree for necessities, preferably clothing and bedding. For me there was a strange feeling of intimacy. I drifted back and forth on a current of emotions, my thoughts spinning with confusion. It was here that my Uncle Leo was resting in peace, after that horrific journey which was to cost him his young life, but what young person would want peace instead of life? I questioned and braced myself to confront these facts, but the memories were like a rubber band tightening around my heart. I suppose the same could have been said about millions of unfortunate souls.

Morning arrived with the ominous threat of another blistering hot day cooped up in a railway carriage. We passed several villages whose names were unfamiliar to all of us. Most of the land was barren and the view very boring. Here poverty reigned supreme and proved heartbreaking to our eyes.

The outlying area was in an appalling condition, the remoteness interspersed with villages, miles of black parched earth. There were glimpses of dry plantations, struggling to produce the season's harvest of vegetables and fruit. Here the reduced rainfall quickly allowed the sun to leach fertility from the already baked soil. We continued through miles of suburbs, satanic mills and factories, farming villages with thatched-roofed cottages. In other remote districts, there were fast-flowing streams, where the women stood knee-deep in water and washed the clothes, beating them endlessly on the rocks that bulged above the surface. Oxen lazily hauled water from the farmyard wells, children shooed cattle which wandered around, chewing mindlessly. In further areas, poor farmers nibbled at the land with dilapidated ploughs, while their women folk sprayed irrigation water from buckets, carried on each side of a bamboo shoulder spar. Here the younger children looked grossly undernourished, their emaciated bodies covered in numerous sores and swamped by countless flies. They apparently seemed happy enough, waving and shouting excitedly as we passed slowly by, with the dust from the train swirling around and forming clouds of brown mist.

They had a war of their own; their situation and sentiments were fully understood, and their misery was valued by all of us. The long journey brought many sights during the tiring days, some of interest, others best forgotten, as we continued, stopping at night at the cities of Delhi, Jaipur and Ahmadabad, and finally the huge port of Bombay loomed on the horizon. Its giant buildings towered skywards like mysterious jagged monuments, concealing the skyline from our vision. It was late afternoon by the time the train came to a halt in the station, where we were besieged by shabbily dressed women with pan-stained mouths. They were trying desperately to sell their fresh fruit. Little boys clamoured like beggars grabbing our small change, then melted away in the crowded platform.

With the luggage safely stowed away in the awaiting coaches, we were soon on our way to the dockside. The streets were buzzing with people of various nationalities, as we passed slowly through. Our instant progress was prohibited by a steady flow of cattle, sheep and goats being herded towards the livestock market, which was the centrepiece in the overcrowded bazaar. It was like a huge recycling plant for pollution, traffic and noise. Even the garbage appeared to be someone's trade in this gateway to India. The city itself was squeezed to capacity, with every ethnic group that this earth could provide, from the wealthy to the beggars. There were limousines to rickshaws, sheer luxury to fervid poverty, signifying past events in this supposed city of dreams. Dozens of market stalls jammed both sides of the main road, parading a bewildering variety of good-quality products by the indigenous inhabitants, who in turn spoke a general variety of languages. The women were looking dazzling in their colourful saris. It was a place of insatiable curiosity and enormous attraction, where religion was a form of entertainment. The hardest part was trying to stay cool.

Rows of well-weathered, modest, brick houses, gleaming in the noon sunshine, lined the sides of the main thoroughfare. Each conveyed a sense of security to those who resided in them. A small patch of well-tended lawn to each front, and a driveway separating them, indicated British residents. As we drifted into the impoverished areas, the badly surfaced streets teemed with men, women, and children. Many were raggedly dressed and some, horribly deformed, begged for any obtainable coins, before returning to their tattered holes.

We finally arrived at the docks. Anchored here in close attendance was an assemblage of merchant ships from various countries, each displaying a barrage of coloured flags from their mastheads, and busy unloading their precious cargo of packages of food and machinery for the armed forces. Further into the basin, massive cranes swivelled in and out of old rusty barges, with their slings full of valuable equipment and, although they were crude by Western standards, their diligent efforts fully compensated for the lack of suitable facilities.

Then there were some liners, already converted into troopships, parading brightly coloured flags, a few painted in uniform grey. Many small boats with triangular ragged sails drifted around in the blustery harbour. Here flocks of gulls screamed, diving in and out of the choppy water, occasionally picking up bits of food that floated on the surface. A hub of noise flooded the dockyard area on our arrival, followed by an announcement over the loudspeaker, a strange deep voice summoning the families to a large impressive-looking building very near to the basin.

Everyone talked nervously about anything that came into their heads, amidst total confusion. The area was restricted to the families, the Red Cross and officers of the Mercantile Marine, although the surrounding locality was congested with military uniforms from numerous Allied countries. It was remarkably strange to see all this security, even though we had lost all certainty of the future.

Inside the waiting area several tables were laid out admirably, accompanied by wooden chairs with padded seats for the forthcoming meal. This we badly needed following the exhausting journey. Suddenly there were raised eyebrows and significant glances were cast, when a representative from the naval department delivered a welcoming speech. He was a tall, thin, wiry man, sporting a well-trimmed hairy covering, and dressed in an immaculate uniform, with a naval rank I did not recognise. He spoke with compelling power and with more than the usual energy, acknowledging the wild applause with a solemn expression. There was no mention of the war, only the restrictions on board the liner, which would be our home, and the various orders that had to be adhered to for our own safety. We sat and listened pensively, although not fully prepared for all of this, and our enthusiasm soon wavered noticeably. The thoughts of a vast ocean ahead and the obvious dangers that lurked in the deep sounded little more than savage. Vague reminders of past journeys stirred in our aching brains; it wasn't an illusion, only another survival structure to enable us to endure the weeks ahead. The long spirited discussion merely dismissed any thoughts of a luxurious cruise, which had been fully imagined by most of the women. Any reflections of a romantic sea voyage were immediately dispelled as no better than a mirage.

After the appetising meal, which was expertly laid out and fully appreciated by everyone present, we were informed that the Dutch liner the SS *Boservain*, would be our temporary home for the next ten days.

The liner stretched the full length of the quay and had a displacement of twenty thousand tons. I stood and gazed, fascinated. It was a welcome relief to return to our cabins after a tiring day, especially with the thoughts of the boat drill exercises hovering at the back of our minds. The daunting sea voyage before our first port of call was not a promise of mounting excitement. Although our cabins were rather small, they were adequate enough to sleep a family of four. There was a tranquillity inside, the sort of place you could hide from the dangers of the world. Then again none of us had attempted a sea voyage of this calibre, so we were found lacking in the mental department.

We eventually joined a small convoy consisting of fourteen ships, troopships and merchantmen, hauling vital food supplies for Britain, accompanied by an adequate destroyer escort. The days that passed were quite pleasant, although rather boring, as numerous hours were spent with us swarming around, like the legions of the lost, attending boat drills on the lifeboat stations. They were often tedious and caused alarming confusion among the passengers, but were essential tasks and, although there were bitter complaints, we accepted these naval procedures as being a major part of our survival, should the need ever arise. We overwhelmed ourselves with positively every detail that was thrown at us, and maintained the illusion of certain survival.

Afternoon tea was an unrecognised meal on board, comprising a few biscuits and a hot drink. The remainder of the menus proffered an amazing selection of food and various delicacies. The days were exceedingly long, especially for the younger ones, who played games on the upper deck. Most of the adults dozed or chatted. These pleasures were harshly inconvenienced by the clumsy lifebelts strapped to our backs, another compulsory order. With the falling of dusk, the blackout restricted all forms of recreation, so the film shows transmitted in the dining area occupied most of the evening. This very enjoyable pastime dismissed the rest of the world from our private little kingdom.

The voyage progressed with utmost caution and awareness. The whole convoy envisaged disturbing possibilities, arising unexpectedly, with alarming results from the deep. The constant fear of doom was repeated in long-running conversations by everyone. Now our habitual progression through nervousness and reassurance appeared to be at full stretch, and there was no alternative. Somehow we had to discontinue harbouring these unthinkable beliefs, which were sharpening up into something more possessive.

Large white clouds floated across the sky, shifting gently eastwards, with the moist touch of a southerly wind, and the air smelt deceptively of an early autumn. Suddenly we were concealed by heavy cloud cover, which seemed to go on for ever through mountainous seas, when great waves exploded onto the decks. Now many of the passengers, including myself, thought we were going to die through starvation, being paralysed by the dreaded seasickness. Numerous meals were continuously being turned away by passengers with aching heads and closed eyes, plus the usual burp way down in the empty stomach. Friendly persuasion was always the suggested method to eliminate this unwanted illness, but the sight of food only increased the burden. With it energy seemed to drain away, as we quickly removed ourselves away from the tables, accompanied by tight chests, swollen throats and eyes streaming with burning tears.

The first glimpse of alien land slid into view as the early dawn arrived, although the landscape wasn't very exciting. Eventually the busy harbour, distant houses and some tatty palms hid behind a curtain of tropical mist. We were then informed that it was Port Suez, gateway to the famous Suez Canal on the North African coast. The dockyard had met with severe air attacks; a few wrecks dotted the fine harbour, and although many of the houses had survived, the water was dirty and awash with debris. It was perfectly clear that, despite the pessimistic reports, the excitement of achieving a safe passage for the whole convoy showed on the faces of the crowds waving enthusiastically on the dockside. All the merchant ships went direct to the unloading areas, but for us, the sharp eyes and ears of the local press had sniffed out the big story.

Excited crowds of all nationalities gathered in their hundreds on the dockside. They were milling around, cheering, shouting and waving at this audacious armada. For many of them life had been savage these past few years. Dozens of small boats circled the troopships, their pennants fluttering in the sharp breeze. The entire assembly signalled that our welcome certainly wasn't muted. To our surprise, we were shocked to learn that many of the residents had worked alongside the enemy, probably because there was no guarantee that the Allies would return so quickly. In most areas, many switched loyalties just to stay alive. However, for the present, they appeared content with their life, and impressed us with their friendliness. There weren't many solid buildings to be seen from the harbour, everything seemed to have been obliterated by the constant air raids. The clawing desert air wrapped itself around you suddenly the moment you descended the gangway, and the remoteness of the place didn't make you feel entirely at home.

Enquiring glances were soon cast at the authorities regarding the discontinuing of our journey. Immediately after disembarking with our belongings, we were shepherded off once again in open trucks to a transit campsite a few miles away in the desert. Everyone was annoyed with the sudden change of plans and the tension and anxiety only increased. The women made no attempt to conceal their disapproval and chagrin, and their frustration edged itself into faces of anger and eyes of disbelief. Their feelings now void of control, some were even reluctant to leave the comfort of the ship. It quickly became obvious that a better approach and a more friendly and carefree manner was required to control some of the more adamant women. For them living in a transit camp, somewhere in the desert, appeared more of a nightmare as the atmosphere of fear invaded their cosy lifestyle. A few dispelled the drowsiness induced by the heat, by remaining calm and unmoved during this encounter with the authorities.

Arriving at the army camp, we were astonished to find it situated at the base of a mountain range bearing the strange name of Gebel Ataqa. The significance of this being that, silhouetted against the horizon, it resembled the attractive shape of a legendary goddess lying there exposed to the heavens, immortalised and now long banished. Although there seemed to be a deadening remoteness and isolation in this alien environment, the whole area had a buzz of activity but was restricted by religious and social cultures.

Each family was billeted in separate tents, which stood in regimental order, personifying accuracy and style. They were large enough to accommodate the average-sized family, but it soon became obvious that movement inside the heavy canvas walls was badly restricted. The covering of sand for carpeting proved very frustrating and inconvenient during the twilight hours. Many objected, while some openly admitted that with care they could overcome this trivial obstacle quite easily. The topic was finally never seriously discussed with annoyance, but with more of a jovial nature.

The whole camp was encircled by an eight-foot steel wire fence topped with barbed wire, and continuously patrolled by British soldiers, giving it the appearance of a prisoner-of-war camp. Italian prisoners prepared, cooked and served all the meals, in a giant marquee perched near the main entrance of the site. We soon settled down to this unreal peaceful life, but were strictly forbidden to leave the compound during the first few weeks. It was considered unsafe to venture too far without an escort, which made us aware of the constant strain on the serving soldiers. Being new arrivals to the Middle East, fresh and enthusiastic, we made no attempt to conceal our delight when informed that the conflict was turning in favour of the Allies. Excitement and tension only spiralled, which annihilated the sun, the sand and the stockade, although in reality it held all of us prisoners.

During the day, the ever-present sinister sun blazed downward like a furnace on the white sand, making the heat seem even worse, bearing down like a heavy weight. In the evenings, the contrast was vast as a gentle breeze drifted in from the Red Sea. Then the sparse desert palms emerging from the white ground took on a magical quality, canopied by the starlit sky. The tents provided a cooler refuge from the sweltering plains and the night air was positively chilly as the sunset and the darkness crept around. Deep into the night, the temperature plummeted to bizarre depths, so trying to acclimatise to this rapid transformation seemed impossible. Behind closed eyes the oil lamps flickered, weaving intricate patterns on canvas walls.

'That swelling on your neck looks rather large and ripe as well,' my mother said one morning. She looked very concerned, much to my irritation.

'It's a boil,' I replied in a whisper, expecting the conversation to end, yet fearing her next remark.

'I know very well it's a boil and it looks ready for bursting,' she replied, showing immediate interest, which worried me, as she gently touched the tender area. She eyeballed me closely, then came the dreaded comment. 'Come on, I think we'll pay a quick visit to the surgery. Besides you don't look too healthy anyway.'

Although cradling my sister, she grabbed my hand and we marched off to the small clinic nestled in a nearby tent. She was quite aware of the temperature that was rising in me. Strains of excited chatter from passers-by eddied on the sweaty air, which passed through the sandy passageways en route to the make-do hospital. Alarm bells of excruciating pain rang loudly in my ears. There would certainly be no sedative for a mere boil, which was now throbbing. My immediate thoughts were that skipping away seemed the perfect solution, but the boil would still be there; besides, I was feeling desperately ill. I certainly wasn't in any condition to go very far. Suddenly instant belief in the angelic image of a pretty nurse in her smart uniform banished all the pain for ever. I coaxed up enough courage within my shivering frame to enter the tent with my mother. The clinic was only used for minor cases and dressings.

We sat and waited patiently in the spare enclosure, while the nurse's services were occupied elsewhere on some unfortunate being, behind a closed curtain. Unannounced quiet moans of endurance, followed by some heavy breathing, dented what little bottle I had. However, the belief that she would generally apply some of her tenderness to a young boy, having already dealt with soldiers, calmed my frustration. Finally the curtain opened and a sombre-looking trooper walked out, with his arm heavily bandaged. A quick glance at his face turned me into a coward within a blink of an eyelid. In the dimly lit interior, my facial expression and feelings also changed instantly when the nurse appeared from behind the dull curtain. She was certainly no seraphic beauty, as I had imagined with optimism, but a stocky young woman with a pleasant smile and built like a warthog. She had a round happy face, but huge arms akin to the cartoon character, Pluto hung from her shoulders. She looked immensely stoical, in a badly creased uniform, and all my doubts about the wisdom in coming increased intensely. Now my knees trembled and my stomach performed the conga. I prayed inwardly that she might suggest that I was a hospital case.

'Hello,' she said in a languid voice, which didn't suit her personality, and motioned me to a chair close at hand.

'Hi,' I replied, my voice trembling.

Her expression was calm and her large mournful eyes held no self-pity.

'What's the matter with you, young man?'

Before I could answer her, there was a short discussion between the adults, and her eyes soon returned to me and the boil. A close examination of the festering abscess confirmed the expected ritual.

'Yes,' she said, smiling modestly, 'it certainly looks ready for bursting and you look as if a good night's sleep won't go amiss either.'

I looked at her with sad eyes already flooding, but never spoke a word.

'Here, place this between your teeth and bite as hard as you possibly can,' she said, handing me a tough piece of leather. Then she delicately placed a wad of cotton wool around the infected area.

I closed my eyes, clenched my fists tightly, gritted my teeth and prayed silently. I felt a large pair of thumbs squeeze the abscess, and didn't have to wait very long. The throbbing magnified and my breath stopped, as colourless liquid streamed through constricted eyelids and the constant pressure increased around my neck. I thought my head was jammed inside a nutcracker, then swoosh, I heard the gentle sound of blood and pus squirt out and any chance of concealing my anguish had long since disappeared. I went limp, I opened my eyes, then closed them again. They seemed to be paddling in a pool of salty water.

'Now drink this quickly, it will ease the pain,' the nurse said, handing me a small glass containing some colourless fizzing liquid. I swallowed the medicine nervously and had no illusions about how I felt. My head started to spin, and all that I could see was gloom, and feel the sticky heat inside the tent.

'There now, that wasn't so bad, was it?' she enquired, examining the tender area.

I nodded, blank and expressionless, wiping away some of my tears with the back of my hand. Then I thought to myself, Yes, it wasn't you on the receiving end.

'Just sit still for a moment,' she said, producing a thermometer. 'I'll have to check your temperature.'

I immediately obliged by opening a wide mouth eagerly, as a thin piece of glass slid under my tongue. Sleep seemed to be knocking at the door as I sat passively on the chair. After wiping away any excess fluid from the painful area, the nurse stuck a huge plaster on the reduced lump. A few minutes passed.

'Yes, hospital for you, young man,' she remarked, glancing at the thermometer between her fingers, after removing it from my mouth. 'You should be in bed, with a temperature of one hundred and three. You're burning up, and need medical attention. Must be some kind of infection that you have picked up.' She sounded confident in her diagnosis.

A quick chat with the orderly, and I was on my way in a battered ambulance to the military hospital a few miles away in the desert.

'You had better behave yourself while you're away,' was my mother's last order. Then she left me to collect some toiletries and pyjamas for my intended stay.

New thoughts flashed through my brain and my imagination began to work overtime... a complete rest in a comfortable bed with clean sheets, cool wards with electric fans spinning from the ceiling and releasing a breath of fresh air, solid walls, compact floors and delicious food with an array of choices, away from the present harsh environment. I continued to daydream as the vehicle bounced up and down on the long dusty track. Approaching my imaginary hospital, I was soon to realise the fatality of make-believe. There was absolutely no indication that the conflict belonged to another world, and I was equally disappointed to discover that canvas was the sheltered accommodation.

'Come on, son, give me your hand,' said the young soldier, when he opened the rear door of the truck.

I stood up immediately and walked slowly to him carrying my few belongings.

'I'll take you to the sister in charge, she'll take good care of you,' he said confidently.

The whole area was a hive of depressing commotion, and my romantic habitat was harsh and ugly. My eyes adjusted to the unpleasant sights, and my ears quickly became attuned to other pitiful sounds from behind Red Cross tents.

A strong smell of chloroform invaded my nose and throat as I entered the sickbay. Once again I was about to witness battle casualties being wheeled in at short notice, drained of all emotion. They never complained, even though their wounds were serious, mostly head and leg injuries. They were stretchered in and out at random. The fortunate ones survived, others didn't. Doctors and nurses worked extremely hard in the intense heat, which suffocated every movement and the sand prohibited normal motion. Other casualties flooded in continuously and those really ill and chronically disabled were probably sent home when fit enough to travel. For me this was a vision of another world, more brutal and vicious than I had ever imagined, a window on human endurance and carnage. The hospital was not a cheery place, with blood and bandages strewn everywhere and the smell of anaesthetic choking the lungs. With sights such as these I carefully concealed my own grievances, the dollops of quinine and that awful castor oil delivered every morning, with the bearer displaying a huge smile at my discomfort.

I spent several hours of spare time being taught religiously about the arts and skills of the board game, Monopoly, by a Scotsman, when so much laughter shielded the pain and adversity in this bleak atmosphere. I finally left the canvas infirmary, fully recovered from my short illness. I took with me many lessons that I had learnt, ones which you wouldn't find in any textbook. I would also carry many courageous pictures in my mind. Yet, above everything, I will always hold the greatest respect and admiration for the integrity and discipline shown by the medical profession.

We were totally unprepared and shocked in mid-December, when during a meal break we were informed that orders had arrived for sailing. It was just an eerie return to another journey, another nightmare, for nothing could distract us from the mathematics of our situation. Today, tomorrow, the war would continue and one day our turn would come, but reason and sanity prevailed. For me personally it was a mixture of childhood, war, and thoughts of loved ones along with an intense feeling of guilt. I was here alive and fully conscious of everything, yet my mental concept was still occupied and controlled by intense fear, a vehicle with a registration number of uncertainty.

Our minds were cocooned in apprehension, when the day of departure finally arrived. We spent most of the morning making sure that our belongings were safely stowed away in the waiting trucks. The journey to Port Suez in the motorised vehicles was thankfully occupied by the constant chatter amongst the women, who had high expectations. There was now a determined air about everything.

As we entered the famous harbour, it was noticeable that there were many government offices, and some well-constructed buildings, but the overall impression was of shabbiness and squalor. The many shops were unattractive and did not provide or sell anything of interest to people like us, although we found it rather exciting to be in the centre of so much effort and support. The human race is not renowned for being the kindest and most considerate of all God's creatures.

There was certainly no evidence of the sea, only the historic canal which appeared to be embedded between great towering slopes of sand. In spite of its admirable harbour, the town itself seemed to be a poor and sluggish area, with very little evidence of further development, the dominant feature being this man-made wonder. Here the police were trying to establish some kind of order, as we left our conveyances for a short walk to a functional-looking building perched solidly on the dockside. We entered a large room with long windows and cracked ceilings, probable attestation to recent air attacks. The inside was decked out like a dining hall, with wooden chairs stacked near the tables for immediate use. There was a long mirror running the entire length of the bar, shelves packed with empty glasses and plates. Numerous multicoloured ornaments decorated the drab surroundings. It lacked any trappings of luxury and the background looked like an interwoven battlefield, with decimated plants and advancing weeds.

Once again came the usual greeting by men dressed in naval uniforms, trying desperately to impose a certain amount of authority, which was hardly surprising, here where there were constant unconfirmed rumours flooding around the shops, and considering the ebb and flow of nervous families jostling for seats in the humid conditions. We were all feeling very tired and irritable, not helped by the consistent reports that we would be boarding some ship anchored in the basin. Trying to assemble ourselves into some kind of order, and jostling for a comfortable position, we finally sat down and waited in an area overlooking the beautiful harbour. It was an area shrouded with giant rusty-looking cranes fully engaged in perpetual motion. The very helpful waiters brought us sandwiches and iced drinks which cooled us down a little, but we still felt weighed down by the oppressive heat and humid atmosphere. We were certainly feeling conscious of the guilt we had for causing so much displeasure to the staff, but the intensity of their efforts and their heroic attempts to be friendly to these mysterious strangers had to be admired.

Finally an interesting discussion was conducted by one of the senior officers, who in turn as a mark of courtesy answered endless demanding questions from many of the unsettled women.

He then informed us, rather surprisingly, that families with a small infant would be personally assisted by an officer, who would chaperon them during any hostilities for the entire voyage. His closing statement cured us of our insatiable curiosity when he informed us rather casually that the British liner, the SS *Orion*, now converted into a troopship and berthed alongside, would be our home for the next two weeks. He also confirmed that we would be accompanied by some eight thousand troops, who were returning home for a deserved spot of leave. The liner had a displacement of thirty thousand tons and was considerably larger than our previous ship. She looked really impressive, in gleaming white, although the paintwork had rusty streaks down her hull, where a continuous flow of warm water pumped out into the basin.

On the opposite side of the docks, giant tugs were hauling corroded container barges low in the water, and seagulls screeched behind in flocks, occasionally pitching into the wake in search of smaller prey at their pleasure. Two hours later we were boarding this floating citadel, trudging upwards on the long steep gangway and carrying some of our small articles, the unwanted trunks being safely stowed away in the massive hold. Now there was a momentary hardening in our stomachs, a flash of tension, which was occasionally displaced with a half-hearted smile. We found the cabins spacious and certainly larger than in the other liner. We welcomed these few hours of spare time to adjust ourselves to another new environment.

The radiance of daylight found us joining a huge convoy in the assembly zone at the mouth of the canal. Here several huge ships of all shapes paraded in dazzling sunlight, yet somehow the weather had turned strangely cooler. The column moved in single file like slow-moving traffic along the misty shape, which resembled a liquid thoroughfare of tremendous width, gently slicing cleanly through the glazed surface, which stretched as far as the eye could see. The vapour, bouncing off in heatwaves, mirrored a ceiling of mist. There appeared to be no twists or turns to this seemingly endless chasm.

There was some choice accommodation in the decks above the waterline, but below, it was a vastly different story. Here thousands of servicemen, the majority of them soldiers, were crammed into crudely converted troop decks which reached way down into the bilges. This was an awesome disadvantage in so many ways, when the ribs and plates of the liner would creak and vibrate violently, especially in heavy seas. High above, the afternoon sun was like a fireball, its rays bouncing off the water in blinding oscillation against a flawless enamelled sky. We moved slowly and effortlessly through the canal, as the main decks were crowded with eager observers, aflame with curiosity amidst a blanket of silence. The women stared morosely at anything or anyone that didn't appeal to them on the sloping plateau of sand.

Eventually our vast procession of stately shipping moved into the boundless surface of motionless deep blue water, the scrupulously clean Mediterranean Sea. Now we had to put our trust in providence and for a moment the war was forgotten. Our immediate thoughts were more of concern with that mystical and omnipotent silence of the ocean itself which looked challenging and formidable, now suddenly disturbed by this huge armada, with some of the escorts scuttling around, exploding their way through the rough sea with enormous difficulty. The gigantic endless swells sweeping them aside in a rebellious motion. The night came as black as a tomb, but there was nothing to see anyway. We plunged in and out of deep swells, as the water bubbled along our sides and reflections of the stars flitted across our beam. Within minutes of our climbing into our bunks, the steady roll of the liner plummeted us into a deep sleep. Soon forgotten were the shallows of the ocean fringes with the storm-tossed waves and their dangers.

With a vengeance dawn broke, and after washing and changing quickly we sat in the dining area for breakfast. Through the portholes we watched fascinated, as the convoy appeared to be struggling at a reduced speed with huge bows plunging in and out of the choppy surface. After the meal, it was time to muster on the starboard side of the ship for our instruction in lifeboat drill, which was compulsory. Fragments of conversation drifted amongst the women who now felt agitated with this new obligation, although they kept their complaints to themselves. Many of us found it almost impossible to maintain an upright position for any length of time, but we applied ourselves with patience to this boring operation, which could be our lifeline. Even though the menu was imaginative and not short of choice, most of the passengers were plagued with seasickness. Many couldn't think of a more inspired reason for being absent from the exhausting exercise. I myself was retaining sour memories of a lost breakfast, and very few of us survived this awful ailment, which never seemed to leave us for any length of time.

The following day we found ourselves in calmer weather, the sea now a velvet carpet glistening under a tropical heatwave, which we found rewarding. A comforting remark that an abundance of fresh air was a reasonable antidote against the reoccurring sickness failed miserably. Although this precaution might have appeared an excellent idea, we knew from past experience that it never really worked on the human mind. Somehow we could never acclimatise ourselves even with the smell of clean, fresh, salt air in our lungs. The safe sanctuary of the stomach was always threatened, and the illusion was soon shattered.

We were flanked on the starboard side by the imposing liner, SS *Strathmore*, with her single funnel, although thought to be unsafe and undistinguished at that time. She was painted from head to stern in the colour of khaki. I always felt that we were impregnable by her presence, but there was no particular reason for feeling this. I was probably more impressed by her grandiosity. Glistening majestically in our wake was the impressive liner, *The Highland Princess*, who looked just as formidable, as her bows dipped up and down in the giant swells. Nevertheless, a flutter of pride rejected any fear that I may have had in these harrowing circumstances.

Most of our time was divided into a number of activities. Games would be played on the upper deck during the calmer periods. A huge variety of films were shown continuously after late supper every night, in the dining area. They were usually comedies, which were predictable, musicals and the popular *Road* series. This was to become a customary jaunt of mine throughout the long voyage. At dusk the upper decks were restricted to all passengers, as the blackout was the order, when everything was enmeshed in a dark net, obliterating the last of the horizon.

One particular day, things looked bad for a moment when a reconnaissance aircraft circled the convoy from a distance. It stayed out of range of the escorts and rumours spread rapidly that our position would immediately be dispatched to any wolf pack operating in and around that area, now a constant reminder that there had been mounting losses at sea.

The sun had set and we had all bedded down cosily for the night, surrendering our extravagant lifestyle in the overcrowded troopship to the peace and tranquillity of our snug cabins. Towards the early hours of the morning an announcement burst through the tannoy system, summoning all the families to the lifeboat station. Within minutes the officer was rapping on our cabin door. We had all practised these demanding drills many times, but panic engulfed our dazed senses as we rushed about frantically. The cabin was now a nest of confusion and commotion. Outside, the gangways soon became areas of purposeful chaos, as running feet pounded the decks in a restless tide of hysteria. Topcoats were slung over nightclothes, shoes and life jackets were all we had time for. My sister was bundled into the arms of the officer, who appeared to be the only one completely in control. Everyone seemed to be heading for a collision course, so fostering any degree of normality made manoeuvring extremely difficult through narrow gangways and watertight doors. Everyone was now clinging tenaciously to whatever means of moral support. We followed the young officer nervously, in sizeable groups, up to the boat deck, where there seemed to be hundreds of people milling around aimlessly. There was a cacophonous din of shouts and screams from young and old alike, and the darkness impeded any reasonable behaviour and stability. The troubled, disturbing, daunting feelings were becoming infectious.

My heart pounded and the blood throbbed in my temples as my thoughts veered to and fro. Hope had scarcely taken hold when suddenly doubts reoccurred and tormenting images filtered through my head. I had visions of a thunderous explosion and the sea's thundering inrush, an endless wait. My mind travelled in a hopeless dream that we had to survive, but flickered like a candle in the wind. My horrific fear was stemmed by a comforting smile and a pleasant wink from the officer standing close to me. I returned a shy smile, and any colour in my cheeks deepened with embarrassment. It was a cold night and the sea air was positively chilly for this time of the year, which left us shivering in our skimpy gear. Emergency blankets were issued to wrap around our shoulders as we clustered around the periphery waiting for the worst to happen. We stood nervously, swaying with the ceaseless movement of the ship, as the chilly sea spray splattered the decks. Nothing seemed to exist except blotchy shapes rolling about on the angry sea. The possibility of the lurking enemy, looming from out of the depths or near the horizon, never occurred to me. I believed, as others believed, that disaster was destined solely for others and for that moment any thoughts of this ship being sunk was the last thing on my mind.

There was nothing but blackness with a hint of undulation, as the sound of the waves splashed against the sides of the liner in the unseen turbulence. High up in the dark sky, the lights of tiny stars winked pitifully through a mist of twilight. The sudden silence, the irritability that hung in the air told a vastly different story. If it was a U-boat attack, I felt sure that many of the passengers had already pictured themselves adrift in a lifeboat, or even worse, clinging to a raft, soaked in salt water and freezing from the damp. Everyone knew the fate that waited for them, even if the sea behaved itself. At least we did have a better prospect than most. There were numerous ships in the area ready to record our position or even rescue survivors should it be necessary. However, given a hit by some well-aimed torpedoes, we should have sufficient time to scramble aboard the lifeboats. After all we had proved our efficiency in the boat drills and besides there would be no second chances. These few precious moments had to be savoured; we had to welcome the semblance of safety and justice in this otherwise lawless sea.

I kept thinking to myself that I wished we had never sailed; any moment now could be our last and all my skylarking days would be over. The minutes passed slowly as the tension increased, and fear drifted in and out of my senses as rapid as the beating of my heart. The darkness was paling in front of us and the sea slid beneath the hull, imparting a gentle rise and fall. We were hopelessly vulnerable in this huge expanse of black water and must have presented a tempting target. It was common knowledge that we all shared a hatred of the exploitation of sea power and the treacherous persecution that accompanied it. I braced myself for any imminent explosion, and the general gloom certainly didn't prevent me from saying a silent prayer. It was something for which I'd been taught to have a total and abiding respect. We huddled together like bees in a hive, although the discomfort was increased by the clumsy life jackets, which we had slipped over our heads. They were another safety clause, a donation not too well received. One huge bulging lump projected from the chest and another from the back, fastened under the armpits with a tight bow. They were now becoming more uncomfortable, with tiredness sapping our energy. With the sleepiness of our eyes we were unable to adjust to all this sudden gloom.

The silence was suffocating as no one spoke, and the murmurs I could hear were prayers being whispered. Occasionally, in the light, perspiration seemed to glisten on some of the weary faces. Has our time come? I asked myself. Will the jaws of the belligerent sea envelop us in one huge gulp like the *Titanic*? We had escaped one brutal enemy and walked straight into the arms of another. I had to chat to myself; everyone else was quiet and withdrawn, most of them having little to say and obviously hoping for some kind of reprieve, for we certainly weren't in a bargaining position. Suddenly an explosion rolled across the surface of the sea and the water seemed to bubble and explode with a heavy thud. I strained my eyes and ears, staring at the incandescent vision, which appeared above the horizon, as the water growled and rippled. Everyone's eyes were transfixed by deep crimson flashes and huge globules of fire, which streaked high into the blackness. The mirrored image snaked across the dark water between us and the burning hulk. Suddenly it sank lower and lower into a trough of emptiness, now lit by a scarlet dazzle of flames. Almost immediately the escorts buzzed and raced between the ships like well-trained bloodhounds. Although the moon was full that night, the light was pale and visibility over the water was inadequate. Suddenly the raging inferno vanished and the sea returned to its placid calm.

Time seemed to drag by and I felt tempted to close my eyelids and surrender myself to sleep, but then the silence sprouted wings to my thoughts… a spread of torpedoes hitting us broadside, the sound of lacerated metal being ripped apart into shreds, carving huge gaping holes in the hull, as floods of black water gushed into the bilges. Then the helpless screams of women and children as panic clouded their brains. I looked around for support, burrowing deeper into my thoughts, trembling and afraid, when a voice rang out, 'Are you all right, son?' It was the young officer trying to console my ever-present terror.

'Yes,' I replied, scarcely able to move my limbs and tottering with fatigue, a sense of unreality overtaking me. Have we really survived? I asked myself. There were more twinkling lights in the darkness; it was the escorts scanning the desecrated area. I felt like running away. The year was now drawing to a close, indication that Christmas would soon be here. It was a time to be decorating the tree, shopping for gifts for loved ones and special friends, sending greeting cards, and making significant wishes for ourselves.

The air grew steadily heavier, and the sea grew steeper, as some of the waves reared higher than the rest. I felt an urge to ask our friend what time it was, when a trace of light appeared and the turmoil died away. The waiting seemed endless before we finally returned to our cabins, still feeling the lingering horror of the havoc we had all witnessed. I was so exhausted that undressing was impossible without pauses for rest, and my eyes were watering by the time I had jumped into bed. Dawn seemed to break before we had even dropped off to sleep, and at breakfast an official announcement was made over the tannoy about the night's misfortunes.

For the next few days, the convoy slipped on without any further mishap towards the unbelievable West, of which we had dreamed for so long. In a short while the sound and light, which had filled the sky on the shores of Sicily, could be seen in the distance. The clamour in the crowded dining hall only confirmed that the rumours suggesting that we weren't too far away from the

Sicilian shoreline were surely correct.

The convoy continued westwardly without any further drama. Everyone had finally settled down and adjusted admirably to the regulated workings of this temporary home. Now life on board had taken on a regular rhythm after the chaos and confusion of a few days earlier.

For a change the sea, usually so boring, now resembled an expanse of peaks in a reduced scale with calm velvet knolls and flowing undulations. I allowed myself the welcome pleasure of the boat deck, now bathed in heavenly sunshine. Soon I became engrossed in the water roaring and hissing along the side of the ship's waterline. She moved rhythmically through this viscous element, producing a continuous flow of bubbles and foam, which swept past in an energetic dance. The sky itself had changed and the tranquillity hung with clouds of sheepskin, which slowly began to overwhelm the deep blue with consumed endeavour. Then suddenly the sun sank as the glitter waned.

Suddenly the horizon grew more and more distinct, and all at once I caught sight of some unusual black dots near the surface, which came and went in a flurry. One of the crew also spotted them. 'Flying fish,' he shouted over to me, as shoals of them clipped the surface of the water, then bore down on the ship in an aggressive manner, finally disappearing out of sight and abruptly taking their leave. I watched fascinated in the company of some of the other children, scampering across the decks from side to side and following the procession with a twinge of excitement. My gaze registered a quiet satisfaction as I breathed deeply and stared towards the infinite blue sky.

By noon the next day only a handful of silky clouds remained as we entered the Strait of Messina, flanked between the rugged shores of Italy and Sicily. The decks were soon awash with curious passengers, stampeding through the gangways, when the tannoy system confirmed alien land in view, looking serene and inviting in the distance. Eventually the day was wearily melting into the night and the sun had paled and died too. However, conversations languished with thoughts of devouring a huge meal in the stillness of the harbour waters, without the discomfort of feeling ill. I stood and observed peacefully, with my hands thrust deep into my pockets. Here the seagulls circled the liner on motionless wings, which faded and blazed in splendour, as they lost and then captured the glitter from the reflection of the flickering water. I felt an urge to reach out and touch them, and for all my weariness, I found it impossible to resist watching God's creatures squawking and scavenging after the waste food, which had been dumped over the side.

A sudden stopping of the engines brought waves slapping against the hull, then a crushing noise, as the huge anchor slid into the water, clamped by lengths of bulky chain link. Moist sand, scattered with great patches of seaweed, crept slowly to the surface, changing the water colour immediately to a muddy green. Only the gentle hum of the electric motors followed, and peace had returned for a while in a breathless hush. There were numerous British warships anchored in the bay, which made us feel safe for the time being.

The expressions on jubilant faces soon went through a remarkable transformation, when requests for shopping visits were instantly denied. Almost instantly this was followed by signs of an initial hint of perplexity on features flushing a deep crimson. We'd spent many years in a tropical climate but without the luxury of electric fans to relieve us from the excessive heat. However, this liner was fitted with air conditioning, so it was refreshing to come inside from the torridity, into an exhilarating atmosphere. Being on the fringe of this foreign and friendly land aroused everyone to a delirious excitement. This in turn removed all the tensions that had accumulated recently but inwardly there were still the tremors of fear. We could not relinquish those, but any illusions of freedom and safety, which we might have had, had already been swept away.

Dawn broke as the sun thrust its power over the skyline, but in the afternoon it was perfectly clear as the sunlight danced on the water. The heat allowed the gentle waves to sparkle as the temperature rose rapidly, and it felt as if the whole world would melt in a sudden rush. On the main deck clusters of passengers loitered, talking and laughing excitedly, as peace seemed to hover. It was only the sound of my brother's voice that pulled me out of my trance, as I gazed at this huge armada. The shoreline had suffered severe bombardment and numerous wrecks dotted the harbour. Inland further spires of masts, funnels and some upper works protruded from the anchorage. An early dawn saw the convoy take on fresh supplies, then continue with their perilous journey. For us, rather surprisingly, we were left behind, which cheered most of us up considerably. But the strong rumours were that the delay was to accommodate troops who had been wounded during the recent landings. There were also indications that we would soon be sailing ourselves.

Suddenly, screaming sirens signalled an air raid, which left me convinced that I was a jinx, which of course was totally untrue. The huge camouflaged planes in immaculate formation hounded the convoy heading West. From our viewpoint enormous fountains of water surged upwards, as sticks of bombs fell into the sea. We were never informed of the outcome of this raid, whether it was successful or not. Fortunately we were unscathed, and sailed a few days later in close company with a single destroyer for escort. It was sunset and the horizon disappeared, as the sun sank into the sea in a blaze of colour. The edges of the clouds were clearly engraved against the blackness, and very soon curtains of overcast mists gathered and consumed the skyline. Now the only sign of turmoil was deep within our own thoughts, as we watched the murky regions of the sea, which looked black beneath an awning of widespread carpeting.

There was never a moment's sense of security, or freedom from fear now that the lookouts had already assembled at their posts. These were dangerous times and we distrusted the peaceful atmosphere. For us it was just an endless wait for another alarm that would have all of us scrambling for safety once more.

Christmas Day, 1943, fell abruptly upon us, but far from the biting cold the sun would impart some of its warmth when it rose above the sea, which was a huge green carpet, looking tranquil and enticing. In the galley they had been working overtime, busy preparing extra-special meals for the festive period. The tree standing in the huge dining area looked dwarfed and isolated. However, it was prettily strung with coloured tinsel and numerous shapely ornaments. The added artificial snow, in the shape of cotton wool, displayed a magical picture, illuminated by twinkling lights. The room itself was also attractively decorated with an assortment of streamers, baubles and some delicate garlands. Even balloons dangled from the ceiling festooned with sparkle. All the tables were spread with coverings of psychedelic crêpe paper and crackers were used to form intricate patterns of fetching elegance. Despite our circumstances, we were filled with emotion when everyone sang carols as part of a continuous increasing uproar, which in turn was followed by silent prayers. Initially everything was prepared for our benefit, but it all appeared meaningless to us for our immediate thoughts were for those who were not so fortunate, hundreds of miles away.

Present conversations remained strictly pleasant and saintly; any topics of the war were definitely avoided. The huge liner plunged forward through mountainous swells, pitching and tossing with its human cargo. Outside was a vastly different story; the sun rose steadily gaining strength as it climbed towards the heavens. The only disturbance was the hubbub of craggy voices in melancholy song, and the clatter of empty glasses on the table. Then darkness fell and the last daylight flickered in our trail, perilously presenting a slender inviting contour against the horizon.

The days passed and numerous whispers floated through the air that the port of Tangier wasn't too far away. In my mind's eye I imagined pictures of gorgeous belly dancers, parading in scanty costumes and snake charmers squatting in nooks, performing rituals with their hideous reptiles to eerie music. There were thoughts of a huge market thronging with Saracen traders, in their flamboyant robes and with rugged features, all of them displaying a varied selection of strange merchandise.

The sight of Gibraltar on the opposite side excited our hearts, home of the British fleet and a crown colony with numerous air bases not too far away. There now was a safe feeling that surveillance would always be constant. We finally entered the Strait of Gibraltar, passing the ape-inhabited rock without stopping. Then stimulation and curiosity hung like a veil, as enquiring faces stared at each other in surprise as we continued with our journey. A hollow sensation weighed heavily in the pit of my stomach, when we were informed that our course was the

North Atlantic.

Suddenly we were hit by a violent thunderstorm as streaks of lightning hissed unmercifully. There were deafening thunderclaps and rain cascaded down, sending cataracts streaming everywhere, gushing from the wide channels of the upper deck, as the liner rolled on gigantic waves. She was taking on a perilous dimension, struggling through the awesome sea and wind-whipped breakers as the stays stretched and creaked in the howling gales. In these conditions the immensity of space could be a blessing or a curse, yet somehow it was the graveyard of so many ships.

Continuous synchronised attacks by packs of German U-boats had already taken a heavy toll on defenceless merchantmen and warships alike. These fronts were formidable and, although bringing large squalls, had proved very successful for the enemy in the past. However, for us a more circuitous route had been selected to outwit the wolf packs – the fearsome Bay of Biscay. This expanse of water was vastly different to the Atlantic, although considerably smaller by comparison. Here mountainous waves made it very difficult for them to operate and exercise their authority, and cruising on the surface was virtually impossible. The hurricane force winds and the turbulence were consistent and ceaseless for lengthy periods.

As we entered this volatile stretch of black water, the waves appeared malign, rearing and subsiding with sporadic menace. Again and again the foam washed over the bows and the sea burst through the gratings. Our solitary escort popped up and down like a lifeless cork, bobbing and weaving as if abandoned to the elements. One moment the stern reared high out of the water stationary, as though extruded from below, and for a few seconds it loomed above the tempestuous sea, then disappeared completely from view. Suddenly the bow would extend momentarily, then vanish without trace. In contrast to the tension and bustle all around, there was peace and tranquillity here. It was periods like these that seemingly made our voyage relatively safe.

The drastic change of weather hit us like a bolt of lightning when we entered the English Channel, the biting cold was cruel and penetrating, but then nature sent us an ally, dense fog. Now we felt safe once more and the long nightmare was nearly over as

British flying boats circled like vultures eyeing a weakened prey. Strangely, though, all those months of travelling away from one war brought us straight into another. Even the women no longer took part in desperate discussions; they seemed to have separated themselves from all their sufferings and the war. The intense cold and memories of horrors no longer plagued them anymore.

Within a few hours we were crossing the Irish Sea, which made us realise that in a short while we would be docking. Dark clouds were spreading towards the horizon, and the sky was threatening heavy rain with a constant rumble of thunder in the distance. 'This is typical English weather and something you will have to get used to,' remarked one of the crew, as we emerged onto the upper deck. Our thoughts were centred on the firm surface of dry land, but the sea spray and chilling breeze were now piercing our bodies, somehow reviving spent memories of a previous winter in the Himalayas. For all of us there was only one real topic of conversation, we had finally arrived in England.

We quickly scampered back to the cabin for some thicker clothing, as we breathed out blue vapour, and everyone followed in the same general direction. There was a sharpish return when shouts of 'Land!' echoed around the ship. We now appeared to be moving very slowly with the engines at half-speed, the waves cowering past, flattened and lustreless. Although we were still unsure of our immediate bearings, the outline became more distinct with the network of defences high in the sky. There were dozens of gas-filled balloons lining the skyline in a protective jigsaw pattern, hanging suspended and drifting lazily with the slight breeze. As each hour passed we felt less and less like evacuees, and needed to be remoulded with new virtues like difference and moral guidance. We also required the knowledge that we would be safe and accepted along this unfamiliar road. There had been months of violent upheavals and so many, many innocent deaths. Now we had acquired an added attraction, as frenzied seagulls greeted us when the liner slowed down. Large ocean-going tugs ranged alongside, gently bumping against the hull. The shielding of their presence lay solely on the pilots hanging out of the wheelhouses and shouting in tones of formality. Their faces looked alert and strained, but for them it was an anxious and necessary period embellished by years of convention.

We sailed through a patch of sunlight, when the clouds broke cover and the embankment stretched away to the north. My eyes didn't linger too long on the wind-tossed liner, as she drifted towards her moorings in Liverpool Bay. I stood motionless on the main deck, amongst a profusion of exuberant faces. There were hundreds of tense voices, of men, women and children raised to fever pitch and the low clouds seemed to amplify every excited sound. It was to be a day full of promise, 2 January 1944. Scanning the dockside, where layers of snow advertised the harshness of an English winter, recent destruction revealed that we had left one nightmare in the Far East and sailed into another. Death usually comes unannounced, but the view made me wonder how many more lives were taken, not by old age or disease, but by bombs and bullets, by a war. Haunted by this fear, a heavy silence descended over me like a shroud. My eyes soon misted over, exposing the innocence of a young boy.

So this is England, I thought to myself, with all the authority of my scholastic wisdom emblazoned across my chest, a country that had acquired a vast empire, one of enormous wealth and power, a nation which I had studied with verve and fascination, yet admired with pride. Everyone must have felt the same as me, soaked in the luxurious sensation of being safe. We had come a long way, overcoming many hardships, not least our own physical pain, but now we were safe. Surely our eagerness to preserve this sanctuary, would strengthen all of us in any forthcoming adversity, and help channel our hostility in a more positive direction. For many of us standing there, it was almost two years since we had started fearfully on this perilous journey. We had breathed the same air, thought the same thoughts, and on balance we'd certainly grown closer together through it all. For a few moments the tension was easing, and the misery of the past months was fading slowly.

Observing the random mingling of people on the quayside, our hearts raced wildly when greeted with a flood tide of jubilation. The wild atmosphere ashore burst forth in a drunken revelry, with the crowd lurching towards the edge of the pier in a blind paralysing panic. Above us the sky was a vast bottomless grey, as we watched through misty eyes, vaguely aware of what was beyond those docks. Now deep in our hearts whatever doubts we had harboured en route were soon washed away by this vociferous assembly. We certainly made no effort to conceal our full spectrum of emotions. It was exactly the kind of reception we needed to build up our faded morale, and the enthusiastic crowds indicated that it was a shared passion. Despite the elated welcome, many were shaking and starting to shiver but not with the cold. This was no fabrication or assumption. We had endured all of the adversities life had presented to us. We had finally arrived, and we had to be survivors. My mind played back, with all the clarity of crystal glass, to that dawn like thunder. The enormity of what had happened exploded into hundreds of thoughts and pictures, which flooded my brain; now I felt that I'd left it all behind.

Most of the servicemen were pleased to be returning home after tough campaigns. Some were badly injured while others appeared to be tenser than a coiled spring. They were obviously fearing painful news after repeated reports of the Blitz and countless bombing raids whilst they were away on duty serving their country. Many were choked with emotion, clinging to the rails and peering eagerly with moist eyes and tightened throats. I can remember the revered silence that preceded our arrival, bringing a huge lump to my throat, and the uncontrollable excitement that heralded the cheers. The faint crying from the women persisted, yet the next day at this time the ship would be void of these merciful sounds. Many of them could feel the panic building within them, like a steady stream being forced into their thoughts by the pounding of their hearts. The question that niggled me was one I'd posed to the mirror countless times. Was I dreaming? The strain was evident on all their faces. This was to be a new challenge, and the more we pondered over the situation the more problems we created for ourselves. Hundreds of uncertain posers raced wildly through their brains, but they knew that none of them could be answered. I had memorised names and faces of past school pals, and wondered what type of friends I would find in this new town. Leaning on the railings of the deck, I felt alone, staring at the water as my hands quivered slightly.

I had studied English at school in earnest, especially the monarchy and London, the Houses of Parliament, the famous tower, and was intrigued by Geography. The classes also touched on the exploits of Nelson, Drake, Raleigh, and even the legendary Guy Fawkes was included in the curriculum, which I found terribly exciting. I was also an expert at looking beyond the known horizon, yet the stimulation of this city was definitely absent. We marshalled ourselves into empty spaces, and many of the women on board were already sobbing; tears of joy and relief were streaming down their faces. Although this fascinating spectacle gave us so much pleasure, we were merely being allowed the privilege of a particular kind of sadness. The penetrating cold was also a continuous element, which we all felt during these moments of strong emotion.

Soon the fading light had begun to rob the impressive skyline, and the horizon slipped away into the emptiness of the darkening heavens. With the customary blackout, for us the night suddenly fell, before we realised that the day had ended, and the world outside receded into an inner universe. By now the port and city were slowly fading under the darkening sky. It was not an ideal time to be transferring families with small children to the various facilities that had been arranged. On deck we stared through the cheerless night, trying to distinguish the shadowy figures rising from the shattered masonry and moving about with frantic speed on the streets near the docks. Further afield it also appeared to be alive with restless people, leaving the congested area of chimneys and shops and treading on the greasy damp streets, with the cold misty drizzle blurring the air.

Unfortunately any form of offshore activity for us was considered hazardous and forbidden. Very soon everything returned to normal and it was time to relax. We all felt dirty, hungry, exhausted and tired eyed, so we were anxious to return to our cabins and respond naturally to the drug called sleep. With us staying on board overnight in the dockyard basin, there was a constant fear of being prime targets for air raids. However, the knowledge that our long journey had been completed in safety and the chain of successes already achieved pleasantly behind, inspired more confidence in us.

Outside, the wind was blowing hard and furious, whipping in from the Irish Sea, a constant reminder of how vulnerable we were and of the warmth we had once taken for granted. The huge liner echoed with sinister creaking sounds from her stays; otherwise everything was quiet except for the occasional stirring from the officers and crew who were on duty.

Dawn had broken over the horizon like a vast immeasurable curtain. The sky was rosy with promise on that day, 3 January 1944, a very special day indeed, we were to take our first steps on English soil. In the basin, dock workers were still busily engaged, discharging vital cargoes from merchant ships. Further away stretched the city with its tall buildings, like unbroken columns of gravestones, looking black against the brightening sky. The sun rose only to introduce a grey winter morning, which certainly didn't look very cheery – it was a paradox. The excitement, which we felt at the prospect of living in England, completely overcame any fears that we might have had. First we were obliged to check in at the main clinic, to acquire a clean bill of health, then have our medical documents officially stamped, before we were allowed to disembark from the ship. It was generally assumed that the hygiene in Britain was of the highest standard, but what we found difficult to understand was that all the mediocre jobs were handled expertly by Europeans, whereas abroad natives were employed for all the inferior occupations.

Now it was quite reasonable to assume that it was no mystery why British culture had survived for so long. Everyone appeared to be well organised; they were also intelligent and vigorous with their work rate.

For a moment the city lay throbbing in the warm sunlight, and a soft cool breeze swept up from the Mersey. The streets hummed with busy, early morning traffic, negotiating the narrow lanes, and overhead the cries of hundreds of birds migrating inland broke the silence. In the distance coils of smoke twisted against the awakening sky. It was the beginning of a new dawn for all, and some of the passengers left the ship for the first time. Everyone was laughing and shouting, their voices rising steadily with their movements.

'Both of you, put your coats on and don't forget your scarves and gloves,' Mother said anxiously, dashing about herself, whilst adding a touch of make-up. Rather unnecessary, I thought, but that could have been boyish impatience. My sister was already wrapped up cosily in a large white shawl and was fast asleep. It was a very damp January morning, but it certainly didn't keep the public from the streets and braving the elements. I suppose all of them had their own private reasons for being there. The paths were hard and slippery beneath the thin blanket of ice, and they walked precariously, their breath clouding the cold air, signalling the graphic purity of an English winter.

Many of the passengers had already left the liner and were trailing through the docks in a migrating stream, displaying pockets of colour in the crowded streets. We scampered down the gangway and waited anxiously for Mother to arrive. She had stopped on the upper deck to speak to the young officer engaged in conversation with one of the crew, obviously recognising him as our guardian during those traumatic periods at sea, when we existed between hope and despair. The air had begun to get a little warmer, so I trotted off ahead of the rest of them, secretly nourishing a period of independence. This feeling of freedom didn't last for long, I ran headlong into a burly figure dressed in a black uniform, with a strange-looking hat perched on his head. There was a slight pause as he stared at me from an enormous height, his face creased in a frown that expressed deep concern. I retreated, taking in a sharp intake of breath, in stunned amazement, which was fuelled by the rumours of their boisterous behaviour.

'Where are you heading for in such a hurry, young man?' he asked hastily but with a tentative quality in his voice.

'Into town with my mother, we're going shopping,' I replied, forcing a very nervous smile and pointing in the direction of her quick approach.

'Well, you had better wait here for her, son, we don't you getting lost now, do we?' he said softly.

'Are you an English bobby?' I asked boldly, having seen pictures of them in magazines and in films.

'I certainly am,' he replied sternly, rubbing his chin with his hand. 'I suppose you have just arrived on that liner,' he said, pointing to area of the ship.

'Yes, we've come from Burma,' I replied excitedly.

For a moment he looked bewildered as he struggled to think of where the place was above the usual noise associated with the dockyard workings. 'Burma?' he enquired with a huge frown.

'It's a long, long way from here,' I shouted with good humour, then ran off to join the family before he could say any more.

The streets were filled with pedestrians, some making their way to work, others probably shopping. There were taxis beginning to wield their trade. Everyone in the city seemed to be out of doors, many jumping onto trams, which ploughed up the centre of the main thoroughfare. Here the power lines stretched black across the sky. With the Christmas decorations swinging in the streets and festive music relayed from inside the shops, there was a faint illusion of future prosperity hanging in the air. For a while the weather remained bright, as we stretched across the busy streets and worked without stopping. We also listened to dozens of strange dialects, which we could not interpret. However, our nerves no longer reacted to these strange sounds, now that everything was back to normal with others present. It was a crisp and cloudy day and most people agreed that it would rain before noon, and wash some of the smog out of the air. They moved about their business quickly and uneasily, with one eye always cocked skywards at the gathering clouds drifting inland from the sea.

'I think it's time we were returning to the ship,' Mother said as we left the baby shop. She had already purchased a few articles, now neatly wrapped and stowed away in our carrier bags.

It looked overcast above and some of the passengers were already heading back towards the docks as midday approached. Many were grappling with new purchases and hand luggage, some were busy shouting at tired children who were misbehaving and pulling in different directions. The last light of the afternoon was fading, and we were weary, so we joined them and were pleased to lose the sense of the crowded city and its busy inhabitants, as we boarded the transport. Time passed and the sound of touching brakes were appropriate when the tram slowed down outside the dockyard. Moving casually, almost sauntering, we stepped off and entered the quayside. After a quick visit to our cabins and the bathroom, we strolled into the dining area like everyone else. It was to be our last meal on board this liner, and we nodded to people we knew with a little more conviction than usual. The authorities had imposed an extra-special menu to please us, and there was also a short speech, impressing us with the importance of our presence. We finally collected our suitcases and travelled with others to our hotel by coach. Now everyone was listening and staring through the windows, and probably trying to remember if they had forgotten anything. The afternoon had started well with a delicious feeling of security and anticipation.

Conversations soon gathered pace as with elation and excitement we stood and gaped wide-eyed at the hotel. Thoughts of a comfortable bed to sleep in loosened my heart a little. Suddenly the doors of the main entrance were opened by a gentleman adorned in a flashy uniform, and suspense quickly gave way to stimulation. He beckoned us with friendship into the foyer, after picking up the suitcases. We then followed him up the stairs to the first floor with remarkable precision. Here the hallways were wide, spotless and adorned with floral wallpaper. It appeared to be getting warmer and the radiators hissed all over with the steam pressure. He unlocked the door to the suite and we stepped inside a spacious lounge, splashed in glorious colour. There was a simplicity in this luxury that was entirely different to the confusion that circled around outside. Through the huge windows I watched the convoys of traffic crawling snail-like, and almost buried in the afternoon haze the Mersey glittered like a mirage. We soon settled down in the wine-coloured suite with matching carpet, waiting to be summoned for the evening meal and by now the best of the afternoon had passed.

It was getting prematurely dark outside, which really surprised us. We also soon recognised that there was no reprieve from the weather, which was intimidating. To our surprise there was the muffled sound of traffic now, and not the sea. Suddenly the view disappeared and the whole city was bathed in darkness, and it took no great sense of imagination to realise that the property was far more extensive than we had visualised, as we strolled into the brightly lit dining area. We sat and ate in silence, except for the steady rumble of traffic outside, whose low vibration we could feel more than we could hear. As darkness fell outside, in the noisy dining area the eager temporary residents ate, talked and discussed their future.

I struggled to wake up the next morning, and from the corridors outside the room came the gentle sound of footsteps and the hum of electric motors. It was now 4 January 1944, and outside, the dawn was grey and overcast. 'Typical English weather,' remarked the hotel clerk rather despondently, although the sun was lurking just behind the tops of the surrounding buildings. It was one of those chilly days, when the darkness extended well into the morning. Breakfast was to be our final meal and the selection was of a large variety. We devoured it quickly and left for the station with tense excitement and great expectations. It was a routine we'd got used to, but nevertheless an important one. This was a collective opinion, as travel can be one of the most rewarding forms of transition.

There was no wind outside, but the biting cold was growing increasingly severe, as we left the hotel timidly, each one desperately trying to break the anxious silence that clouded our entry into the awaiting coach. We felt isolated amidst this torrent of relief and delight, which carried our fragile hopes for the uncertain future. We moved away, and it was a slow idyllic journey instead of a stormy passage, everything feeling in tune, in harmony. We gradually lost sight of the hotel, treading through the heavy traffic en route to Lime Street station. Now some of the anger had left us and was replaced with a little sadness. We tried desperately to unravel our own confused thoughts and mixed emotions. We were also plagued with many questions on less sensitive matters, partially out of a blend of anxiety and boredom.

There were literally hundreds of people milling everywhere, porters loading and unloading baggage cars, trains arriving and leaving periodically. We had never witnessed an assortment on such a large scale, civilians and armed forces moving around impatiently. It was a maelstrom of confusion and utter madness, as people barged about in some kind of ritual panic, everyone immersed in the discernible tension, which was in the atmosphere engulfed in steam and smoke. Here everything represented immense industry and high-powered commerce. There was a hint of vast sums of capital and international power.

'Mum,' I shouted. 'That man over there will know which train we need to catch.' I pointed to a solitary policeman standing observing the crowds. He was a figure similar to the one with whom I had previously become familiar. He carried himself erect, unsmiling and immobile, and had a look about him, a look of purpose, with a cool friendly smile.

'Good afternoon, officer,' Mother said, facing him. 'Could you please direct me to the correct platform for the Selby train?'

He thought to himself for a moment, then he replied politely, 'Certainly ma'am, you want to be on platform number seven.' He pointed us in the appropriate direction as he spoke. His voice exerted as much charm and reassurance as he could command. He was an imposing majestic figure in his immaculate black uniform.

Mother thanked him as we moved on. Meanwhile other passengers were busy hauling themselves aboard the train that would be travelling on our route. Their coded words above the commotion revealed the information we wanted to hear. After we had viewed everyone suspiciously, it gradually dawned on our tired minds that the train standing there was indeed ours. Then a friendly porter safely stowed away the heavy luggage in the baggage compartment.

Above the usual noise associated with the stampeding crowds on a railway station, there was a sense of pride in our achievement, as we climbed aboard the stationary carriages. We fortunately managed to find some available seats amidst all the confusion. However, despite the physical and emotional exhaustion of the wearing day, we finally settled down in the compartment. Others shuffled around energetically for space, with politeness in their efforts, with the eyes of the city upon them. We seemed to have lost several hours moving around, and still couldn't welcome the cold weather. Now we were exhausted, all in and hoping that the train would soon be moving on. We remained silent in the jolting carriage, each totally occupied with our own private thoughts and imagining what strange faces would be greeting us at the end of the journey. I'm infected by travel and watched zones of totally different vegetation pass by. The transition seemed to go on for ever, and in the darkness it was difficult to imagine our bearings.

Very soon the hours drifted, as we stopped at various cities, where people descended with their luggage, either visiting or returning home from work. Many villages flashed past in the semi-darkness, as the train maintained its speed. Suddenly it would slow down and the couplings would shake violently. Along the corridors people were trying to look through the misted windows.

The journey unwound slowly and the train finally stopped at Selby station at 6 p.m. on 4 January 1944. It felt really good to open the door and escape the stuffy compartment. We had survived in this largely thankless but necessary task, now its justification was there for all of us to see and acknowledge. The sky was cloudy and all the stars were hidden as we half dragged ourselves from the carriage. Moving forward nervously along the platform, we felt an urgent need to keep going as some doubt was creeping into our progress. It was a gloomy-looking evening, as the blue dimness of the blackout obscured our view. There was an electric eeriness of silence, followed by the shuffling of unsteady feet, as we struggled with the hand luggage. Human voices predominated on the platform and enquiring faces turned in our direction, and gradually the significance of our presence resulted in the sound of a young woman's voice.

'Hello, you must be Gwen and the children,' she said, looking very elegant in a WAAF (Women's Auxiliary Airforce) uniform.

'Yes,' replied my mother, after pausing for the regulation look of enquiry.

Then they kissed each other briefly on the cheeks.

'I'm Edna, Arthur's younger sister,' she said pleasantly, and her voice had the timbre of sweet-flowing time. 'This is my husband, Bob, and my brother, Bill.

In the dim light they both looked thoughtful, understanding and very helpful. It was great to feel the elasticity of their alliance.

'You must be Colin, the young man of this family,' she said, holding out her hand.

I nodded, beaming at her remark. Her smile was bubbly and

infectious, and I was feeling slightly embarrassed at her delightful smile and by the candour of her gaze. We waited anxiously in the shadows for a few minutes, as she explained our future movements. She impressed us with her enthusiasm and her eagerness to be very gracious.

There was a flurry of activity as the main trunks were unloaded off the train onto a trolley by both of the men, and locked up in the station storage room until the following morning. The visibility was almost nil, as through the blackout we squinted through tiny droplets of rain thrown from the sky.

Finally, after the hurried introductions, we walked slowly down the silent streets to our temporary home at 13 Douglas Street. As soon as we knocked, the door was opened immediately, and our reception made us feel happy and optimistic. My grandmother was waiting patiently, with the rest of the relations, next to a neatly laid table. There was little room in the lounge, where a coal fire burned brightly, much to our delight. Great, I found myself saying silently at the sight of some delicious food. We needed something, especially after the bone-shaking, teeth-rattling journey. It felt as though Our Maker had conspired to feed us, despite the steady rationing. Some things were predetermined to happen, and we appreciated every moment of it. After the meal, there was the minimum of words and preliminaries, so we went straight to bed because of our tiredness.

I awoke to a typical English January morning, cold and bleak, almost two years to the very day on which I had left my aunt's home, days of laughter and belonging. Maybe these cherished gifts cemented the foundation that had guided me through all those traumatic periods for whatever reason. I had survived, journeying through thousands of miles in adverse conditions, on trucks, trains, aircraft and ships, seen places and countries I had never imagined even existed. I had suffered some pain and anguish, witnessed some of the horrors of war and heard stories of those who had experienced a fate far worse than mine.

Adjusting to this new environment was certainly going to prove very difficult with the blackout, rationing, traffic and even the residents themselves. There was an entirely different world out there than the one to which I had been accustomed. Any further schooling was also not permitted for a short period, until all our personal documents had been investigated by some government regulation. This was going to take some time, and as the months progressed, I would soon be reaching the compulsory leaving age of fourteen years. One could qualify for admission to either the grammar or technical schools, which were associated with the town, through a series of examinations. Unfortunately these had been conducted during my absence, so not surprisingly I now viewed my career as an uphill battle. With most of the children occupied at school, my closest companion was my baby sister, whom I would take on regular walks in her new pram. It was a peaceful and satisfying privilege, which gave me an enormous amount of pleasure, basking in our mutual affection without concealing my delight. However, occasionally, a blush of embarrassment would surface, when I was approached cautiously by some of the local women who grabbed my attention and showed a little more than the usual interest in the young stranger from the Far East. I enjoyed their obvious friendship and appreciated their overall kindness, as we chatted endlessly. The normal discussion was the war, which seemed to be at the centre of every conversation, followed by my long journey, the dreadful weather, which only added unwanted depression and the terrible shortage of fresh food.

We had survived the first few months of the year and now continued into the second period. Days of quiet thoughts followed, with long periods of silent contemplation, and memories produced loss of tangible explanations. Suddenly the silvery veil of happiness slowly dissolved, when one of those moments in life slowed into another direction. The cloak of sadness hovered like a dark cloud, when a turn of events was to usher more pain into my life. This was also to be an unwelcome stage, when my mother noticed a steady decline in my sister's health. This soon resulted in continuous visits to the local surgery. Immediate speculations eventually concluded that she had pneumonia, and she was promptly admitted to the children's ward in the Leeds General Infirmary a few miles away. As usual the impending fear started to pump again, and a blind numb horror began to suffocate me once more. I was feeling marooned in nothing…

Eventually an admission to the local school was granted in early June, releasing in me a wave of excitement. It was an ideal opportunity to meet the other young children at the new school. The beginning of new friendships was mixed with the essences of an early summer, offering a contrast of freshness. There was also a change of residence, more spacious lodgings on the outskirts of the town. Suddenly the mists of time left a cloud of foreboding over us as my sister's condition worsened, and an appointment was made for a visit from a specialist paediatrician. It was to be a lonely and monotonous period for me, as the harrowing days passed into weeks. The same anxieties and fears of the preceding year were reoccurring in my thoughts, now the joy and pleasure of my new-found privilege were fading fast. I felt very lonely and a great sadness began to swallow me up with a vengeance.

My couple of months of schooling passed quickly till the advent of the summer holidays. Unfortunately my genetic inheritance would clash with the compulsory leaving age of fourteen before the school reopened. The lessons that were taught had been learnt a long time ago, and all sense of the cosy attraction soon disappeared. Now the glorious green summer had departed and the trees were looking bare and unprotected, but, despite the circumstances and the painful emotions I still felt, I was now growing up.

September opened up a new life for me, which I accepted humbly and with courage. I was genuinely excited at the prospect of starting my first job, and there was no tougher grounding for a young inexperienced lad. I felt competent about my ability, and was inspired by the thoughts of working with men. It also gave me a sense of purpose to earn a small wage, with which I could assist my mother.

It was a miserable Monday morning and the rain poured down in sheets, as I walked to work in the shimmering dawn. Draped in an oversized boilersuit, generously handed down to me by a friendly neighbour, brown boots, topcoat and a flat cap, I proceeded to begin my working life as an apprentice riveter in the local shipyard, not too far away from my home. I wanted to appear industrious, intelligent, open-minded and quite capable of listening to all the advice given to me. Ambition beat inside me in a steady rhythm, and I could also dream of never confining myself to a single path of success. Somehow, though, I was sensing more than irony in the fact that my future education was to be conducted in the bowels of a ship. I was firmly overcome with the injustice of that fact.

My sister's health was fading fast, and one night while we were alone my mother told me that she had spinal meningitis and the signs were ominous. I fully understood how she felt by the tightness of her voice, and the tears that streamed down her face. The mood around the room darkened in an instant, and it scared and enraged me into a moment of solitude. There was something horrible in what I felt. The sorrow in Mother's expression was so frightening that I needed a shield, so I jumped into bed and sobbed, finally drifting off into a restless sleep. My stepfather had also arrived at our lodgings on compassionate leave from his regiment. Together they made regular visits to the infirmary, even though the inconvenience of the railway system had to be adhered to. I plunged fearlessly away from those early preliminaries, consumed by the firm belief that she would soon be cured of this terrible illness and would shortly be returning home.

The next few weeks slipped painfully by, and in the evenings I found myself possessed with impatience for my mother's return home from the hospital. However, there were no unnecessary conversations, so I made myself as inconspicuous as possible, then quietly cherished, like a treasure, thoughts that my sister's young life had not yet been stolen, and lived with that conviction. The pain and discomfort hovered like a guardian angel. Soon there was loss of enjoyment of life and a loss of companionship. The burden was now uncontrollable, but sometimes when you believe in the impossible the incredible comes true. As we are blessed by a God, it never hurts to pray, so with a gentle air of purpose, I knelt with my hands together in supplication.

'Please don't take her life; she is so very young, and you did take my other little sister away. Mother has told me that she is very ill, but I know that you can make her better soon. You must also know that I do love her very much. Please help her, I beg of you,' I silently prayed with an ache in my heart.

Even if my constant prayers had been heard they were never answered, as the grey day finally fell upon us. She never recovered from her illness, and passed away peacefully on Friday 6 October 1944, aged sixteen months, in the Princess Elizabeth ward of the Leeds General Infirmary. The sad news devastated me, and tears streamed down my sorrowful face. I was in an endless stupor. My mother spoke to me for lengthy periods, as I tried to understand what she was saying, but I really didn't want to. Grief had become a constant shadow and the reality of her loss appeared so large that I suddenly felt afraid again. I would certainly never forgive the betrayal by the friend, to whom I had prayed constantly to save her young life. On the day of her funeral, Monday 9 October, the household was in a permanent state of heartache and I didn't want to be part of it, certainly not because I didn't care – I'd loved her very much – but I had become very disillusioned with life in general. I needed to reassemble my thoughts, rediscover my own feelings. I tried desperately to recollect pleasant memories, which I had experienced a long time earlier, but this proved very difficult and my mind only filled with unpleasant reminders.

It was one of the saddest days of my life, and all I wanted was to be left alone. My grief was like a vulnerability pouring through me, an emptiness. I kept trying to replenish my feelings with happy memories of her tiny self. For the moment my life felt very fragile. Perhaps it had something to do with the way she died, being snatched away from our lives without a smile that I could remember for ever. I found it very daunting to realise that she was gone and to tell her I loved her, so I single-mindedly slipped away and went for a long walk into some nearby woods against my parents' wishes. I trudged along with glazed eyes, alone, in a silence which to my ears flooded all the noises of the earth, and wept a spate of tears as heavy as mercury. The intense pain slipped into a hollow somewhere within me, a niche that had not been breached in a long time. With this feeling of isolation, it was extremely difficult to accept the reality of losing another little sister. I was stricken with a sense of loss and longing so intense that it made me feel very ill.

The days and weeks passed in a steady procession, but even so I still felt horribly insulated from reality. Because of the war, houses were in short supply, so we moved on once again to new empty premises at the opposite end of the town. It had been a butcher's shop prior to the war. I looked round helplessly at my bedroom, which was situated directly over the empty shop itself. The huge bay window below had been shuttered off since its closure throughout the war years.

It had been a depressing Christmas of 1944. There was no tree, no tinsel glistening on the branches, and no ornaments or streamers embellishing the room. The New Year also had passed in a silence, which one could distinguish very clearly, as we remembered the tragic deaths of others. It was moments like these that made it impossible not to think about everything that had happened. In my quieter moments there was a natural yearning for certain dreams to come true, no matter how far-fetched they might seem. I thought of my other little sister, all alone in the Himalayas. Now there would be no flowers on her grave, thick moss would have smothered it and no one would take care of it anymore. My stepfather remained very quiet for a long time, then he returned to the army a broken man. The loss of his only two baby daughters in succession was to take a heavy toll on our lives. Not to sound bigoted, because it was no fault of mine, I would never speak to him again as the years passed.

I consider myself very lucky to be alive, some people have all the luck, I am probably one of them, but who knows. Life has to go on regardless of the pain, and it isn't disloyal to move on, nor does it destroy what we had before.

Chapter XII

It was a long walk to my place of employment from our new home at the opposite end of the town. In the shifting darkness, the journey of over two miles appeared to be endless. The sky that morning was a perfect deep blue and innocent of clouds as the daylight broke. I walked briskly, pausing occasionally along the dark streets, where there appeared to be no signs of life. It was no surprise that I was still feeling uneasy and saddened in my heart over past events. Hanging from my shoulder was the haversack packed with sandwiches substituting for the dinner that I would receive in the evening after completing the day's work. The initial busy hours slipped by rather quickly, shortening the Friday morning in early January 1945. By mid-afternoon the clouds had lifted from the heavens, leaving behind a weak sun, which shone like a worn out torchlight. It was still brutally cold now that the winter had set in, and snow-bloated clouds flocked in the sky like frightened cattle.

One section of our riveting squad wore thick overcoats whilst working below decks in the ship tied to the 'Brown Cow' jetty on the River Ouse. This was aptly named because it was the nearest point along the river bank to a cosy little public house of that name nestling on a sharp bend near a village. The holder-up, who was the leader of our squad, and myself, were in the bottom of the hull. On the deck above, the other half of the team, two riveters, when required pounded the white-hot rivets to secure the steel sheets together. Several feet above, on the top deck, the hotting lad pumped the bellows of the coal fire with one foot. The glowing flames would smoulder the new black rivets into incandescent pieces of metal for our benefit. As required the lad would then drop them accurately into a small box cushioned with coal dust, for my convenience. The job didn't pay that much as an apprentice, but at least it provided some assistance for my mother each weekend. The main reason for our endeavour, apart from the modest reward each Friday, was the war effort.

This company, Cochrane and Sons Shipbuilders, was under contract to the Admiralty, supplying dan layers for use in the Royal Navy. The enclosed area where we worked felt like being inside a steel catacomb; it smelt unaired, musty and damp. Movement was limited in the cramped conditions of the bilges. I clutched the hot piece of metal in my tongs and tried to insert it into the adjoining hole for immediate entry. Occasionally the orifices were slightly inconsistent, which prevented an ideal embedment. A steel punch was then required to enlarge the cavity before continuing.

'Take it back, son, these holes are very bad and don't match at all,' said the gaffer hurriedly.

Without any hesitation I returned to the open area, and calmly bending slightly forwards replaced the rivet back in the box. I was totally oblivious to the fact, that the hotting lad was on the point of dropping another one. Almost instantly there was a sound of hissing, the awful stench of something burning, flesh being charred. Unfortunately a rivet was resting firmly on the back of my neck.

I leapt into the air, screaming obscenities, in a state of indescribable panic. The glowing metal piece had slipped down my back and lodged above the belt around my trousers. I felt intense pain near my spine like a muscular earthquake, and my head was spinning with feverish activity. I no longer had the strength of a child, as I screamed out for instant help. Suddenly this compact area began to turn dark, and the world outside grew fainter and fainter and consumed by a hazy mist. Amidst all the commotion, I felt lost and abandoned overwhelmed with the strangest feeling that something awful had happened, in a timeless vision. I felt inflamed, and shivered all over. Somewhere in my deep subconscious I appeared to be stumbling, reaching out in desperation for something to cling onto in panic and disbelief.

Sweat trickled down my forehead and stung my eyes, even the shuddering in my body would not stop. Now I was losing my senses, and the excruciating pain felt like the end of the world. Beneath the many layers of clothing, the area close to my spine was feeling like an ever-increasing bubble about to explode. I was gasping for fresh air, choking, coughing as I breathed, and my limbs trembled. Fortunately, within minutes the saving grace was a right cross to the jaw, which rendered me semi-conscious as the lights went out instantly. During the remaining few moments of stability that followed, four very worried and concerned men raised my limp body by the arms and legs then waited patiently for the hot piece of metal to burn its way through the many layers of fabric that I was wearing. This extra protection was deemed a necessity against the bitter cold, when working deep down in the bilges of a ship on a January afternoon in Northern England.

Slowly regaining consciousness, I was too buried in my own thoughts to say anything. I felt pain and with it came the all too familiar feelings of guilt and intense anger. Strangely enough I didn't feel tired, and numbness deadened the pain caused by the unpleasant movement in a speeding vehicle. I saw houses, shops, and people spinning past through a blurred window of a motor car. Somehow the tension was only making it worse. I needed to relax, so I gripped the dashboard tightly with my fingers. Time passed very slowly, and I vaguely remember being perched in a warm salty bath, which stung like hell. It only prolonged the agonising pain, which formulated all kinds of whirling images in my mind.

I was most anxious to hear some kind of voices but there wasn't a sound, only a distant, almost muted echo. Suddenly all that I could smell was the stench of anaesthetic, which I then automatically associated with the buzz of a hospital. I gazed through watery eyes at a white uniform, standing near what I thought was a medicine cabinet. Yet there was no feeling of any sort of relief, only a touch of embarrassment. However, I was in no condition to withdraw myself from this bizarre nightmare.

'Yours is certainly a very unusual case. How on earth did this happen to you?' she murmured. Then she gently sponged me down with some of the warm water.

I just shrugged my shoulders and buried my face in my hands. 'I really don't remember,' I replied. Then I winced as the liquid touched the burnt area, making me flinch and shudder.

There followed a few more tender words of compassion from a voice that was almost a whisper. However the embarrassing condition that I felt I was in left no room for dignified conversation. I glanced around for signs to distract me from the gloomy channel of my own thoughts.

Time hovered painfully, and although I was still in a daze, the familiar feeling of depression came over me. I suddenly found myself lying on my stomach in a comfortable bed, surrounded by peering faces. The interval of silence was frightening, as I stared through confused eyes at graceless furniture in the accident ward in the Selby War Memorial Hospital. Occasionally the faint sound of voices seemed to come and go, in a confusion I couldn't quite distinguish. At one end of this compact little ward, a roaring coal fire crackled and sparkled, generating warmth. The iridescent flames danced like imaginary shadows and the rustle of footsteps across the wooden floor echoed in the distance. I eventually dozed off in a moody silence and the medication rolled me towards unconsciousness at an alarming rate.

The ward suddenly burst alive, with the usual routine sounds of bottles and bedpans clanging. The warm rays of the rising sun shone through the window, and the early dawn woke me to the clipped chatter of happy nurses completing their night shift. However the welcome daylight was going to bring discomfort and considerable pain, as the sound of the agony trolley began its usual rounds.

'Good morning, young man. How are you feeling today?' said a gorgeous young nurse as she removed the thin sheet covering my bare back.

I stared at her, mesmerised by her tender voice and hesitant about answering as I was still in a daze. 'I don't really know for sure,' I replied nervously.

'Now the important thing is that you keep very still and be brave, I need to change your dressing,' she said softly.

For a moment I wanted to run away as fast as possible, but couldn't. 'I'll be all right, I promise,' I said quietly, turning to face her and putting on a brave face.

'Please hold on tightly, because this is really going to hurt,' she said in a tone scarcely above a whisper.

I became suspicious, but concentrated on her advice by grinding my teeth, shutting my eyes and strangling the pillow.

The whole operation was rather primitive but a necessary part of the practice, so the nightmare began. The sulphonamide powder and Vaseline gauze had stuck to the burned area and had to be removed briskly in one swift movement. There was a sudden jab of intense pain as pieces of raw flesh left my tender back, followed by silent tears of anguish falling from tired eyes. The urge to smile dissipated rapidly, when a kindly remark was aimed to please, but through her voice I could feel an honest note of compassion. I was startled by the strength of how I had clenched my teeth together and tightened my jaw, for it certainly eclipsed any excessive pain that I might have felt. The pounding in my head was soon soothed by the touch of soft hands wiping away the discharge of pus. This was followed by several new dressings.

'I'll need to change them again tomorrow,' she said, looking very concerned and full of sympathy.

Helped by the easy flow of conversation, it was simple to tolerate those steel instruments each morning.

The weeks passed pleasantly in this homely environment and the wounds healed slowly. However, after I had given it considerable thought, the long interval signalled the end of my apprenticeship as a riveter in the shipyard. It was also to be the beginning of my adolescence, when my intimate thoughts developed unusual tenderness. I found myself besotted with this petite blonde nurse with blue-grey eyes and a dazzling smile, forever looking radiant in her perfectly starched white uniform. She was extremely attractive with a milk-and-honey complexion of Scots-Canadian ancestry. Although I had developed a special feeling for her, and found myself wishing I were older, I regretfully withheld my emotions, and respectfully accepted her position of authority by always addressing her as 'Nurse Crossland'. She had a unique loveable kindness, which featured, in her appearance, and her personality was marked by an extreme refinement. Even her tenderness fuelled pangs of admiration in everyone, more so in yours truly.

Perhaps I was a victim of my own innocence, but I was certainly wrong to believe that these sweeping changes were transitory and would soon disappear. Discipline was hard and sometimes unreasonable in the nursing profession, especially with the upheaval of a war. Strangely though, in this small hospital, the rules were occasionally waived without the nurses being too irresponsible. Her tolerance towards all the patients went far beyond her loyalty to the medical profession. Her off-duty periods often found her tiptoeing into the ward very late in the evening. She would be welcomed with a huge smile as she entered, her pretty face framed in a cascade of long blonde hair. It was only for a short visit and a chat with me, usually about the recent film she had seen or the music she had danced to in the local ballroom that particular evening. Although tired herself, in her eyes shone the brilliance of the moon that penetrated the darkest depths of the night, sending a warm tremor through me. Because of rigid laws ration books were lodged with the hospital authority, but her meagre two ounces of sweets never failed to visit my locker in the shape of Pontefract cakes and wine gums.

Winter passed, soon the trees were returning to life and the earth began to awaken beneath the shining sun. In places patches of grass began to sprout through the disappearing snow, and tiny streams ran along the edges of the road. Now my felicitous stay finally came to an abrupt end, as my recovery and time for healing was complete, much to my annoyance. On the morning of my sad departure, there was an unexpected surprise as a farewell gift from her, a strange and unusual reward in the shape of a huge kiss, planted firmly on my mouth by this delectable nurse. It deposited an impressive red lip print of embarrassment and a flash of surprise on my face when viewed by an approving audience in close attendance. Though flooded with high emotion, I trembled with excitement and smouldered with overpowering pride. How freely one's thoughts flow when the tender strings are plucked! For me it was something really special for I now felt that my heart belonged to her.

Many, many years have now lapsed since my childhood and adolescence, but that is without significance. Somehow even today loved ones are still remembered with a small degree of anxiety, and the tears, which have been intermittent with the passage of time, often return. I count myself extremely fortunate to have survived. Probably the strict discipline that I was used to helped to make that possible. I really don't often think about what happened now, because survival breaks the news that those we have cherished have left us. One of the most important things that make us human are the people we love dearly. When they have gone then there is nothing left, for only death is final in a world we always knew existed.

My mother was a strict disciplinarian throughout her early life, making many of her own rules and abiding by them righteously. However, in her later years, time healed the contention, and she changed beyond all recognition, pushing aside most of her beliefs. She religiously preached that we as Christians should learn to forgive and forget the horrors that had passed. Her strong principle was that absolution was the supreme healer of pain and liberated those who have suffered. Not surprisingly I would never bow to her insistence, when she left her infectious advice hanging in the air. She was to recognise this fact in the reality of her own private life, usually seeking inspiration and strength in total belief. She was fuelled by the ideology that, although God's mills grind exceedingly slow, they grind exceedingly small. Vengeance would come from His hands alone. Now and again, she would come to terms with her credence with absolute reticence inside her home, often listening to her memories above the silence, but the silence was always more compelling. She herself became a very generous and compassionate individual, but suffered from the voracity of predators and parasites, when she welcomed them into her humble dwelling. Many of them soon profited generously from her failing health and naivety.

Shortly before her final days on this earth, having herself endured tremendous suffering and crippling agony in a hospital bed, she held my hand and although she could only vaguely recall anything or anyone from the past said, 'I've always loved you, son. You were my first-born and there's something special about the first-born. Somehow you seemed to be away from me most of the time so I gave my feelings to Trevor.'

There was sadness in her eyes. I sighed deeply, studying her with a sombre glare yet savouring her words of love.

'Please don't think too badly of me, will you?' she said softly.

These last few words were slow and heavy.

'I never have, Mum,' I replied sadly. It was the very first time that I had ever heard those delightful words from my mother. I felt a stab of guilt, when I kissed her and held her hand tightly before I left. I suppose part of caring is feeling intense pain; they seem to go together. Although I prayed regularly for her to get well, I knew she would never be able to cope with the unprecedented trauma of three major life-threatening operations. The removal of both of her legs on separate occasions, then further amputation of one of them from the hip joint, was beyond human endurance. Unfortunately there was no cure for the deadly infection of gangrene. I needed all my strength when she sighed, and there was a slight twitching at the corners of her tender smile from someone in a great deal of discomfort. How strange that through her pain and distress there seemed to flow a special composure and her closeness to death gave her a godlike peace. For a moment I thought of my father, and tried to analyse the many differences between life and death. I could understand the making and destruction of humans, but the child inside of me would always mourn.

My own personal feeling regarding the most satisfying gift that we possess, is that it is when we can abstain from visiting cinemas, theatres, and denounce the artificial ceremonies of life and just open our eyes to the marvels and wonders of this earth, and immerse ourselves in the quiet beauty of it all as we hug the secret of the deep awareness of the pleasure that we have within ourselves with an expression of something being right with the world. Like a kind of September song, whatever the purpose, it rhymes.

Most of us feel indifferent to the Japanese because of their savage and merciless campaign, and still recriminate against them for whatever reason, such was the apathy induced by the overwhelming hatred of this cruel and enigmatic race, something profound and engraved induced by their heartless disregard for human suffering with a system controlled by violence and slavery; the mutilation of the human mind, and the degradation shown by the Oriental behaviour; their procreating of slavery to a pitch of interminable fatigue; their saturation starving of human souls, and their pathological dedication to destroying with unspeakable slaughtering; their negative ridicule of every human dignity and virtue fused with their appetite for torture and ruthlessness, which proved insatiable. The scale of all this orchestrated evil went beyond the realms of sanity. It was certainly the most calculated exhibition of brutality ever designed by mankind, in this misconceived and unreliable world.

It is my own private judgement, without bordering too much on aggression and while cutting out the undercurrents of hostilities, that there are millions who will agree with my statement. Forgiveness! I will never go along with that phrase, noble as it may appear. My mother would probably have forgiven, but then she was a better person than I. Time and age have distorted nothing, my memory is vividly accurate, and it's a great privilege to have clarity in thought in moments like this. Even after all these years, my thoughts are drawn back to all my loved ones and the places that we shared together. I will certainly never ever forget, far too much has happened. If I have sounded frivolous and prejudiced, I can plead excuses, for I am a victim of my environment and upbringing. We need to respect the earth, to live in harmony with each other, for death comes soon enough. That is something no one can change. Anybody who hurries it is a damn fool.

It's very strange to summon one's youth, and half a century is a long, long time for one to recollect and revisit the past; childhood, adolescence, the process of passing into maturity into obsolescence. The world is full of abandoned and undernourished children, many of whom do not get a substantial foundation in their existence. I know that I did, for I have been extremely lucky in my life. Even though I have known excessive pain, I have also known devoted love. However, I will always remember the sacrifice that was paid.

THE END